**Electricity
and
Electronics**
BASIC

Electricity
and
Electronics
BASIC

William F. *Barnett* Steinberg
Supervisor of Industrial Arts
San Diego City Schools

Walter B. Ford
Professor, Electricity—Radio
Industrial Arts Department
San Diego State College

THIRD EDITION

AMERICAN TECHNICAL SOCIETY CHICAGO, U.S.A.

621.3
S819e

Cover Photo Courtesy CBS Hytron

PRINTED IN THE UNITED STATES OF AMERICA

PREFACE

That "Electricity and Electronics—Basic" is a successful book is indicated by its use in hundreds of schools throughout the country for seven large printings and three major editions. In revising this edition, advantage was taken of the experience of hundreds of teachers who have used it in the past. Their valuable suggestions have been incorporated to make possible a more readable book which includes the latest developments in the field. New material has been added, and the original text revised to reflect the trend for upgraded, up to the minute material in the field of electricity and electronics.

From the awe-inspiring achievements of nuclear science and the spectacular advancements in aviation to the innumerable discoveries that have added comfort and convenience to our daily lives, we are constantly dependent upon electricity and electronics. You may never operate an atomsmasher or guide a space ship, but if electric lights, the automobile, the telephone, radio, or television enter into your activities you need to know something about the basic principles that are utilized in all of these.

Anyone who wishes to feel at home in the world of modern technology must be familiar with the fundamentals of electricity and electronics. To make it possible to acquire this familiarity quickly and easily is the purpose of this book. The necessary information is presented in a direct and simple manner. Each step is clearly illustrated by photographs and drawings.

Color is used in the illustrations to provide clarity and as an asset in the learning process. Experience has shown that color, properly used, is a valuable tool in illustration. Its overuse, for effect, is distracting and destroys its value. The use of color simply for decoration has been studiously avoided.

As you proceed through the text you will gradually learn the convenient symbols used by engineers and technicians in all fields to represent electrical and electronic equipment on diagrams. At the end of each unit of study, there is a group of "Review Questions." These are provided to assist the reader to test his knowledge and to check his progress.

"Interesting Things to Do" is what the authors have called the many fascinating projects that enable you to demonstrate and apply what you learn in the text. These projects are not only interesting but produce useful articles and develop practical skills. Few tools are necessary and generally only materials commonly found in a home or school shop are required.

The knowledge of electricity and electronics gained from this book will open up new and inviting paths. A great number of vocational opportunities exist and they are multiplying rapidly in the area that is leading progress in most occupational fields. A variety of exciting hobbies offer themselves. And you will have the keen satisfaction of grasping the essentials of an important part of your everyday life.

CONTENTS

USING ELECTRONICS FOR COMMUNICATION

INTERESTING THINGS TO DO

ELECTRICITY FOR EVERYDAY LIVING

USING ELECTRICITY FOR COMMUNICATION

SUPPLEMENTARY PROJECTS

LIFE SUPPORT FOR 14 DAYS IN SPACE

The spacecraft Gemini, manned by two astronauts and filled with electronic apparatus, will orbit the earth for two weeks as its electronic equipment gathers vital information for our nation's first flight to the moon.

This Electrical

and

Electronic Age

~~~~~~

UNIT 1
THINGS ELECTRICITY CAN DO

Electricity and Electronics

It is very difficult to separate the meaning of the two words *electricity* and *electronics*. The field of electricity is usually thought of as electricity that is used in magnets, generators, motors, lights, and heaters.

The field of electronics is usually thought of as electricity that is used in radio, television, and other equipment where electron tubes and transistors are needed.

In the Home

We are so accustomed to flipping a switch in our homes and having a room instantly flooded with light that we seldom think of what is happening behind the scenes to make this possible. Yet back of every home lighting system there are a number of interesting devices. The names of these devices are strange to most of us. As we proceed with the study of electricity we shall become very familiar with the names and the electrical equipment they represent and learn what an important part they play in bringing electricity into our homes.

Probably the most important use of electricity in the modern home is for producing light, either by the common light bulb or fluorescent lamps. In addition to furnishing light, electric lamps of the ultraviolet type can bring the effects of sunshine into the home

Courtesy Frigidaire Div.—General Motors Corp.

◆ 1. Electricity and electronics play an important part in the operation of a modern kitchen. The chicken shown in the electric range can be cooked by high frequency radio waves within 6 to 8 minutes. Pies require only 3 minutes to bake.

Courtesy Allied Radio Corp.

◆ 2. Transistorized intercom units provide communication between all rooms of a modern home. Requiring little current to operate, they may be left on over long periods of time to monitor a sleeping child or serve to call the family to dinner.

and also kill harmful germs in the air. Electric lamps of the infrared type can provide us with radiant heat.

How many electric motors are working in your home to lighten household tasks and provide for your comfort? If you gave an answer offhand without stopping to count them you would probably fall far short of the correct number. In the average modern home electric motors operate the clothes washer and drier, refrigerator, garbage disposal, fan, electric razor, clock, furnace blower, and workshop equipment. The uses for electricity in the home do not end with furnishing light and motor power. Electrical heating provides for the comfort of the family by operating the range, toaster, waffle iron, water heater, coffee maker, heating pad, iron and ironer, clothes drier and electric blanket.

◆ 3. Operating a computer that is electronically controlled. Both business and industry use various types of computers. For commercial businesses these machines may be pro-grammed to handle billing, payrolls and inventory. In industrial plants they are vital in solving difficult problems in research and production processes.

On the Farm

Electricity is just as important to the farm as it is to the modern city dwelling. About two-thirds of all farms use electricity to lighten the chores as well as to serve in the home. Many of the jobs that were formerly done by hand and required many man-hours may now be done with electricity in a fraction of the time. These include pumping water, grinding feed, milking, and many of the other jobs which are found around a farm. Small portable radio units make it possible to keep in contact with workers in remote areas of the farm.

In Industry and Business

When we think of the many ways in which electricity helps to run a modern home, we are apt to overlook the part it plays in keeping the wheels of industry going. Actually, only about one-third of all of the electricity produced in our power plants is used by farms and homes. The remaining two-thirds supplies the needs of commercial and industrial plants. The average modern manufacturing plant uses in the machines which it operates, over 10,000 kilowatt-hours of electrical energy a year. Let us consider some of the ways in which this tremendous amount of electricity is used in industry.

◆ **4. This is a schematic diagram of a trans-oceanic radiotelephone link that enables you** to call foreign lands from your own home.

In the great steel industries electricity is used in practically every process from the time the crude iron ore is taken from the earth to when the finished product in the form of flat steel sheets is ready for delivery to manufacturing plants across the nation. Electric shovels are used to dig the ore and electric cranes load it into freight cars or ships and unload it again at the steel plant. Electric conveyors carry it to the blast furnaces in which the iron is changed into steel. The rolls which form the steel into sheets are driven by electric motors. When the finished sheets of steel reach the manufacturing plants, electric motors operate the machines which shape them into some of the appliances that contribute so much to our way of living. These electric motors help produce radio and television chassis, and many appliances found in the home.

For Communication

Primitive man depended upon fire, smoke, or drum signals to send his thoughts to his neighbor. Modern man has only to lift the receiver of his telephone and dial a series of numbers to send his voice to the most distant point of our nation. And with little more effort he can talk with someone in a foreign land or on a ship hundreds of miles from shore. See Diagram 4.

Mobile radio units installed in cars or aircraft and transistor units that may be carried in one's pocket provide communication networks for police, fire departments, aircraft, industrial and military purposes.

Small transistorized units, called Citizen's Band Transceivers, which operate on frequency bands that require no license, serve an important function in the uses mentioned above as well as providing a fascinating hobby for the electronics enthusiast.

Courtesy Allied Radio Corp.

◆ 5. Blocks away from home or friends this bike mounted walkie talkie offers real two-way communications. This Citizens Band Transceiver may be used in a wide range of applications from industrial and recreational uses to a convenient means of keeping in touch with young children from the home. Citizens Band transceivers require no license and can be operated by anyone.

For Lighting

Not very long ago we were limited in our working and playing time to the hours of daylight. In order to make the greatest use of their plants, many modern industries operate on a 24-hour schedule, which only adequate electric lighting makes possible. While the largest electric lamp in the home rarely provides more than a few hundred candlepower of light, the lamps used in industry are rated in terms of thousands of candlepower.

Cities depend on electricity to light streets and expressways, and to operate the numerous lights and signals necessary for the control of traffic along them.

For Transportation

In the field of transportation, electric power is replacing many means of transport using such fuels as coal and gasoline. Diesel-electric engines have replaced the steam driven locomotive of the past and the subways, elevated trains, and trolleys used in the city are all electric.

Today, hardly any form of transportation exists which does not depend on electric power for its operation. It is required for jet aircraft, the submarine, and the ocean liner as well as the family car.

None of these could function without electricity to operate their motors, generators, ignition and lights.

7:20 A.M. STARTS MOTORS IN COMPRESSORS TO BUILD UP PRESSURE

7:30 A.M. TURNS ON LIGHTS IN CORRIDORS AND LOCKER ROOMS

7:15 A.M. SWITCHES ON OVENS AND PLATING BATHS

7:40 A.M. TURNS ON LIGHTS IN MAIN PLANT

7:00 A.M. TURNS UP HEAT OR AIR CONDITIONING

7:55 A.M. TURNS ON POWER FOR MACHINE TOOLS

8:00 A.M. SOUNDS STARTING SIGNAL

Courtesy IBM

◆ 6. Up to 40 remote operations—lights, motors, heating and air conditioning systems, as well as clocks, time recorders and signals—can be automatically controlled by a central control system. Before the plant opens . . . during the working day . . . after close-down, the electronic control system will maintain automatic and efficient 24-hour supervision.

For Automation

The word *automation* has become a common one in industry. By means of automation, complete manufacturing processes are performed entirely automatically. With electric timing devices and relays, many jobs which were formerly done by hand power are now being done with electricity. It permits much-needed manpower to be used elsewhere. Many industrial plants are now being automatically made ready for the day's operation before the first worker appears on the job.

Courtesy Hughes Aircraft Co.

◆ 7. The spacecraft, Surveyor, is designed to make a controlled landing on the moon. Its mission will be to analyze the moon's surface, measure its radiation and magnetic charac-teristics and transmit TV pictures back to earth. Its electric power is obtained from solar cells.

In Research

Little could be done in a modern research laboratory without the aid of electricity. Nearly all of the measuring devices used in developing nuclear power for the use of mankind are electrically operated. Geiger counters which detect the presence of uranium are run with batteries. X-ray machines, used for medical purposes and by industry to detect flaws in metal castings, and the recently developed X-ray microscope which permits even closer examination of defects within men or machines, all depend upon electricity for their operation.

With travel in outer space an ac-complished fact, scientists are now preparing to land men on the moon within the present decade. To make this achievement possible much information about the moon must be obtained before the journey can be attempted. This will be collected by an unmanned spacecraft called the "Surveyor." Since weight limitations prevent the use of batteries, scientists are depending on the sun to provide the electrical power for operating the controls of the spacecraft and sending the desired information back to the earth. Thin wafers of silicon, called "solar cells," will be used to convert sunlight into electricity.

Courtesy Philco Corp.

In the Military

In this age of missiles, satellites, and nuclear weapons, the military has been responsible for the development of some of the most advanced electronic devices in the world today. While many of these new devices must be classified as secret, the world at large knows of the vast ring of radar stations that sur-

◆ 8. The United States Air Force has perfected a far-seeing "third eye"—airborne television. Now the military command can watch the TV screen as though it were a living, moving map.

round our country to warn of hostile movements against us. The newspapers, magazines, and television keep us informed of the almost daily developments in new electronic military devices. Through television we are able to watch the progress of our ballistic missiles and space probes as they are launched from Cape Kennedy.

However, as thrilling as these devices may be, they show only a small part of the responsibility of electronics in our national defense. Each firing of a missile, space capsule, or routine flight by our Strategic Air Command requires a

Courtesy Bendix

◆ 9. The reflected sound waves from a sonar unit are used to show the location of an enemy submarine, or ship. Submarines are also capable of launching missiles from under water aimed at land targets hundreds of miles away.

vast network of communication around the world to coordinate the preparatory planning. Radar, radio, sonar, television and telephone enable the military command to keep track, not only of our own ships, missiles, and aircraft, but those of every other nation as well.

REVIEW QUESTIONS

1. List the ways in which you have used electricity since getting out of bed this morning.

2. Make a list of the number of electric motors that you have in your home.

3. What is the size of the largest lamp used for lighting in your home?

4. Name several uses for the electric lamp.

5. What part of all of the electric power produced is used by farms and homes?

6. What is meant by the word *automation*?

7. How do scientists learn about conditions in the upper atmosphere?

8. Tell how electricity is used to protect our shores from invasion by another country.

UNIT 2
FUTURE DEVELOPMENTS IN ELECTRONICS

In the Home

What does the future hold for us in new electrical and electronic developments? We can almost rub our lamp like Aladdin, make a wish for some new electrical development, and be reasonably certain that our electronics and electrical laboratories can produce it. The research laboratories are working constantly to produce a more efficient lamp. In the not too distant future we will have a really "cold" elec-

tric light. This type of lighting has already been developed in the laboratory. See Figure 10.

The kitchens of our homes are well on the way toward becoming electronically operated. While most operations involved in cooking can now be done by electric devices, the housewife will in the future be able to "program" her dinners far in advance. The meals will be cooked, the dishes cleaned, the floors swept and polished, all by pushing a

Courtesy Westinghouse Electric Corp.

◆ **10. A "cold" lighted room in the home of tomorrow. Electroluminescent panels made with phosphors and transparent conductive** materials will replace light from conventional lamps with a soft pleasing glow.

series of buttons on a master control unit.

In the field of entertainment we may look for a flat wall screen to replace our present television as shown in Figure 12. The development of the "light amplifier" has made this possible, and it should be but a short time before this becomes a commercial reality. Also, soon to be available is a TV recorder which will allow us to "tape" programs from our television set. The recorder can be set to tape programs while we are away from home so that these programs may be enjoyed at our convenience. The tapes can be stored and replayed just as the tapes we now use for Hi-Fi.

The television telephone by which one may see the person to whom he is

Courtesy Kay Laboratory

◆ 11. A television telephone that will make it possible to see the person at the other end of the line.

speaking has already been developed. See Figure 11. This may soon be put into general use.

Courtesy General Electric Co.

◆ 12. A practical method of direct light amplification may be the key to large-screen television sets, which are thin enough to hang on a wall or to be used as room dividers.

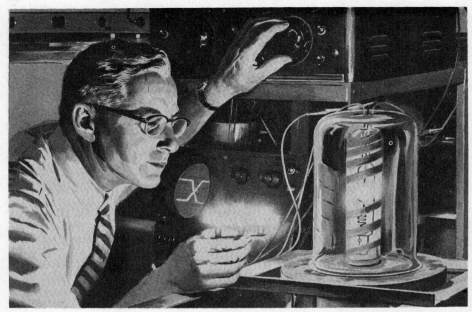

◆ 13. Electricity produced directly from heat lights small lamps in the laboratory of General Electric scientist Dr. Volney Wilson, inventor of the thermionic converter.

In Industry

In the industrial field we shall probably see automation take over more and more of the operations which are now done by manual labor. Perhaps we shall see a whole manufacturing operation from the raw material to the finished product, built entirely by means of electrically controlled machinery. Human attention will be required only to keep it operating in correct working order.

Many new developments are possible with the use of radar. One of these is the automatic control of automobiles on the highways. We may one day see automobiles traveling safely along our roads steered solely by means of radar. The same principles will be applied to controlling our airplanes. Radar will guide them safely to their destinations, from take-off to landing, without the aid of human hands.

A journey into space may be an adventure of the future. The construction of space ships that can travel to other planets is now being studied. When the time comes for these space ships to be built, electronics will play a most important part in their operation.

In Medicine

It is said that the ancient Romans knew of electricity and used electric eels in the treatment of mental illnesses.

Today, in medical research and

Courtesy Westinghouse Electric Corp.

◆ 14. In the future electricity will be produced in power plants using atomic energy as the fuel.

treatment electronics offers a great contribution to the welfare of mankind. One of the projected advances of the X-ray now used by doctors and hospitals is the color X-ray which will aid in the diagnosis of many illnesses. Currently in the planning stage and soon to be in production are electronic monitoring devices which will indicate and record a patients' condition as indicated by blood pressure, pulse rate, temperature, and other body functions. A form of "radio pill" has been developed containing electronic circuitry which when swallowed transmits data on the internal conditions of the patient. Since future space travellers must stay in cramped positions for long periods of time, electronic devices may well be used to provide exercise by means of electrodes connected to muscles of the body. The development of the Laser, a device which projects an intense beam of coherent light, and of great interest to industry, is opening the way to advanced means of surgery. It has already been used in delicate operations on the eye and is expected to be of great value in the treatment of tumors and other diseases.

REVIEW QUESTIONS

1. What new electrical device can you think of that might be developed for the home?

2. Explain what is meant by "cold" electric lighting.

3. For what purposes, other than lighting, can electric lamps be used?

4. What new development may replace our present day television tube?

5. What electronic device may someday be used to make highway travel safer?

UNIT 3
OPPORTUNITIES IN ELECTRICITY AND ELECTRONICS

Electricity and Electronics as a Vocation

Probably no other industry provides better job opportunities than the field of electricity and electronics. New electronic developments are made almost every day, and each of these developments provides new jobs. Everywhere we look, electricity and electronics are being used more and more. The tremendous growth of electrical devices means that more people are needed to design, install, and repair these items.

Basic jobs in electricity and electronics may be divided into six levels: (1) assembler, (2) construction, (3) maintenance and repair, (4) communication, (5) technician, (6) engineer.

Courtesy Hughes Aircraft Co.

◆ 15. A technician watches an intense beam of light from a "Laser" unit pierce a hole through a sheet of extremely hard tantalum in less than 1/1000 of a second. Research work with Lasers is but one of the many interesting areas of research being done in electronics.

Assembler

Assemblers can be found in any plant that manufactures electrical or electronic equipment or components. Assembling jobs include such positions as chassis assembler in a radio manufacturing plant, coil winder in an electric motor plant, or a cable installer in an aircraft factory. Each position requires special training for each specific job. Some very intricate work is required of the assemblers who place small parts on a printed circuit board used in a television set.

Most of these jobs require good finger dexterity, ability to follow directions closely, using hand tools, and an understanding of the types of schematic drawings required for a particular job. Many assemblers must also learn how to use certain test equipment to determine whether or not the finished product will function properly.

Construction

Construction electricians perform the various tasks relating to electrical work on all types of building projects. They install electrical fixtures, heating devices, lighting circuits, and other types of equipment using electricity. The ability to read blue prints is important in electrical installation work as well as skill in the use of tools. The construction electrician is important to all building trades.

Other jobs that might be classified with construction are: the ship electrician who installs the wiring and electrical equipment in ships, the tele-

Courtesy Radio Corporation of America

◆ 16. Making the final tests on an ultra-high-frequency transmitter before it is shipped from the plant.

phone installer who runs the telephone lines into homes and factories, and the stage electrician who provides lighting and wiring in motion picture studios and on theater stages.

All construction jobs must follow specific electrical code requirements, and the ability to read wiring diagrams, and calculate electrical formulas are all essential for the construction electrician's job.

One of the best ways to learn the electrician's trade is through an apprenticeship program. Apprenticeship is an approved program of supervised on-the-job training supplemented by related trade instruction. Most apprenticeship programs require a high school diploma with course work in mathematics, electricity, and science.

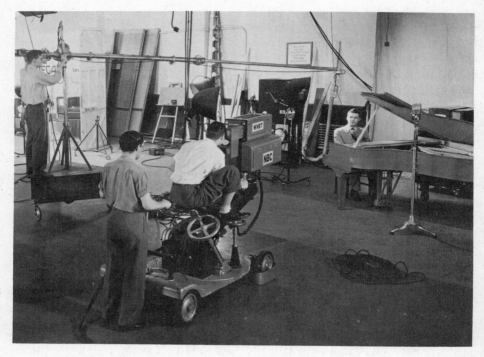

◆ 17. Many skilled electrical and electronic technicians are needed in the production of a television program. A government license is usually required for jobs in this field.

Maintenance and Repair

More people are employed in the maintenance and repair of electrical and electronic equipment than in any other phase of the industry. Maintenance electricians are responsible for keeping in good working order the tremendous amount of electrical equipment and machinery used in the home and in the nation's industrial, commercial, and government buildings. This field of work includes the skilled craftsman who inspects, repairs, and maintains electrical wiring, motors, generators, transformers, and other types of electrical equipment. A very

important individual in the maintenance field is the electrical appliance repair man who works on home equipment such as electric toasters, waffle irons, washing machine motors, and electric clothes dryers. Each of these maintenance jobs requires special training, tool skills, and a knowledge of electrical principles.

In electronics, one of the best known repair fields is the servicing of radio and television sets. All types of electronic equipment require specially trained service men. Hearing aids, computers, transmitters, test instruments, and stereo amplifiers need the attention of a skilled maintenance man when they fail to operate properly. These men have a high degree of skill, a good understanding of electronic theory, and they must know how to use the many types of special test equipment.

Training for maintenance and repairmen of electrical and electronic equipment may be obtained from special technical schools, military service schools, and from some industrial training programs. Most of these training schools require a high school diploma and desire students who have enrolled in mathematics, science, electricity, and electronic courses.

Communication

Probably the best known use of electronics is found in the field of communications which includes radio, television, radar, radio relay systems, telemetering, ship radio, telephone, and facsimile transmission. The ability to communicate using electronic equipment plays an important part in the safety services provided by aviation, coast-guard, police, fire, forestry conservation, highway maintenance, and special emergency service. Many types of positions involving the use of electronics can be found in each of the areas of communication. For example, a television station employs operators to maintain and repair the transmitter, to control the sound and adjust the picture, to operate the camera, to run the motion picture projector and adjust the lighting. Each of these highly skilled individuals must work together when the station is

transmitting a program.

It is often difficult to separate the communication operator and the technician, as they have a great deal in common. In many cases the operator of a particular piece of communication equipment is also the technician who designs and repairs the equipment. The general speed-up in the communications field has resulted in an increased need for individuals to operate and maintain a variety of communication equipment.

Many of the positions in communications require a special operators license which can be obtained by examination from the Federal Communications Commission. High school courses in mathematics, science, and electronics provide a valuable background in planning such a career. Obtaining an amateur radio station license and building and operating an amateur station is also good training.

Technician

The term "Electronic Technician" is used to designate a worker performing electronic activities requiring technical and related training, which provides direct support to the engineer or scientist in specialized areas of work. It includes those jobs involving research, design, and the development of electrical and electronic circuits. Testing and modifying experimental electronic devices is also part of the technician's job.

In addition to working on all types of communication equipment, technicians become specialists in such fields as industrial measuring, recording, in-

Courtesy General Electric Co.

◆ 18. Two engineers, directly in back of gate, are observing the effect of 10,000,000 volts of an artificial lightning discharge.

dicating and controlling devices, navigational equipment, missile and space-craft guidance, electronic computors, and many other types of equipment using vacuum tubes and semiconductor circuits.

There are many types of technician positions, and a number of different titles are used, such as, electronic computor technician; electronic circuit technician; electronic instrument technician; electronic research technician; and systems testing technician. Technicians are employed by industry and the government to conduct tests; direct installation; experiment; and operate equipment using electrical and electronic principles. For example, a technician working on a proposed printed circuit must first experiment with the arrangement of wires and components, so that they may be properly assembled. He plans methods of testing the unit by using test instruments and changes the arrangement of parts, so that the device operates correctly. To do all of this, he must understand electronic theory and use the mathematical computations necessary to plan, operate, and test the circuit.

Technicians usually qualify by obtaining training above the high school level. Training can be found in junior colleges, technical institutes, vocational schools, in-plant training, and the armed forces. Typical courses include electrical and electronic theory, mathematics, physics, and drafting.

Engineering

The engineer is responsible for conducting research, designing, experimenting, and creating new ideas with electrical and electronic devices. Electrical and electronic engineering is one of the most rapidly growing professions, and with the advances made in our technology and the increased use of electronics, the demand for electronic engineers continues to grow.

The major areas of work in this branch of engineering include electrical or electronic machinery and equipment manufacturing, telephone and telegraph, power, illumination, transportation, and communication. Areas of work such as nuclear energy, missile guidance systems, servomechanisms, computors, and automation require large numbers of electronic engineers.

The electronic engineer's work is exacting, and he must learn to work alone or as a member of a team. Much of his time is used working on ideas, sketches, mathematical calculations, and in writing reports and specifications. Engineering requires considerable above average ability, exceptional aptitude, and achievement in mathematics and science.

There are many areas of specialization within the field that may appeal to persons with particular interests. For example, the illumination engineer who has a keen artistic sense may find his ideal occupation in the motion picture industry or in the theater, while the electronics engineer with an appreciation of music may find his greatest opportunity in one of the many positions concerned with the recording and reproduction of high fidelity music. Similar interests might be stated in other areas of specialization.

A good high school background in the fields of mathematics and science are essential to enter the field of engineering. Most electrical or electronic engineers obtain a college degree in engineering. To those who have the ability, the opportunities in the field of engineering seem to be unlimited.

REVIEW QUESTIONS

1. What field of electronics would you choose as a vocation?

2. Why should jobs in electricity and electronics be plentiful in the future?

3. List the jobs that a good service electrician should be able to do.

4. What type of electronics work requires a government license?

5. Name as many electrical or electronics engineering jobs as you can.

Making Use

of

Magnetism

UNIT 4
PERMANENT ARTIFICIAL MAGNETS

Everyday Uses of Permanent Magnets

To understand electricity we must first know something about magnetism. *Magnetism* is not the same as electricity, but it plays a very important part in the construction and operation of many electrical devices.

Almost everyone has picked up pieces of iron with a magnet or has seen a small magnet hold itself to a metal surface. This simple principle, of holding on to certain metals, is used for many practical purposes around the home. The tack hammer shown in Illustration 1 is a magnet used to hold tacks firmly to the hammer head so that the user will not have to hold the tacks

◆ 1. The magnetic tack hammer is a very useful tool for upholstering or where tacks must be driven in hard-to-get-at places. The magnetic head is usually in a horseshoe form and the opposite end of the head is non-magnetic.

with his fingers. In the kitchen, magnets are attached to potholders so that

◆ 2. This note pad holder consists of a steel backplate and several small permanent magnets. These magnets hold paper and pencils when placed on the metal back.

they will "stick" to the stove, refrigerator, or other metal surfaces. Magnetic strips are used to hold sharp knives, small magnets hold notes to a metal plate on cabinet doors (Photograph 2), and cabinet doors are held closed with magnets. Some games use magnets to keep miniature players on a metal playing board.

All around us magnets are used; however, most people do not know how materials are magnetized. Illustrations 1, 2, and 3 are examples of how some permanent magnets are used. They are really artificial magnets because they were not magnets in their

◆ 3. In traffic courts, magnets in miniature plastic automobiles will hold the vehicles to a metal board so that positions of various automobiles that have been involved in an accident may be illustrated.

REPULSION BETWEEN
LIKE POLES

MAGNETS

REPULSION BETWEEN
LIKE POLES

MAGNETS

ATTRACTION BETWEEN
UNLIKE POLES

◆ 4. When the ends marked *N* are brought together, there is a tendency for the two bars to move apart or push each other away. The same is true if the ends marked *S* are brought together. Now if the end of one bar marked *N* is brought near the end of the other bar marked *S*, the two bars will pull themselves together.

natural form. Something had to be done to the material to change it into a magnet.

◆ 5. The top magnets were placed so that the like poles were near each other. When iron filings were sprinkled on them, a pattern formed, which shows that the two like magnetic fields push each other away. In the lower magnets, with unlike poles placed close together, the magnets have a strong attraction for each other. The iron filings form the path of the magnetic field.

Magnetic Action

If the ends of two bar magnets are placed near each other, they will either pull together or stay apart. See Illustrations 4 and 5. We can easily see that the ends marked alike tend to repel each other, and those marked unlike tend to attract each other. The *N* and *S* on the bars are commonly called *poles* and are referred to as the *north pole* and the *south pole* of the magnet. With this information, we can now state the first principle of magnetism: *Like poles repel each other and unlike poles attract each other.*

◆ 6. The ball bearings shown in the photograph represent the molecules in a piece of steel. A magnetized piece of steel has all of the molecules aligned so that the like poles are all in the same direction.

◆ 7. Each ball or molecule is marked to show that it has a north and south pole. In this unmagnetized piece of steel the molecules are not arranged in an orderly pattern.

Structure of Magnets

Not all pieces of steel are magnets. Two pieces may look exactly alike but one may attract other steel objects and one may not. The one that attracts another steel object is called a *magnet*. What makes the difference between the magnetized and unmagnetized pieces of steel?

Steel, like all things, is composed of very small particles called *molecules*. It is believed that each molecule has a north and a south pole the same as a whole magnet. In a piece of steel that is magnetized, these very small magnets have arranged themselves in an orderly fashion. Photograph 6 illustrates how the molecules have been arranged so that all north poles point in the same direction and, of course, all south poles will be pointing in the opposite direction. In the unmagnetized steel the molecules are arranged in a very irregular manner, as shown in Photograph 7. In this random arrangement of the tiny magnets, they tend to neutralize each other and thus the steel is unmagnetized.

Magnetic Induction

The unmagnetized steel may be magnetized if we stroke it with a magnet, as demonstrated in Photograph 8. The magnet will make the tiny molecules arrange themselves so that all of the poles bear in the same direction. This is called *magnetic induction*.

Magnetic Compass

If a piece of magnetized steel is suspended and left free to rotate, it will turn so that one end points north and

◆ 8. This piece of steel is being magnetized by stroking it with a permanent magnet. One pole of the permanent magnet is placed at one end of the piece of steel and pulled the full length of the steel. At the end of the stroke the magnet is lifted away from the steel and before starting the second stroke the magnet is again placed at the original starting position. After repeating this several times the steel will become magnetized. This is called *magnetic induction*.

the other end points south. This is because the earth is a huge magnet with
north and south poles that attract the
poles of the suspended magnet. This is
the principle of the *magnetic compass.*
The compass uses a very light, thin
magnet that rotates freely on its pivot.
The end of the compass that points
north is commonly referred to as the
north-seeking pole. The magnetic compass is an important aid to all types of
navigation. Through its use, ships at
sea are guided safely to port, explorers
are protected from becoming lost, and
airplanes are kept on their course.

The first compasses made by man
centuries ago used a piece of *lodestone,*
which means "leading stone." It is an
iron ore that is naturally magnetic.

The north magnetic pole is not
always in the same position; it shifts
slightly from year to year. It is in the
vicinity of Hudson Bay in northern
Canada, as indicated in Photograph 9.
The changes in location of the poles
are quite small and for most purposes
the pole is considered to be approximately 12° west of the geographical
north when a compass is read in New
York City, and approximately 18° east

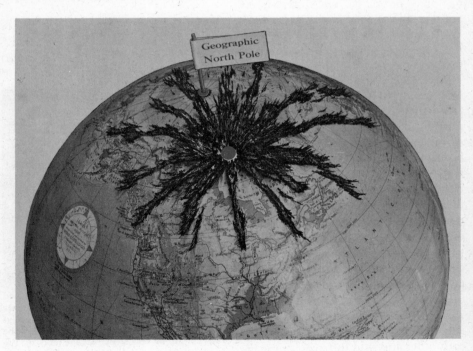

◆ 9. The iron filings on the top of the globe
illustrate the magnetic field of the earth. Not
everyone realizes that the earth's geographic
north pole and its magnetic pole are not the
same. They are approximately 1400 miles
apart and the compass points to the magnetic
pole. The fact that these two poles are not
the same makes it necessary for air or sea
navigators to recognize this difference when
plotting courses.

◆ 10. With this chart you will be able to determine the variation from true north that is indicated by a compass in your locality.

of the geographical north when read in San Francisco. In a narrow strip through the United States, from Michigan to Georgia, the compass will point true north and south all of the time, because the magnetic pole is directly in line with the north pole. See Illustration 10. The difference between true north and the compass reading at any place on the earth is called *variation*.

A permanent magnet may lose its magnetism by being hammered, dropped, or heated. All of these means cause the molecules to change their positions and thus the steel will lose its magnetism. On the other hand, an ordinary piece of steel will acquire magnetism if it is pointed north and hammered. The attraction of the earth's magnetism aligns the molecules.

Metals That Make Magnets

Permanent magnets are made in many shapes and sizes, as seen in Photograph 11. The common types are *horseshoe* and *bar* magnets. They are made of hardened steel, because it retains its magnetism for a long period of time. Soft steel can easily be magnetized but will not hold its magnetism. It is believed that soft steel loses its magnetism easily because the molecules of steel are free to move and thus change position readily. In hard steel the molecules are not so free to move.

A steel alloy, which is steel mixed with other metals such as tungsten, chromium, cobalt, or nickel, will make a very strong permanent magnet. Recent developments in the use of alloy steels have produced magnets which

◆ **11. Typical examples of commercial magnets. Each magnet has definite north and south poles regardless of its shape.**

have a much greater magnetic field than the hard steel magnets. One of the best alloys for making magnets contains aluminum, nickel, and cobalt. This type of alloy is commonly called *alnico*. Uses for permanent magnets other than those shown in the illustrations are in radio speakers, electrical measuring instruments, telephone receivers, generators, and motors. We shall learn more about these uses later.

Magnetic Materials

Metals which are attracted by a magnet are called *magnetic materials*. These are iron, from which steel is made, cobalt, and nickel. Other metals, including pure aluminum and copper,

zinc, and lead will not be attracted by a magnet and are called nonmagnetic. Materials other than metals, such as wood, textiles, etc., are never magnetic.

Magnetic Field

Magnetism will pass through all materials which are nonmagnetic. This can be illustrated by placing a piece of paper or glass on top of a magnet and sprinkling iron filings on it. The iron filings will become magnetized and drawn toward the magnet even though the paper or glass is between the filings and the magnet. Photograph 12 shows how the filings will form a definite pattern which is similar to the invisible magnetic field produced by the magnet. This magnetic field is always present around any magnet.

We can get a stronger magnetic field if two unlike poles are brought closer together. The closer the two poles are together without touching each other, the shorter the path will be for the magnetic field to travel. Each pole will have a greater attraction for the other and also they will have a stronger pull for other magnetic materials. If we should bend a bar magnet into the shape of a horseshoe, we would then find the magnetic field to be stronger.

◆ **12. The iron filings show the lines of force that are always present between the poles of any magnet.**

INTERESTING THINGS TO DO

1. Showing the Magnetic Field Surrounding a Single Magnet.

a. Place a bar magnet on a flat wooden surface and cover it with a sheet of paper. Sprinkle iron filings on the top of the paper and tap it lightly until a pattern forms. You now have the picture of a magnetic field. Observe that the lines tend to go from one pole to the other. Also note that the strongest field is close to the ends of the poles.

b. Sprinkle iron filings on a horseshoe magnet covered with a sheet of paper. You will notice that the magnetic field is now concentrated between the two poles. Why is there a greater magnetic field shown by the horseshoe magnet than by the bar magnet?

2. Showing the Magnetic Field Formed by Two Magnets.

a. Place two bar magnets on a flat surface, end to end, so that the north poles are approximately 1″ apart. Cover the bars with a sheet of paper and sprinkle iron filings on the paper

the same as in *1a*. Observe the pattern of the magnetic field. What is happening to the magnetic field?

b. Place two bar magnets on a flat surface, end to end, so that the north pole of one and the south pole of the other are approximately 1″ apart. Cover the bars with a sheet of paper and sprinkle iron filings on the paper. Observe the pattern of the magnets. How does it differ from the pattern of *2a?*

3. Making a Permanent Magnet by Induction.

a. Place an old hacksaw blade in a vise and with a pliers break off a piece about 2″ long. (To avoid having the blade break into several pieces do not let it extend over 2½″ beyond the vise jaw.) Obtain a permanent magnet and stroke the blade with the magnet. Test the blade to see if it is magnetic by trying to pick up some small nails. Why has the blade become a permanent magnet?

b. Obtain, two ¼″ straight-shank twist drills, and magnetize them by induction, using a very strong magnet. Be sure to stroke each drill with the same pole of the magnet and keep each drill pointed in the same direction. Then place the two drills parallel on a flat surface about ⅛″ apart. Keep the sharpened ends pointed in the same direction. Observe what happens to the drills. Why do the drills push each other apart? Reverse the direction of one of the drills. What happens and why?

4. Making a Compass.

Obtain a piece of spring steel approximately ³⁄₁₆″ wide and 1″ long (an old clock spring is excellent for this purpose). Shape the spring to a point on one end. Center-punch the spring in the middle so that it will balance on a pivot. It is easier to balance the compass if the center of the spring is raised as in Photograph 13. The pivot can be made by sharpening a brad on each end and forcing one end into a block of wood. The wood block should be about ¾″ thick and 1½″ square. A small hole can be made in the block with another brad, making it possible

◆ **13. Compass Constructed from a Clock Spring**

to push the pointed pivot in with your fingers. A drawing of the points of the compass can be made on a piece of paper and glued to the block. Magnetize the spring steel by induction. Place the magnetized spring on the pivot. If it does not balance, grind the heavy end until the steel compass needle balances perfectly. Compare the direction in which the spring points with that of a standard compass. Why does it point towards the north magnetic pole? What happens if the north pole of a bar magnet is brought near the north-seeking pole of the compass?

REVIEW QUESTIONS

1. List the uses that have been made of permanent magnets in your home.

2. Why are man-made permanent magnets called artificial magnets?

3. What are the poles of a magnet called?

4. State the basic law of magnetism.

5. When a piece of steel becomes magnetized what change takes place?

6. What is meant by *magnetic induction?*

7. What do we call the end of the compass that points towards the north?

8. What is the difference between the geographic north pole and the magnetic north pole?

9. Explain why a compass is important to all types of navigation.

10. Find out the approximate compass variation for your locality.

11. Why does the compass point true north and south in certain locations?

12. Why does hard steel retain magnetism?

13. What materials are used in making very strong permanent magnets?

14. List some nonmagnetic materials.

15. What is meant by a *magnetic field*?

16. What material did ancient navigators use for a compass?

UNIT 5
ELECTROMAGNETS

How Permanent Magnets Are Made

We have discussed how a permanent magnet may be made by stroking a section of hard steel with another magnet. Another method of making a permanet magnet is by *electromagnetism*. If insulated wire is wrapped around a hard piece of steel and the two ends of the coil are then connected to a source of electricity, such as a battery, we have what is called an *electromagnet*. If the battery is left connected for a short time, the steel will become magnetized and, when withdrawn from the coil, will be found to be a magnet.

Coil Polarity

What caused the coil of wire to magnetize the steel? We can find out if, after removing the steel core from the coil, we reconnect the coil to a battery source of electricity. Now iron filings may be sprinkled around the coil and a pattern will develop like that shown by the bar magnet. A compass may be placed near the coil and it will point

◆ 14. Compasses have been placed in the magnetic field of a coil that has been connected to a dry cell. Each compass points in the direction of the magnetic field. We can see that one end of the coil attracts the south pole of the compass. This shows us that the coil has definite north and south poles the same as a bar magnet.

in the direction of the magnetic field. See Photograph 14. This field can also be called the *lines of force*. The lines of force around the coil have a north and south pole just like the permanent magnet. The south pole of the coil will attract the north pole of the compass.

Importance of Electromagnets

Of all the functions of electricity, one of the most important is in the *electromagnet*. Many devices use the principle of electromagnetism in their construction. Without its use our entire industrial world would stop func-

tioning. All electric motors are dependent upon it. Automobiles use it to start and to keep running. The sound coming from a radio is dependent upon it. The television picture is focused by it. The power that provides heat and light for our homes is generated by it. Many more uses could be listed, as electromagnets are working for us continually. See Photograph 15.

How an Electromagnet Is Made

When we made a permanent magnet with electromagnetism, we used hard

CONTACT POINTS

ARMATURE

COIL

◆ 15. The buzzer is an application of an electromagnet. Its vibrating motion is made through the use of a contact point. When the buzzer is connected to a source of electricity the coil attracts the armature. As soon as the armature is pulled toward the coil the points open and the coil loses its magnetism. The armature then returns to its original position where the points again make contact. At this time the electromagnet once more pulls the armature to the coil. The vibrating motion is the result of the electricity being continually turned off and on. The metal pointer in the photograph shows where the tone of the buzzer can be adjusted.

steel for the magnet. This was done because we wanted to retain the magnetism in the steel. Electromagnets are used in many electrical devices which require a very strong magnetic field and also require the magnetism to be started and stopped rapidly.

If we connect a coil of wire to a source of electricity, we will find that it will have a very weak attraction for iron. Now if we insert a piece of soft steel into the center of the coil, we will find that the electromagnet will lift a number of steel objects. This increase in magnetic strength is due to the soft steel core, which provides a better path for the magnetic field. Disconnecting the battery from the coil will cause the steel objects to drop from the core. This shows us that a soft steel core loses its magnetism easily. It also illustrates that when the coil is disconnected from the source of electricity, the electromagnet is no longer operating.

Basic Principles of Electromagnets

We have now stated the two principal requirements of an electromagnet: (1) It must have a strong magnetic field which can be concentrated through the use of a steel core. (2) It must have a soft steel core so that the magnetism can readily be controlled.

◆ 16. This is a small shop-made electromagnet that can lift several hundred pounds. A pen light cell was used as the source of electricity for the electromagnet to support a man weighing 180 pounds. Large commercial electromagnets are used to lift heavy steel objects weighing several tons.

The electromagnet can be made stronger or weaker, depending upon how strong the source of electricity is and upon the number of turns of wire around the core. We can increase the strength of the magnetic field if we can increase the power of the electric-

Both coil symbols are now in common use.

Two lines always indicate a magnetic core.

◆ 17. In a modern door chime a coil-and-plunger, often called a *solenoid*, is used for its operation. When the door button is pushed, the plunger is pulled into the coil against one of the chime tubes. As the button is released a spring pulls the plunger back out of the coil against the other chime tube. From this starting and stopping of the electricity we are able to get the two different tones from the chimes.

ity. Likewise, if the number of turns of wire around the core is increased, this too will increase the strength of the electromagnet. These two factors will be more fully explained in another section of this book.

Coil and Moving Plunger

Devices that require opening, closing, pushing, and pulling by remote control usually use an electromagnet consisting of a coil and steel plunger, commonly called a *solenoid*. If we wind a coil of wire on a nonmagnetic hollow form, such as cardboard tubing, and connect it to a battery, it will set up a magnetic field around the coil. This field consists of lines of force that pass through the center of the coil. A small piece of soft steel placed near the hollow opening of the coil will be drawn into the coil, as shown in Illustration 18. This attraction, which causes the piece of steel to be pulled into the center of the coil, is due to the magnetism of the coil magnetizing the steel core. The molecules of the steel align themselves because they are attracted by the magnetic poles of the coil. We then have a coil acting like a magnet and magnetizing a steel core—the coil and the steel core attract each other. When the battery is disconnected, the coil loses its magnetism and, since it is made of soft steel, the plunger also loses its magnetism. This moving plunger can be used to push or pull various devices whenever the electricity is connected

♦ 18. When the battery is connected to the coil, the plunger is magnetized and pulled into the center of the coil. When the battery is disconnected, the coil and plunger lose their magnetism and the spring pulls the plunger back.

to the coil. If a spring is hooked onto the plunger, it will return the plunger to its original position as soon as the electricity is turned off. See Photograph 19.

♦ 19. A rear view of the coil-and-plunger used to provide motion in a commercial advertising sign. In operation the flashlight cell is connected to the coil of wire so that it pulls the steel core toward the center of the coil. As the plunger goes through the coil the battery is disconnected by the movement of the plunger. This permits the plunger to pass through the coil and after reaching the top of its swing it returns to the starting position. At this time the coil is reconnected to the dry cell and the plunger action starts over again. The device must be started by hand.

INTERESTING THINGS TO DO

1. Making a Permanent Magnet by Means of Electricity.

Make a hollow tube by wrapping a piece of thin cardboard (tagboard)

2″ x 2″ around a ¼″ wood dowel. See Illustration 20. Using a fast drying glue, secure the overlapping cardboard. Be sure to avoid gluing the tubing to the dowel so that it can be removed easily. Out of heavy cardboard or 1/8" masonite, shape two round washers about 1" in diameter. Drill a hole in the center of each washer so that they can be fit snugly over the ends of the cardboard tubing. Drill a 1/16" hole in one washer close to the center hole. A second 1/16" hole should be drilled near the outside edge of the same washer. Glue one washer to each end of the tubing. Insert one end of a spool of No. 22 magnetic wire through the inner 1/16" hole in the washer. Wind four, close-spaced, even layers of wire on the tubing and bring the end out through the outer hole in the washer. The two coil leads should be left about 6" long.

Obtain a piece of hard steel approximately 1/4" x 3". This can be a section of hacksaw blade, clock spring, or tool steel. Insert the steel into the center of the hollow coil. Connect the two ends of the coil to a dry cell for about ten seconds. Disconnect the cell and remove the hard steel core. Test the steel to see if it will attract small nails. What has happened to the steel? Hold one end of the steel near the north-seeking pole of a compass. Mark the polarity of your magnet.

2. Using a Plunger-Type Solenoid.

Obtain a piece of soft steel 1/4" in diameter and about 2 1/2" long. Insert the soft steel about halfway into the center of the coil made in Number 1. Connect one end of the coil to a dry cell, and momentarily make contact with the remaining coil lead to the other terminal of the cell. What hap-

◆ **20. Electromagnetic Coil**

pened to the soft steel core? Why did this occur? How can this principle be used on other electrical devices?

The coil that you have wound can be used on a number of different electrical projects such as a buzzer, door chime, motor, electrical lock, relay, or switch.

3. Making a super-electromagnet
Materials needed:

1 Piece iron pipe, 4" pipe size, 2 1/8" long
1 Piece sheet steel, mild, 1/4" x 5" x 5"
1 Piece sheet steel, mild, 3/8" x 5" x 5"
1 Piece steel rod, mild, round, 1 1/2" diameter, 2 1/2" long
2 Eye bolts, steel, 3/8"
2 Hexagon nuts, steel, 3/8"
8 Machine screws, R. H. steel, 8-32, 3/4" long
360 Feet magnet wire, 18 ga., enamel or cotton covered
1 Piece sheet metal, 20 ga., 6" x 8", for wire spool (*see text*)
1 Piece plastic tubing, size 18, 2" long.

The secret of this electromagnet's tremendous holding force on very small battery power, shown in Figure 16, is the nearly perfect magnetic contact between the top plate and pipe and a similar contact between the bottom plate, core, and pipe. This requires that the parts which go together be turned and faced on a lathe to a mirror-like surface. For those who

◆ **21. Cross-section drawing of a super electromagnet.**

have the ability to perform the necessary lathe operations, and also the welding experience to weld the center core to the top plate, the magnet will open up the fascinating field of electromagnetism with many exciting experiments.

Four inch pipe usually has an outside diameter of about 4½", but since that measurement may vary somewhat the steel pieces for the top and bottom plates are specified larger so that they may be placed in a lathe chuck with ample clearance.

Turn and face the parts in a lathe to get the smoothest possible surfaces on the parts which fit together. The bottom plate should be about ¼" wider than the diameter of the pipe. Drill the center of the top plate for a

press fit with the center core, press the core into place and weld the two pieces together, as shown in Figure 21. Secure the top plate and core to the pipe with steel machine screws, as shown in the drawing. Place the magnet shell in a lathe and face the ends of the core and pipe so that the two pieces will be perfectly in line. Drill and tap the magnet core and bottom plate and secure the eye bolts in place with hexagon nuts. Drill two ⅛" holes in the top plate for coil leads.

Make a form out of copper, aluminum, or brass, on which to wind the magnet wire. *Do not use iron or steel.*

This form should fit snugly over the center core and should be slightly shorter than the iron pipe. Wind 360 feet of magnet wire on the form and insulate the coil leads with pieces of plastic tubing. To prevent breakage of the coil leads they may be joined to pieces of stranded wire within the form, or they may be brought out to an insulated terminal strip mounted on top of the magnet.

If the magnet is to be used to lift one or more persons, it is advisable to link the top and bottom plates together with a loose piece of chain. This will prevent the bottom plate from striking the person being lifted in case a weak dry cell allows the two parts to separate.

REVIEW QUESTIONS

1. What happens when a coil of wire is connected to a source of electricity?

2. When a piece of hard steel is placed in a coil connected to a source of electricity, what happens to the steel?

3. Give another name for *magnetic field*.

4. Make a list of some electrical devices that use electromagnets.

5. What effect does the steel core have on the magnetic field in an electromagnet?

6. Why isn't hard steel used in electromagnets?

7. What is a coil and moving plunger usually called?

8. Explain why a soft steel core will be pulled into the magnetic field of a coil.

How Electricity Is Produced

~~~~~~

UNIT 6
THE ELECTRON THEORY

Structure of Matter

Matter is anything that has weight and occupies space. It may be in the form of a solid, such as copper in an electrical conductor; a gas, such as hydrogen; or a liquid, such as water.

Using water as an example, let's analyze the structure of matter. If we took a drop of water and continued to divide it until it could not be divided further and still maintain the chemical properties of water, the smallest particle remaining would be a *molecule* of water.

Next, let's take this molecule of water and pass an electric current through it. This action will break down the molecule still further into its two component gases, hydrogen and oxygen. But these gases no longer have the properties of water. A substance that can be broken down into two or more basic parts, such as water, is called a *compound*.

The hydrogen and oxygen which combined to make the water and which cannot be broken down further are known as *elements*. The smallest particle of an element which still has the chemical and electrical properties of that element is an *atom*. To make a molecule of water, two atoms of hydrogen and one atom of oxygen are needed. See Illustration 1.

The Nature of Electricity

Before the acceptance of the electron theory, the effects of electricity could be seen, felt, and measured but could only be described as a mysterious force that traveled through a conductor at a speed of 186,000 miles per second. The electron theory is widely accepted today as an explanation of the flow of electricity through a conductor.

According to the electron theory, the atoms which make up all matter are

◆ 1. Hydrogen and oxygen atoms unite to form a molecule of water.

composed of 3 types of particles, *protons, electrons,* and *neutrons.* The atoms of different materials vary only in the number and arrangement of these particles.

The electron is a particle of negative electrical charge revolving around the center of the atom, similar to the earth revolving around the sun. The center of the atom contains the positively charged particles called protons and the neutral particles (neutral in that they bear no charge) called neutrons. This center is termed the *nucleus* of the atom.

We have noted that there are two types of charged particles, positive and negative. Since the positive charge of the nucleus of the atom attracts the negative charge of the electron, we can say that *opposite charges attract.* In other words, there is a force of attraction between positive and negative charges.

When considering weight, we must note that the proton and neutron weigh about 1847 times as much as

the electron. Thus the total weight of the proton and the neutron will determine the weight of the material.

For the sake of clarity, the structure of an atom is usually represented by a series of progressively larger orbits. But the paths of the electrons are generally thought of as following the inside circumference of spherical shells, one inside the other. The force which holds the electrons in their paths, preventing their breaking outward, is the attraction between the positively charged protons and the negatively charged electrons. The force which prevents the electrons from moving inward is centrifugal force, which is the force tending to make a rotating body move away from the center of rotation.

Except for the electrons in the outer shell, the particles of an atom are held tightly together and tremendous forces are required to pry them apart. Since the electrons in the outer shell are farthest from the nucleus, they are least attracted by the positive charge. In materials such as copper and silver which have only one electron in their outer shell, as shown in Illustration 2, the electron may be easily dislodged. This characteristic makes these

◆ 2. Arrangement of electrons in a copper atom.

materials very good electrical conductors.

An aluminum atom consists of 13 electrons revolving around a nucleus of 13 protons and 14 neutrons, as shown in Figure 3. The distribution of electrons in an atom requires that there be eight in the outer shell for stability. Any number of electrons less than eight in the outer shell causes them to become unstable. As the number of electrons are decreased, instability increases. These unstable electrons are known as "free" electrons because they can move easily to another atom. An aluminum atom has only three electrons in its outer shell and it is this property that makes it a fair conductor. If we examine the illustration of a copper atom, Figure 2, we can see why copper is a far better electrical conductor.

An atom of copper has only one free electron in its outer shell where an atom of aluminum has three. The single electron in the copper atom will move more readily to another atom than will one of the electrons in the aluminum atom. Also, the electrons in the aluminum atom revolve around the nucleus within three shells, while electrons in the copper atom require

♦ 3. Arrangement of atoms in an aluminum atom.

♦ 4. When the negatively charged electron moves from the dry cell to atom *A* it forces the electron from the outer shell of atom *A* to atom *B*. The electron from atom *B* moves on to atom *C* where it displaces the outer electron and forces it to atom *D*. This movement continues on to atom *E* and through the remainder of the circuit to the positive terminal of the dry cell.

four shells. This places the electron in the outer shell farther away from its center, which reduces the attraction from the positively charged nucleus and further decreases the force required to move the electron to another atom.

Since the movement of electrons along a conductor corresponds to the flow of electricity, some means must be provided to start the electrons in motion. When an electrical circuit is connected to a source of supply, such as a dry cell, negatively charged electrons tend to flow from the negative terminal of the dry cell through the conductor. This movement dislodges a negatively charged electron from the outer shell of an atom within the conductor and forces it to the next atom. The newly arrived electron forces the electron in the outer shell to the next atom where a similar action takes place in adjacent atoms until the positive terminal of the dry cell is reached, as shown in Illustration 4. While this step-by-step movement may seem like a slow process it is actually occurring at the speed of light, or approximately 186,000 miles per second.

UNIT 7

MAKING ELECTRICITY WITH CHEMICALS

A Simple Cell

Chemical action is one method of providing a source of electricity. Certain materials, usually metals and carbon, when placed in a liquid solution can produce electricity. A simple cell for producing electricity can be made by placing carbon and zinc in a solution of salammoniac. Salammoniac is used to clean soldering coppers and is available in powder or bar form. Salammoniac is known chemically as *ammonium chloride* and may be obtained in powder form at any drugstore. If the bar salammoniac is used it will be necessary to break off several small pieces and pound them into a powder. The powder can then be mixed with the water in a glass.

A piece of zinc is placed in the glass with the salammoniac solution and a rod of carbon is put in so that it does not touch the zinc. A short length of insulated wire is then connected to the zinc and another wire to the carbon. The other ends of these wires are hooked to a 1½-volt flashlight bulb. The bulb will light, and the cell of zinc, carbon, and salammoniac is developing electricity. See Fig. 5.

Electrons

What makes our cell produce electricity? The solution of salammoniac and water, called an *electrolyte,* starts acting on the piece of zinc so that very small particles, not visible to the human eye, gather all around the zinc. These particles are called *electrons.* All electrons are considered to be negative particles of electricity. The electrons will pile up all around the zinc until there is not room for any more to get on it. The zinc which has all of the electrons around it is called the *negative electrode.* A minus sign (—) is usually used to indicate the negative electrode. See Fig. 5.

Since all the electrons in the solution have gone to the zinc, the carbon is without electrons. We call this point where there is a shortage of electrons the *positive electrode.* A plus sign (+) is usually used to indicate the positive electrode. In electricity when we have a large number of electrons at one place they tend to try to move to a

SINGLE CELL

Terminals of a cell are identified by the length of lines.

MULTICELL BATTERY

Cell symbols are combined to represent a battery.

DIRECTION OF ELECTRON FLOW   FLASHLIGHT BULB

ZINC STRIP

CARBON ROD

SALAMMONIAC SOLUTION

◆ 5. A simple cell made of zinc, carbon, and a solution of salammoniac. The three requirements for a complete electrical circuit are all connected together—a source of electricity, the cell; the two connecting wires; and the object that works from the electricity, the bulb. The flashlight bulb is connected to the zinc and the carbon. The electrons start flowing from the zinc through the wire and the bulb so that they can get to the carbon. This flow of electrons is what is called a flow of electricity. The flow of electricity is then negative particles, called electrons, going from a point where there are many extra electrons to a point where there are very few.

place where there is a shortage of electrons. The electrons in the electrolyte solution flow to the zinc. In order to allow the electrons on the zinc to reach the carbon, an outside path must be provided.

Primary Cells

Cells which cannot be recharged are called *primary cells*. When we made the cell of zinc, carbon, and salammoniac it was a primary cell because it could not be recharged. The cell went "dead" because the zinc was dissolved in the electrolyte.

Direct Current

The flow of electrons from a cell through a circuit is called *direct current*. Direct current is a flow of elec-

tricity that is always in the same direction. A primary cell has one terminal that is negative (−) and the other that is positive (+). When the terminals were connected to a flashlight bulb, the electrons flowed from the negative terminal through the wire and bulb to the positive terminal. This is a direct current source of electricity because the electrons always travel in the same direction. The abbreviation for direct current is DC.

The Dry Cell

A primary cell that can be carried easily and handled without spilling the electrolyte is called a *dry cell*. See Illustration 6. These dry cells are used in flashlights, pen lights, radios, telephone circuits, and in many other

SEALING COMPOUND

ZINC CAN

CARBON POST

ELECTROLYTE PASTE

SPACER

EXTERIOR VIEW
OF A DRY CELL

CROSS-SECTION
OF A DRY CELL

◆ 6. The outside of a flashlight cell is covered with cardboard but the container is a zinc can. The center post is a carbon rod held in place at the top by an insulating material. Under the insulating top and in the zinc container can be found the electrolyte, which is salammoniac in paste form with black manganese dioxide added.

places where direct current is needed. They differ mainly from the wet cell, in that the electrolyte is made of a paste instead of a liquid.

The dry primary cell will have about 1½ volts. See Fig. 7. As in the wet cell,

the carbon is the positive (+) terminal and the zinc is the negative (−) terminal. The action is the same as in the wet cell. When the zinc is dissolved the cell goes dead.

Single dry cells are found in many shapes and sizes. Large cells are used where longer service is needed. Usually the larger the cell the longer it will last. Of course, when cells must be carried, as in flashlights, they are made small so that they are light in weight.

The Alkaline-Manganese Cell

An undesirable characteristic of ordinary dry cells is the forming of gas bubbles on the surface of the electrodes. This reduces the active area in contact with the electrolyte and limits the current output from the cell. This action is called *polarization* and a depolarizer in the form of manganese-dioxide is usually combined with the electrolyte to reduce its effect.

◆ 7. This experiment demonstrates that regardless of the size a single dry cell will produce only 1½ volts.

The polarizing effect frequently gets ahead of the action of the depolarizer and then the cell requires a period of rest to return it to a working condition.

Recent developments in dry cells have brought about improvements which reduce materially the effect of polarization, thereby increasing current output capability and useful life several times over that of a similar size zinc-carbon type cell. One such cell, known as an *alkaline-manganese* type is shown in Figure 8. This type of cell has a potassium-hydroxide electrolyte of high conductivity which provides low internal resistance, and electrodes with large surface areas which reduce polarization to a minimum. These features provide a dry-cell capable of withstanding reasonably heavy current drain with little change in terminal voltage and one that will operate satisfactorily even under extreme low temperature conditions.

The Mercury Cell

Like the Alkaline-Manganese cell, the mercury cell is capable of maintaining a reasonably high current output with no appreciable change in its terminal voltage. It has a longer useful life than other type dry cells, extending up to two years, according to the claims of one manufacturer. It is capable of withstanding extreme hot and cold temperatures, which makes it an excellent source of power for portable electronic equipment where those conditions prevail. One advantage of the mercury cell over other

◆ 8. Typical construction of an alkaline-manganese cell. The effects of polarization have been reduced by increasing the areas of the anode and cathode elements.

types of dry cells is that it may be obtained in small button-like sizes which make them desirable for hearing aids and other electronic devices where space is limited. A sectional view of a mercury cell is shown in Figure 9. Note the similarity in con-

◆ 9. The mercury cell takes its name from the mercuric oxide used as a cathode. This type of cell provides a useful life of several times over that of a similar size dry cell.

struction with that of an alkaline-manganese cell. Both cathodes are near the outside of the cells and the same type of electrolyte, potassium hydroxide, is used for each cell. One of the main differences between the two cells is that the mercury cell uses mercuric oxide for a depolarizer while the alkaline-manganese cell uses manganese dioxide. Since both the mercury cell and the alkaline-manganese cell use highly caustic potassium hydroxide, *never* attempt to cut one of these cells open, otherwise serious injury to the eyes or skin may result. The chemical action which causes current to flow in a mercury or alkaline-manganese cell is similar to what we learned when we studied the chemical action of a simple cell. The voltage of a mercury cell is 1.35 volt.

◆ 10. A modern radio B battery is made up of many wafer-like 1½ volt cells. The photo shows some of the 45 cells which provide a total of 67½ volts for the battery.

Batteries

When more than 1½ volts is needed, dry cells are connected so that the voltage of the cells can be added together. See Illustration 10. In a flashlight using two dry cells, the voltage produced by the two cells is 3 volts. When dry cells are placed together in one container and are connected to provide more voltage we call this a *battery*. These cells may be round in shape much as the pen light cell or can be made flat so that they will pack more compactly. Radio batteries are made to deliver various voltages, usually 1½, 6, 22½, 45, or 90 volts.

The Storage Cell

One of the disadvantages of the dry cell is that when it has been used for a period of time the cell becomes discharged and must be thrown away. A cell that can be used over and over again by recharging is called a *secondary cell*. This is the type of cell found in the storage battery that is used in automobiles. A storage cell that is being used as a source of electricity will run down, but after recharging it is ready for use again.

In the simple primary cell we used two unlike materials such as zinc and carbon in an electrolyte solution. The most common type of secondary cell is called a *lead-acid cell* since it contains plates of lead for both the positive and the negative terminals, and sulfuric acid and distilled water for the electrolyte. We can construct a simple storage cell by putting a dilute solution of sulfuric acid in a glass container. Extreme care must be used in handling sulfuric acid as it is very dangerous. If the acid comes in contact with any part of the body it will burn the skin, and it will also burn holes in clothing. The acid should be diluted by first pouring the water into the glass and then adding the acid very slowly. Two strips of lead are next placed in the acid solution so that they do not touch each other. These metal strips are both alike and the cell will not produce electricity until we do something to change one of the pieces of lead.

The cell needs to be *charged;* this can be done by using a source of direct current electricity such as that found in two dry cells. The dry cells should be connected so that they will produce 3 volts, the positive terminal being connected to one strip of lead and the negative terminal to the other strip. We can see that some action is taking place in the electrolyte as bubbles start to appear in the solution. As the charging process continues, the lead plate connected to the positive terminal of our dry cell will start to turn brown. The negative plate will show little change in color. After about ten minutes we can disconnect our dry cells and test the storage cell to see if it produces electricity.

Charging and Discharging a Storage Cell

When the cell has run down we can recharge it and use it again. During the charging process, two changes occurred in the cell. The plates became different in color, with the positive plate turning brown. The brown coat-

1. Terminal Post
2. Vent Cap
3. Sealing Compound
4. Cell Cover
5. Filling Tube
6. Electrolyte Level Mark
7. Inter Cell Connector welded to lead insert
8. Lead Insert in cover and plate strap
9. Plate Strap
10. Separator Protector
11. Negative Plate
12. Separator
13. Positive Plate
14. Negative Plate with active material removed to show plate Grid
15. Plate Grid
16. Container

The Electric Storage Battery Co.

◆ 11. The illustration shows the interior construction of a typical 12-volt automobile battery.

ing on the positive plate is chemically called *lead peroxide*. This charging has made the two lead plates different, one of the requirements of a primary cell. The electrolyte solution changes from a weak solution of sulfuric acid to a stronger solution of the acid. The change in the metals and the formation of stronger acid always occur during charging. The voltage of the fully charged cell is about 2 volts.

Commercial Storage Batteries

Besides the advantage of recharging, the storage cell is much better than the dry cell where continuous heavy use is required. In automobiles the storage battery is used to start the engine, provide power for the ignition circuit, and as a source of electricity for lights and accessories. Since more than 2 volts are usually necessary for these purposes, the battery is made of six lead-acid cells connected to provide 12 volts. In some automobiles a 6-volt storage battery is used.

Testing a Storage Battery

One method of testing a storage battery is to test the acid in each of

POSITIVE GROUP — SEPARATORS — NEGATIVE GROUP

◆ 12. Each cell of a commercial battery is made up of several negative plates and several positive plates held apart from the others, by insulated separators. These separators may be made of such insulating materials as wood, fiber glass, or rubber, and they keep the negative plates from touching the positive plates. In the cell all of the negative plates are connected together and all of the positive plates are connected together so that the cell will be able to handle heavy demands for electricity. The plates are made of a lead grid framework. The negative grids are filled with spongy lead and the positive plates are filled with lead peroxide.

the cells by means of a *hydrometer*. The hydrometer contains a float inside of a glass tube. The float will rise with liquids heavier than water. A term, *specific gravity*, is applied when comparing the weight of different liquids with that of water. Water is given a value of 1.000 in weight, which is called its specific gravity. See Fig. 13.

When a battery has been in use for some time the electrolyte becomes lower in the cells. This is due to evaporation. Pure water, called *distilled water*, must be used to refill the cell. After a battery has been in service for a long time it will lose its capacity for being recharged. This is because the paste becomes loose in the grids of the plates, and the plates start to buckle. At this time the battery must either be rebuilt or replaced by a new one.

The Nickel-Cadmium Cell

The introduction of small portable power tools and electronic equipment that require more current than can be provided by dry-cells has brought

Unscrew Vent Plug

Discharged 1.150

Half Charged 1.225

Fully Charged 1.275–1.300

◆ 13. When sulfuric acid from a fully charged cell is drawn into a hydrometer it will read about 1.300, as the acid is heavier than water. This heavy acid made the float stay up higher in the liquid than it would with water. When a battery is discharged, part of the acid has returned to the plates. The solution in the cell now has less acid than before and the specific gravity will read about 1.150.

CONTACT SPRING

POTASSIUM HYDROXIDE

GASKET

CADMIUM NEGATIVE ELECTRODE

SEPARATOR

PERFORATED METAL SPACER

NICKEL HYDROXIDE (POSITIVE ELECTRODE)

◆ 15. Cross-section view of a button-type nickel-cadmium storage cell showing basic elements. Improvements which have done away with replacing water and allowing gas to escape from the cell have made it an excellent source of power for portable equipment.

◆ 14. Photographs above show a drill and hedge trimmer which are independent of long power cords. Their source of energy is nickel-cadmium batteries which are very compact, produce energy for many hours, and are easily recharged.

about the improvement of the nickel-cadmium storage cell to where it may be used as readily as a dry cell. Like a conventional lead-acid storage cell the nickel cadmium cell in its original form required occasional refilling with water and provision for the escape of gas generated within the cell. The modern improved cell contains a nickel and a cadmium electrode with a potassium-hydroxide electrolyte. In operation the nickel electrode reaches full charge before the cadmium electrode thereby preventing the generating of hydrogen gas from the cadmium. Oxygen generated at the nickel electrode reacts with the cadmium and forms the electrochemical equivalent of cadmium oxide. Since no provision need be made for the escape of gases, the cell may be sealed and used like a conventional dry cell. Nickel-cadmium cells are very popular with transistor radio owners, since they can be recharged by means of a simple transformer, half-wave dry rectifier combination.

INTERESTING THINGS TO DO

1. Making a Simple Wet Cell.

In a pint glass jar mix a solution of water and salammoniac. Keep adding powdered salammoniac to the water and stir the solution until no more salammoniac will dissolve. Obtain an old dry cell and remove the center carbon rod. Cut a strip of zinc about 1" wide and 6" long. Place both the zinc and the carbon in the solution so that they do not touch each other. Connect a wire to the carbon and another wire to the zinc strip. Attach the other ends of the wires to a 1½-volt flashlight bulb. Why does the bulb light? What is happening in the cell?

2. Making a Simple Storage Cell.

Pour a dilute solution of sulfuric acid into a pint glass jar. Use EXTREME CARE IN HANDLING THE ACID. If the acid needs to be diluted, be sure to put the water into the jar first and add the acid slowly. Obtain two lead strips approximately 1" x 6". Place these two strips in the electrolyte solution so that they do not touch each other. Connect one wire to one lead strip and another wire to the other strip. Two dry cells should be connected so that they produce 3 volts.

◆ 16. A Simple Storage Cell

To do this connect the negative terminal of one cell to the positive terminal of the other cell. One wire from the lead strips goes to the remaining negative terminal of the two cells and the other wire goes to the remaining positive terminal. The storage cell is now being charged. Notice what is happening to the lead plates. Let the charging action continue for about ten minutes. In place of the two dry cells, connect the wires from the storage cell to a flashlight bulb or a buzzer. What is happening? Why do we call this a *secondary cell*?

REVIEW QUESTIONS

1. Define an atom.
2. What holds the electrons in their paths around the nucleus?

3. Why are silver and copper good electrical conductors?
4. At what speed does an electron

move from atom to atom in a conductor?

5. What are the three requirements for a complete circuit?

6. Explain the difference between a wet and a dry cell.

7. What is the difference between a primary and a secondary cell?

8. What is meant by *electron flow*?

9. In a primary cell what happens when the cell goes dead?

10. Explain what we mean when we say that a direct current is flowing.

11. How does the size of a dry cell affect its operation?

12. What happens when a storage cell is being charged?

13. State the purpose of the separators in a commercial storage battery.

14. How can you determine the charge of a storage cell?

15. Why do commercial storage batteries have more than one plate for each cell?

16. What is the main difference between a standard dry-cell and an alkaline-manganese cell?

17. State some advantages of a mercury cell over a standard dry cell.

18. Is a nickel-cadmium cell a primary or a secondary cell? Explain your answer.

Letter symbols in a circle identify rotating machines.

Letter symbols in a circle are used to identify any instrument.

UNIT 8
GENERATING ELECTRICITY WITH MAGNETISM

◆ **17. The galvanometer is connected to the two ends of the coil. Holding the bar magnet in one hand, we should then push it through the center of the coil of wire. Immediately we will notice that the needle of the galvanometer moved in one direction and then comes back to zero in the center of the dial.**

◆ **18. When we pull the magnet back out of the coil the meter needle moves in the opposite direction and then comes back to zero.**

Batteries are very useful for providing a source of electricity but they are limited in the amount of electricity that they can produce. To produce great quantities of electricity, a method of making it by means of a magnetic field is generally used. The generators and dynamos found in electric plants throughout the world use the principle of electromagnetism to make electricity.

Moving Bar Magnet

To produce electricity by a magnetic field we need a coil of wire and a magnet. A coil can be wound of about 25 turns of wire around a 1″

hollow tubing. To indicate that electricity is being produced we need a very sensitive instrument called a *galvanometer*. A galvanometer is used to show that a very small quantity of electrons is flowing in a circuit. Usually the pointer or needle of the meter points to the center of the dial when not in use. When electricity flows through the meter, the needle will move either to the left or right.

Each time we push the magnet toward the center of the coil the galvanometer needle will move in one direction, and each time we pull the magnet out, the needle will move in the other direction. If we leave the magnet inside of the coil the galvanometer needle does not move. To produce electricity, as shown by the galvanometer, we need to have the magnet moving in or out of the coil. See Illustrations 17 and 18.

Turn the bar magnet around so that the other pole is pushed into the coil first. Now we will notice that the needle moves in the opposite direction. This shows us that the direction of the galvanometer needle movement depends upon which direction the magnet is pushed or pulled. The direction that electricity flows depends upon which direction the bar magnet is moving.

Moving Coil

If we hold the bar magnet steady in one hand and place the coil so that the hollow center can be moved back and forth over the magnet we will again notice the galvanometer needle moves first in one direction and then in the other. The coil can be turned over so that the opposite end starts moving over the magnet first. Now the needle will move in the opposite direction. From this we can see that electricity can be produced either by moving a magnet in a coil or wire or by having a coil of wire move over a magnet.

Induced Electricity

Why did the coil and bar magnet produce electricity? When we studied magnetism in Unit 4 we found that a magnet always had a magnetic field around it. When either the magnet is moving or the coil is moving, the wires in the coil are cutting through the magnetic field of the magnet. Cut-ting through the magnetic field by the coil produces what is called *induced* electricity. Electricity can be induced in the coil only when either the magnet or the coil is in motion.

Alternating Current

The bar magnet, when pushed in or out of the coil, made the galvanometer needle move first in one direction and then in the other. This was due to the cutting of the magnetic field which induced electricity in the coil. This induced electricity is a flow of electrons through the coil and galvanometer. When the bar magnet was pushed into the center of the coil, the electrons began to flow in one direction. As soon as the magnet was stopped, the electrons stopped flowing in the circuit. Electrons started to flow again in the opposite direction when the magnet was pulled out of the coil. The flow of electrons, first in one direction, then stopping and starting to flow again in the opposite direction, is called *alternating current*. This is different from direct current, which always flows in the same direction.

Alternating current electricity, which is abbreviated AC always flows first one way through the circuit and

ALTERNATING CURRENT SOURCE

This symbol is used to indicate any source of alternating current.

then reverses and starts flowing in the other direction. We later shall find that there are many reasons why alternating current is used.

Frequency

The faster that we move the bar magnet in and out of the coil the faster the electrons must change direction of flow through the coil and galvanometer. The electron flow changes direction every time the magnet changes direction. We say that the electrons have completed one *cycle* of flow when the magnet has been pushed into and pulled out of the coil once. One cycle of electricity might be compared to an automobile engine that turns over once. The engine in making one revolution has completed one cycle of its motion before it starts the second revolution. To make a second cycle of alternating current we must plunge the magnet in and out of the coil again. Each time we do this we complete one cycle of alternating current.

The number of cycles completed in one second is called the *frequency*. We can develop a frequency of 10 cycles per second alternating current by pushing the magnet in and out of the coil ten times every second.

The frequency of alternating current coming into most homes is 60 cycle. This means that the alternating current is changing direction 120 times every second.

A Simple Generator

If a coil of wire is moved in a magnetic field we know that the cutting of the lines of magnetic force will produce electricity. This is the principle of the *generator*, which is used to produce most of the electricity that we use. A generator has a moving coil that can be rotated in a magnetic field. The rotating coil is usually called an *armature*. The magnetic field can be made of two magnetic poles such as found in a horseshoe magnet. See Illustration 19.

◆ 19. To obtain electricity from the rotating coil we must be able to connect onto the two ends of the coil. This requires the construction of special devices called slip rings or a commutator. The contact to the slip rings or commutator is made by two brushes. The drawing shows how the brushes are always in contact with the two ends of the coil through the use of slip rings.

◆ 20. This drawing of an A. C. generator shows that the maximum voltage will be developed when the armature conductors are cutting the maximum number of lines of force. The single armature turn is shown to simplify the drawing and not to indicate that it would be sufficient to light the bulb. Actually, a very large number of turns of wire would be required on the armature to develop enough voltage to light the bulb.

◆ 21. In this drawing of an A. C. generator the turn of wire representing the armature has rotated 90 degrees, or one quarter turn. Since it is not cutting any lines of force, no voltage is being developed.

Alternating Current Generator

To make contact with the coil as it rotates, two separate rings are placed around the shaft of the armature. One ring is connected to one end of the coil and the other ring to the other end of the coil. The rings must not touch each other and must not touch the armature shaft except through an insulating material. These two rings are called *slip rings* (Figures 20 and 21). As they rotate two *brushes* made either of soft copper or carbon are always in contact with the rings.

When the coil rotates in the magnetic field, made by the two poles of the magnet, the greatest amount of electricity is produced in the coil when it is cutting the largest number of lines of force. The coil is cutting the largest

number of lines of force when it is moving directly across the ends of the two poles. See Figure 20.

The coil cuts the fewest lines of force when each part of the coil is moving farthest away from the center of the magnetic field. The amount of electricity produced in the coil is large when the coil is moving between the two magnets. No electricity is produced when the coils are cutting none of the lines of force. See Figure 21.

When a coil was moved in and out of a magnet, we said an alternating current was being produced because it would cut the magnetic field first in one direction and then in the other direction. This same action takes place as the coil rotates between the two poles of the magnet. The induced electricity flows out through the brushes first one way and then the other, as the coil is rotated in the magnetic field. The alternating current is not

ROTATING
PERMANENT MAGNET
FIELD

STATIONARY
ARMATURE
COIL

◆ 22. This photograph shows how alternating current can be developed with stationary armature coils and a rotating permanent magnet field. As the magnet rotates it induces an alternating current in the stationary coils. Slip rings are not necessary on this generator. Generators used on bicycles are of this type.

constant and is changing in amount depending upon where the coil is in the magnetic field.

Alternating Current Wave Form

The action of an alternating current generator can be shown by a graph known as an alternating current wave form, Figure 23. As the armature rotates between the poles of a magnet, the voltage generated rises to a maximum at 90 degrees, then drops to zero at 180 degrees, as shown by the half-cycle wave form. As the armature passes through the 180 degree point to complete the cycle, voltages of the same value as the first half-cycle will be generated, but of opposite polarity because the armature will be cutting magnetic lines of force in the opposite direction. This is represented on the graph by the loop below the line.

◆ 23. Alternating current wave form.

◆ 24. A drawing of a simple direct current generator. The armature is now cutting the maximum number of lines of force. One brush is always in contact with the side of the coil going up on the left side of the armature. The other brush is in contact with the side of the coil going down on the right side.

◆ 25. As the armature rotates a quarter of a turn, the coil is cutting a minimum number of lines of force. At the same time the coil, through the commutator, changes connection with the brushes. This produces direct current electricity.

Direct Current Generators

To obtain direct current from a generator we use a *commutator* instead of slip rings. The commutator (Illustrations 24 and 25) consists of a single ring cut in two so that each half is separated from the other on the armature shaft. One side of the commutator is connected to one end of the coil and the other side to the other

◆ 26. A graph may be used to show a direct current generator wave form. This is similar to the alternating current waveform only both loops are above the line to indicate that the generator output is a pulsating direct current.

end of the coil. Brushes make continuous contact with the commutator to pick up the electron flow from the coil. During each half rotation of the armature, the brushes make contact with a different end of the coil. See Illustration 25.

Thus through the use of a commutator we are able to get direct current from the generator. This direct current is varying in strength the same as the alternating current. The difference is in the electron flow, which is always in the same direction for direct current. We call this changing in strength of direct current *pulsating* direct current. See Illustration 26.

Commercial Generators

One of the requirements for all generators is that we have some means

Courtesy Delco-Remy Div.—General Motors Corp.

♦ 27. Automobile generators usually have a number of coils on the armature. The end of each coil comes out to a separate section of the commutator. These sections are insulated from each other and are called *segments*. The segments are connected to the coils so that each can deliver its electricity to the brushes.

Most automobile generators use an electro-magnet for the magnetic field. The electro-magnet provides a strong magnetic field for the armature. The coils used to produce the electromagnetism are called *field coils*. These field coils receive their electricity from the armature.

of power to rotate them. The army uses hand power to turn over some of their portable field generators. Large generators are run by water turbines, or by gasoline, steam, or diesel engines.

Most generators built commercially have more than one set of coils in the armature. By having more coils in the armature it is possible to produce a more constant supply of electricity. This is because some of the coils are always directly across from the poles of the magnet. It is at this point that the greatest amount of electricity is

Courtesy Westinghouse Electric Corp.

♦ 28. Modern railroads use electric power to drive their trains. This train uses a diesel engine to operate a large electric generator. The generator is then used to provide electricity for an electric motor that' moves the train.

◆ 29. Modern electric power generators are streamlined and compact. This steam-driven generator is capable of supplying electricity to a city of 225,000 people.

induced in the coil.

The automobile generator (Illustration 27) uses a commutator to produce direct current electricity. Since the brushes deliver direct current to the field coils each pole always has the same north and south polarity. This type of generator is used for direct current arc welding and many other places where direct current is needed.

Most alternating current generators also use electromagnetic field coils instead of permanent magnets. The magnetic field must always have the same poles and the same polarity. This is not possible with alternating current electricity because the electrons are flowing first in one direction and then the other. We can see that if the field coils were connected to the slip rings of the alternating current generator the poles in the field would always be changing. Alternating current generators, like direct current generators, must have constant north and south poles for the electromagnetic field. Some method must be used in alternating current generators to supply direct current to the field coils. This can be done by having a separate generator to produce the direct current, or, by having two generators connected together on one armature.

INTERESTING THINGS TO DO

Making and Using a Galvanometer.
Use the small compass constructed in Unit 4. The wooden base should be approximately 1½″ square. Cut two pieces of heavy cardboard the same length as the base and wide enough so that the top of the cardboard will be approximately ⅛″ above the top of the compass needle. Glue the two pieces of cardboard on the sides of the base as shown in Illustration 30. Wind about 40 turns of No. 28 magnet wire around the compass. In order to be able to see the compass it is best to wind 20 turns on one side of the needle and the other 20 turns on the other side as shown in the picture. This completes the construction of the galvanometer.

Obtain a piece of cardboard tubing about 1″ in diameter and 2½″ long. Wind approximately 100 turns of No.

◆ 30. Shop constructed Galvanometer indicating electron flow.

22 wire on the form. Connect the two ends of the coil to the two leads on the galvanometer. Keep the coil and galvanometer about 18″ apart. Push a bar magnet into the coil. Now move the magnet back and forth through the coil. What happens to the compass needle? Why?

REVIEW QUESTIONS

1. What is the purpose of a galvanometer?

2. How does reversing the poles of the bar magnet affect the movement of the galvanometer?

3. Why does a coil with a moving bar magnet produce electricity?

4. When alternating current is produced, in what direction do the electrons flow?

5. How does alternating current differ from direct current?

6. What is the number of cycles completed by an alternating current in just one second properly called?

7. In 60-cycle alternating current how many cycles are completed in one minute?

8. What is the difference between commutators and slip rings on generators?

9. When a generator is rotating, at what position is the largest quantity of electricity produced?

10. List the different types of power used to turn generators.

11. In automobile generators how is the magnetic field obtained?

UNIT 9

PRODUCING ELECTRICITY WITH FRICTION, HEAT, LIGHT, PRESSURE AND GASES

Static Electricity

Probably everyone has had the experience of receiving a shock from touching the door of an automobile just as he started to get out of the car. Possibly you have received a shock when you walked on a heavy rug and then touched another person. These shocks were caused by *static electricity*.

When riding in an automobile your body moves against the seat and back cushions. Rubbing against the cushions gives your body a charge of static electricity. When you touch the door of the automobile, this charge jumps to the door and you feel a shock. The charge was neutralized by the metal of the door. The same is true when you walk across a rug; the friction of your shoes against the rug produces a charge on your body. When you touch someone, the charge is neutralized by the other person.

Static electricity is made by friction which is the result of two different nonmetal materials, called *insulators,* rubbing against one another. Most insulating materials are what we call *neutral.* They have an equal number of negative and positive charges. If we rub two different materials together, one will rub some of the electrons off the other. The material which has gathered electrons onto it is said to have a negative charge, and the one that has lost electrons is said to have a

◆ 31. An example of static electricity can be shown by rubbing a comb against a piece of wool clothing. The comb becomes charged as the electrons are rubbed onto it from the wool. When the comb is touched against a small scrap of paper, it will attract the paper and pick it up. The comb, which has a negative charge, repels all of the electrons on the edge of the paper nearest to the comb. The electrons on the paper next to the comb go to the opposite end of the paper. The negative comb now attracts the positively charged edge.

positive charge. As the electrons jump from one point to another we see a spark and feel a shock.

Charges of static electricity can be compared with magnetism. In magnetism unlike poles attract and like poles repel. The same principle is true in static electricity: *Unlike charges attract each other and like charges repel each other.* See Illustrations 32 and 33.

Problems Caused by Static Electricity

Static electricity in many instances

◆ 32. Both glass rods have been rubbed with a piece of silk. The silk rubs the electrons off of the glass, making them positively charged. Since both glass rods have a positive charge they will repel each other.

◆ 33. The glass rod hanging from the string has been rubbed with a piece of fur. The glass takes electrons off the fur, giving it a negative charge. The other glass rod was rubbed with silk, giving it a positive charge. The two unlike charged glass rods will attract each other.

is destructive and we need to find ways to control it. Trucks carrying gasoline become charged from the gasoline sloshing around in the tank and from the friction of the tires on the highway. This static charge could result in a spark which might ignite the gasoline. As a result all gasoline trucks have a chain or tape dragging on the ground to prevent the charge from developing. Rotating belts used on machinery can develop a static charge. When these belts are used around explosives it is necessary to ground the parts making contact with the belts. This grounding prevents the charge from developing, and thus prevents a spark that might cause an explosion.

Uses for Static Electricity

Some very important uses have been found for static electricity. Probably the most well known is the flue precipitator (Illustration 35) which is used in removing dust and smoke from the air. Clothing brushes with plastic bristles pick up the lint from clothing because the plastic bristles become charged with electricity due to the friction caused by rubbing them against clothing.

Courtesy General Electric Co.

◆ 34. Static electricity is responsible for lightning. The friction caused by the small droplets in the clouds gives the clouds a charge of static electricity. When the charge becomes strong enough in the cloud, it discharges to the earth. This discharge of static electricity from the cloud to the earth results in a huge flash and a loud noise.

POWER SUPPLY
II5V A-C

POWER PACK
(Source of high voltage)

COLLECTOR CELL
(To collect particles)

6,000V D-C
TO POSITIVE
COLLECTOR
PLATES

13,000V D-C
TO IONIZER
WIRE ASSEMBLY

CLEAN AIR

BAFFLE
(To distribute
air uniformly)

PRECIPITATED
PARTICLES

POSITIVELY
CHARGED
PARTICLES

CHARGING
PARTICLES

AIRFLOW

UNCHARGED
PARTICLES

DIRTY AIR

PRECIPITRON
FRAME ASSEMBLY

IONIZER
(To charge particles)

Courtesy Westinghouse Electric Corp.

◆ 35. The precipitator is used as an air cleaner. It consists of one set of plates that have a high negative charge and another set of plates that have a high positive charge. The dust or smoke is first given a negative charge as it passes by the negatively charged plates. These particles then flow past a set of plates that have a positive charge. The negatively charged particles are attracted to the positive plates.

Sanding belts are sometimes coated by static electricity. The abrasive is charged by placing the grains in a very strong static electricity field. This charging makes the grains of the abrasive stand on end as iron filings stand in a magnetic field. While the grains are held on end, they are glued onto the belt. The end grains make a much sharper edge for sanding.

The Thermocouple

Heat can be used to develop very small amounts of electricity. If we twist a piece of constantan wire and a piece of iron wire together and heat them where they are joined together, a small quantity of electricity will be developed. See Photograph 36. We can indicate that electricity is being produced if we connect a galvanometer to the ends of the two pieces of wire. The producing of electricity by heating two different kinds of metal is called the *thermocouple* method.

The thermocouple method of making electricity is used to measure high temperatures. Two different metals such as platinum and iridium are joined together and are placed in a

◆ 36. A match will provide enough heat to generate electricity from a thermocouple.

◆ 37. One use for a thermocouple is to automatically control a gas furnace so as to maintain an even temperature at all times.

heating unit. The electricity developed by the heating of the two different metals is shown by a galvanometer. As the temperature is increased the voltage produced by the thermocouple increases. This increased electricity makes the galvanometer needle move farther on the scale. The scale on the galvanometer is marked to read degrees of temperature. Thus by reading the scale of the meter, we can tell the amount of heat being produced. This type of meter is called a *pyrometer*.

Automatic gas furnaces sometimes use thermocouple electricity to open and close the supply valve. The pilot light of the furnace heats the two different metals to produce the electricity. When the wall thermometer, called a *thermostat*, closes the circuit due to changing of the room temperature, the thermocouple (Illustration 37) develops electricity to operate a coil and steel plunger device called a *solenoid*. This solenoid opens the gas valve. As soon as the room reaches the correct temperature the wall thermostat opens the circuit and the solenoid shuts the gas off.

The Photoelectric Tube

Certain materials such as potassium, sodium, and caesium when held in the light will give off small quantities of electrons. These materials, called *photosensitive*, are used in *photoelectric* cells. A photoelectric tube (Illustration 38) consists of a curved plate coated with the photosensitive material. A rod of metal is placed near the curved plate. Both the rod (*anode*) and plate (*cathode*) are sealed inside of a glass

PHOTOSENSITIVE PLATE (CATHODE)

ROD (ANODE)

◆ **38. Photoelectric cells can be used for many purposes.**

tube. When light shines on the curved plate it gives off electrons. We know that electrons are negative particles of electricity and that they will go to a place that has a positive charge. By connecting the rod to the positive side of a battery it will attract the electrons given off by the plate. The brighter the light that shines on it, the more electrons it will give off.

The ability of light to produce a flow of electrons in a photoelectric tube is used for many purposes. In almost all cases the photo tube must be used with some type of amplifier to make the small flow of electrons strong enough to do work. Doors are opened by having a light shine on a photoelectric tube. When someone walks between the light and the photoelectric tube the electrons are stopped momentarily. The amplifier circuit is so arranged that when the electrons stop it will turn on the motor that

♦ 39. A shop constructed exposure meter using a photoelectric tube to make photographic enlargements. The photo tube picks up light from the photographic enlarger. This photo tube is connected to the meter so that the amount of light on the tube will be recorded on the meter. The meter is calibrated to indicate the length of time in seconds necessary for each enlargement.

♦ 40. A simple Light Meter.

opens the door. Burglar alarms, lights, and many types of machines are controlled by photo tubes. One very common use for the photo tube is in the light meter used to measure the amount of light shining on a particular place. See Photograph 39.

The Selenium Cell

To develop power through the use of sunlight has been the goal of many inventors. The use of selenium makes this goal attainable. Selenium is another material that will give off electrons when light shines on it. Selenium is used in the new type of cell called a "sun battery" (Photograph 40). When artificial light or sunlight shines on the selenium surface of the cell a small voltage is generated by the cell. Several of these cells may be connected together to produce increased amounts of electricity. Many uses can be made of this cell wherever artificial light or sunlight is available. Light measurement, automatic light control, light beam communication, timing devices, and many other commercial applications are possible with the sun battery.

Pressure Produces Electricity

Very small quantities of electricity can be produced when pressure is applied to some kinds of crystals. These crystals, such as quartz or Rochelle salts, will generate electricity when they are squeezed between two metal plates; and if a very sensitive meter is connected across the plates, voltage will be indicated. The greater the pressure that is placed on the crystals, the greater the resulting voltage. This ability to generate electricity by compress-

◆ **41. A photograph and sketch of a crystal phonograph pickup. As the needle vibrates in the record grooves, these vibrations are delivered to the metal plates next to the crystal. These vibrations press on the crystal and a voltage variation is then produced by the crystal between the two metal plates. The varying voltage is then fed into an amplifier.**

ing a crystal is known as the *piezoelectric effect* of crystals.

Crystal Phonograph Pick Up

A good example of the piezoelectric effect is found in crystal phonograph pick-up arms. These pick-up arms use a crystal such as Rochelle salts with a needle attached as shown in Figure 41. As the needle rides in the grooves of the phonograph record, it is vibrated

PHONO PICKUP

This symbol represents any type of pickup.

back and forth by small variations that are found in the record grooves. These variations are due to the sound vibrations that were impressed in the record when it was manufactured. Since the needle is connected to the crystal, the vibrations picked up by the needle are applied to the crystal. Thus, a varying pressure is placed on the crystal. This variation in pressure produces a weak voltage change which is then sent to a phonograph amplifier. The phonograph amplifier increases the varying voltage produced by the crystal and the electrical impulses are then converted back into sound waves by the loud speaker.

The Crystal Microphone

Another method of using crystals to generate electricity is found in the crystal microphone, often used in broadcasting stations or public address systems.

When someone speaks into a crystal microphone, the sound waves strike the crystal in the microphone and compress it. The sound waves are converted into a weak electric current by the crystal. This small current is then fed into an amplifier where the signal is made strong enough to operate a loud speaker.

Crystal Vibration

Another piezoelectric effect of a crystal is its ability to vibrate or produce mechanical motion. When a voltage is applied across a pair of plates that have been placed on opposite sides of a crystal, a vibration will be set up by the crystal. The number of vibra-

◆ 42. Fuel cell electric power generator.

tions per second that will be produced by the crystal is very constant. These vibrations are called the frequency of the crystal, which is basically determined by the type of crystal and its thickness. Such crystals are usually cut from quartz and are used in broadcasting stations, for example, where fixed frequencies are very important.

The Fuel Cell

Scientists are working constantly to find new methods for generating electrical power. Occasionally, they are able to reach back through the years and pick up a partly developed idea, apply modern research techniques to it and produce a device that has the glamour of a wonderful new discovery. Such has been the case of the recently developed fuel cells, which hold promise of producing electrical power at efficiencies as high as 85 percent. A modern turbine generating station does well to operate at an efficiency of 40 percent.

Sir William Grove, an Englishman, is credited with having built the first primitive model of a fuel cell in 1839. Other workers followed down through the years, but only recently has the fuel cell been brought to its present high state of development by research for an efficient source of power for space travel. A drawing of one type of fuel cell is shown in Figure 42.

In the fuel cell shown in the drawing oxygen and hydrogen unite to form water and in the process releases electrons which flow from the negative electrode to the outside terminal when the cell is connected to a load. The water vapor formed by oxygen uniting with hydrogen flows into the radiator-condenser, where heat is removed and the vapor condensed into water. The pump separator forces the water into a tank and sends the exhaust hydrogen back into the hydrogen inlet of the fuel cell. One advantage of this type of fuel cell for space craft use is that the water salvaged from the cell would be useful for all space crew requirements, including water for drinking.

INTERESTING THINGS TO DO

1. Generating Static Electricity.

Cut several small pieces of scrap paper and place them on a flat wooden surface. Charge a comb by rubbing it on woolen clothing. Hold the comb near the scrap pieces of paper. What happens? Why?

2. Making a Thermocouple.

Cut a piece of constantan wire 6″ long and a piece of iron wire the same length. Wire sizes between No. 14 and No. 20 will be satisfactory. Twist the two wires together for a distance of about $1\frac{1}{2}$″. Connect the opposite ends of the wire to a very sensitive galvanometer or a low reading milliammeter, an instrument that measures small currents. Heat the twisted ends of the wires with a match or a gas flame. Why does the needle on the meter move? Reverse the two wire connections to the meter. What happens?

3. Making a Simple Light Meter.

Obtain a selenium photo cell or a sun battery. Connect the two leads from the cell to a milliammeter (0-to-1 or 0-to-5 milliamperes). Be sure to connect the red or positive lead of the cell to the side of the meter marked "positive." Hold the face of the cell toward the window in your room. Observe the reading of the meter. Place the cell directly under a light bulb. How does the meter reading compare with the one taken from the window light? This meter may be constructed and calibrated for use as a light meter for photographic work.

REVIEW QUESTIONS

1. In what ways are static electricity and magnetism similar?

2. List some of the problems caused by static electricity.

3. Name several uses made of static electricity.

4. What are the requirements necessary to produce electricity by the thermocouple method?

5. Name several commercial uses of the thermocouple.

6. How does a photoelectric tube operate?

7. Why is it necessary to have an amplifier when using a photoelectric tube?

8. Make a list of purposes for which the photoelectric tube is used.

9. What is the principal material used in the sun battery?

10. Suggest a new type of use that might be made of the sun battery.

11. What is the material used to produce electricity by pressure?

12. Explain how pressure is used to produce electricity in a phonograph pick-up.

Basic Electrical Circuits

UNIT 10
MEASURING THE VOLTAGE

Voltage and Pressure

We have said that the voltage of a dry cell is 1½ volts and that the voltage of a storage battery is 6 volts. You have probably heard that the electricity in your home is 115 volts. The various voltages indicate the amount of pressure that each of these sources produces.

Voltage is the pressure or force that

VOLTMETER

The letter "V" indicates a voltmeter symbol.

pushes electrons through an electrical circuit. A single cell of a storage battery produces a pressure of 1½ volts. When three cells are connected together they produce three times as much pressure as one cell. The voltage of the battery is 4½ volts. The greater the pressure or voltage the more electrons will be forced to flow through a circuit.

Voltage might be compared to the water system in a city. Most towns have a large tank that is used to force water through pipes to the houses throughout the community. The water pressure is available whenever the faucet is opened. If the water in the tank gets low the pressure in the system is low.

◆ **1A.** In the photograph the five steel balls have been placed in a clear plastic tube so they are pushing down on the scale used for measuring weights. These balls are providing enough pressure to force the pointer of the weighing scale to the center of the dial. Electrical pressure may be compared to this. The voltmeter is showing electrical pressure forcing the needle to the center of the scale.

◆ **1B.** This photograph shows the pointer of the weighing scale almost at the bottom of the dial, indicating that the weight has been increased. The addition of the five steel balls in the plastic tube has increased the pressure and the increase may be measured by the scale. The electrical pressure increase may be compared to this. The voltage was increased and the voltmeter shows this increase.

In electricity, the source of electricity produces the voltage the same as the water tank provides the pressure. The greater the voltage, the greater the force of the electricity. This force is called the *electromotive force* and is measured in *volts*.

Producing an Electromotive Force

The electromotive force, or voltage, may be produced by generators, dry cells, batteries, thermocouples, photoelectric cells, or sun batteries. Generators are the most common source of voltage and are used when large quantities of voltage are needed. Batteries are usually used where it is not convenient to use generators and where direct current is needed. The other methods of producing voltage have

limited use except in special places where small quantities of voltage are needed.

COMMON VOLTAGES

Some very common voltages that can be obtained from various devices are listed below:

Thermocouple	Few thousandths of a volt
Dry cell	1½ volts
Storage battery	6 and 12 volts
Door chime transformer	12 to 24 volts
Home outlets	110 to 120 volts
Electric lines into homes	110–220 to 120–240 volts
Transformers on power poles	2,400 to 4,200 volts
Power company substation	12,000 to 69,000 volts
Power company generators	12,500 volts
Long distance transmission lines	287,000 volts

Using Voltmeters

A voltmeter is used to measure electromotive force. The meter is connected directly across the two terminals where the voltage is to be measured. One connection of the meter goes to one wire of the circuit and the other connection to the other wire as in Illustration 2.

◆ 4. Measuring the voltage of a storage battery with a meter having a 0-to-25–volt scale.

IeO-VOLT LINE

300

150

+
–

◆ 2. When measuring the voltage of a power line, one terminal of the voltmeter is connected to one side of the line and the other terminal of the meter to the other side of the line.

When selecting a voltmeter it is necessary to know whether the electricity is alternating current or direct current. Direct current meters will not read alternating current voltages and alternating current meters will give incorrect readings of direct current.

It is also important that the meter

◆ 5. A wiring diagram of Photograph 4. Wiring diagrams, sometimes called *schematic diagrams,* use electrical symbols to show how the parts are connected.

75   100   125
0 25 50   150
Pattern No. 72
Alternating Current

◆ 3. This is a drawing of one type of meter scale. The divisions found on the scale vary with the type of meter used. The reading on the scale above indicates 111 volts AC.

used have the correct scale for the voltage to be measured. If the voltage is too high for the meter it will burn out the meter.

To measure the voltage of a storage battery that delivers 6 volts, a direct current meter that has a full scale reading of 10 volts is generally used. If the meter had a 0-to-200–volt scale, the 6 volts of the storage battery would move the needle so slightly that it would be difficult to obtain an accurate reading. A meter that had a 0-to-1–volt scale could not read the 6 volts and would probably be ruined because it was not designed to read more than 1 volt.

When measuring the voltage of direct current electricity, it is necessary to notice the polarity of the meter.

◆ 6. Measuring the voltage of a radio B battery. When connecting the meter it is necessary to observe the polarity of the battery and the meter. Minus goes to minus and plus goes to plus.

One terminal of the meter is marked with a + and is sometimes painted red. This is called the *positive* terminal of the meter and is connected to the positive terminal of the battery. The other terminal of the meter is connected to the *negative* post of the battery. The voltmeter is connected directly across the source of electricity. See Photograph 6.

Most homes use alternating current electricity and the voltage of the outlets is from 110 to 120 volts. When measuring the outlet voltage, an alternating current meter must be used. The scale can be a 0-to-150–volt or a 0-to-200–volt. See Photograph 7. Alternating current meters do not have a polarity marking as the direction of electron flow is always changing. The meter is connected directly across the outlet with one terminal of the meter going to one side of the outlet and the other terminal to the other side of the outlet.

Some meters called *multimeters* (Photograph 8) can be used for both alternating current and direct current. Separate connections are shown

◆ 7. Using an alternating current meter to measure the voltage of a wall outlet.

◆ 8. A multimeter that will measure AC and DC voltage, resistance and direct current.

◆ 9. If the fingers of the left hand are wrapped around the coil in the direction of current flow, the thumb will point toward the north pole end of the coil.

on the cases of the meters where the terminal leads may be connected for either AC or DC. These meters very often have various scales that can be selected by moving a switch on the front of the meter case.

◆ 10. The magnetic forces of attraction and repulsion cause the coil of the meter to turn so that the unlike poles of the coil and the magnet are brought closer together. If the voltage or current is increased, the coil becomes a stronger magnet and it turns further due to the greater magnetic force between the poles of the coil and the magnet. The pointer shows the voltage reading on the scale.

The Principle of the Moving Coil Meter

Most direct current electricity is measured with a meter using a moving coil. The moving coil meter is often called a D'Arsonval movement meter in honor of the famous French Physicist who introduced the moving coil galvanometer in 1882. The meter operates on the attraction and repulsion effect between magnetic poles.

When direct current flows through a coil of wire it becomes an electromagnet which has a north and south pole. The direction of the magnetic field of a coil may be determined by using what is known as the "left hand rule." This left hand rule is illustrated in Figure 9.

If a coil is suspended between the poles of a horseshoe magnet as shown in Figure 10, the coil will turn so that the north pole is near the south pole of the horseshoe magnet and the south pole of the coil will be attracted to the north pole of the magnet. It is this movement of the coil when current is flowing through it that produces the meter readings on most direct current meters.

Construction of the Direct Current Meter

The moving coil of the D'Arsonval meter is made of several turns of insulated wire wound around a rectangular aluminum frame, Fig. 11. Aluminum is used so that the weight of the coil will be as light as possible. The coil is placed between the poles of a very powerful permanent magnet, and is mounted so that it is free to turn. Steel pivots at the top and bottom hold the coil between jeweled bearings so that the coil can turn with very little friction, Fig. 11 (inset). Attached to the coil is a light weight pointer, called the meter needle, that moves across the scale of the meter. A coiled spring returns the pointer to the zero mark on the scale when the meter is not in use.

Damping the Moving Coil

The moving coil of the meter is mounted between the poles of the horseshoe magnet at a slight angle so that as the current flows through the coil the poles of the coil will be either attracted or repelled by the poles of the permanent magnet. The amount of movement of the coil is determined by the force that the magnetic field exerts against the permanent magnet. The stronger the current flow through the meter the greater the movement of the coil and needle.

Since the moving coil is mounted on jeweled bearings its movement could make it swing back and forth like a pendulum. To avoid this swinging of the coil a method called damping is used. The most satisfactory method is called electrical damping. By using an aluminum frame on which to wind the coil, the movement of the frame in the magnetic field causes an electric current to be induced into the frame. The induced magnetic currents are in such a direction that they oppose the motion of the coil and thus the coil comes to rest very quickly. A device called a zero adjustment is used to

Daystrom Inc., Weston Instrument Div.

◆ 11. The moving element of the meter must be light weight. It uses a metal frame for damping. Inset shows bearing.

Daystrom Inc., Weston Instrument Div.

◆ 12. The principal parts of a permanent magnet moving coil meter. The permanent magnet is a circular one called a "core" type magnet.

Daystrom Inc., Weston Instrument Div.

◆ 13. A representative type of voltmeter which uses the movements shown above.

place the pointer at the zero mark on the meter scale when the meter is not connected in a circuit.

The Direct Current Voltmeter

A voltmeter is always connected directly across the two points to be measured in a circuit as in Figure 2. Since the moving coil has comparatively few turns of wire, it cannot be connected directly across the voltage source as this would burn out the coil. To reduce the current and to obtain the desired scale reading a resistor is always placed in series with the moving coil when the meter is used as a voltmeter, Fig. 14. The resistor is called a multiplier and its size determines the full scale reading of the voltmeter.

In most electrical circuits it is necessary to use a voltmeter that will not place very much of a load on the circuit. If this occurs the meter draws too much current, and will reduce the circuit voltage so that the meter will not give a true reading of the voltage present when the meter is not in the circuit. Voltmeters which use large resistance multipliers are desired since they place a very small load on the circuit.

Alternating Current Moving Coil Meters

If alternating current is connected directly to a moving coil type meter the needle would just vibrate. Alternating current flows in one direction and then in the opposite direction so rapidly that the meter would be unable to respond to these fluctuations. The moving coil meter can be used

METER TERMINALS

MULTIPLIER RESISTOR

◆ 14. The multiplier resistor is connected in series with the coil of the movement. The resistor is usually located inside the case of the meter.

to measure low frequency alternating current voltage if a device called a rectifier is used. The rectifier, which will be studied in Unit 29, changes alternating current into direct current so that the meter will operate properly.

Effective Value of Alternating Current and Voltage

Both alternating current and voltage vary with the changing electron flow from zero to a maximum and then back to zero again. The amount of energy produced by alternating current is not the same as for direct current. Direct current usually provides a constant voltage but with alternating current the voltage is continually changing from zero to a peak and then back to zero again. It is necessary to determine what the *effective* voltage of alternating current is. Mathematical calculations show that effective voltage or current of alternating current is equal to .707 of the maximum value (Figure 15). Alternating current meters are made to read the effective voltage as it is the effective voltage that helps us in determining the amount of energy that is being produced. An effective voltage of 100 volts alternating current produces the same amount of energy as 100 volts of direct current. In most homes, for example, the voltmeter will read 117 volts when connected to a wall outlet. The peak voltage of alternating current in the home is actually about 165 volts.

The effective value is known mathematically as the root-mean-square, or *rms* voltage. This effective value of alternating current is the equivalent of a direct current value that will produce the same amount of power. A.C. meters read the effective value.

Moving Iron Vane Meter

The moving coil meter operates only on direct current. To use the moving coil meter on alternating current it is necessary to use a rectifying device with the meter. A very common type meter used to measure low frequency alternating current is called a *moving vane meter*. Such a meter uses two iron vanes placed inside a circular coil as in Figure 16. One of the iron vanes is stationary, and the other iron vane which is movable is connected to the meter pointer. When the coil is in a circuit so that the current flows through it the iron vanes are magnetized by induction. The moving vane and the stationary vane become magnetized so that they have like poles at the top and like poles at the bottom. Since like poles repel each other the moving vane is pushed away from the fixed vane. Even when alternating current is connected to the meter coil, the two vanes always have like poles op-

◆ 15. A sine wave illustrating the peak value and effective value in one cycle of alternating current. The peak and effective values are reached twice during each cycle.

posite each other so that the pointer will move. A coil spring keeps the two vanes close to each other when current is flowing through the coil.

When it is used as a voltmeter a multiplier resistor is connected in series with the coil the same as for the moving coil meter.

◆ 16. A moving vane meter movement. A repelling force is developed between the two iron vanes when current flows through the coil. One vane is fixed and the other is pivoted so that it will move when the magnetizing current flows.

INTERESTING THINGS TO DO

1. Measuring Direct Current Voltage.

Obtain a storage battery and a 0-to-15–volt direct current meter. Connect two insulated wires to the meter. Connect the positive terminal of the meter to the positive post of the storage battery. The other terminal is connected to the negative post of the battery. What is the voltage reading? What happens if you reverse the connections to the meter?

Measure the voltage of each cell of the battery by connecting the leads from the meter to the terminals of each cell. What is the voltage of the cells?

2. Measuring Home Outlet Voltage.

Obtain an A.C. meter with a 0-to-150–volt scale. Connect two insulated leads to each of the terminals of the meter. The other ends of these leads are connected to an attachment plug cap. Be sure the connectors are tight and that the wires do not touch each other. Plug the cap into the outlet voltage. What is the voltage reading?

3. Constructing a Neon Bulb Voltmeter.

Materials needed to construct the neon bulb voltmeter:

200,000-ohm, ½-watt carbon resistor
500,000-ohm carbon potentiometer
Pointer knob for potentiometer
Neon bulb, type NE–2
One pair of test leads about 3′ long
Hook-up wire
A 2″ length of mailing tube. This tube should be large enough in diameter for the potentiometer to fit in one end.

Cut a piece of cardboard the same diameter as the mailing tube. Make a

◆ 17. Neon bulb voltmeter.

hole in the center of this round disk large enough for the shaft of the potentiometer to fit through. Glue the round cardboard disk to the mailing tube. Cut a small oblong hole in the side of the mailing tube. Check to see that the hole will be large enough to see the neon bulb but not large enough to permit the bulb to come through the hole.

Before placing the parts in the mailing tube, solder all of the connections as shown in Drawing 18.

Place the parts inside the mailing tube and mount the potentiometer so that the shaft extends out of the end covered by the cardboard disk. This end of the tube can be covered with white paper as it will be where the dial markings are placed when calibrating the meter. The pointer knob can be tightened on the potentiometer shaft.

Using a clear cement, glue the neon bulb inside the tube so that it is visible through the hole already cut in the tube.

Calibrating the Meter. Radio B batteries or a power supply with dif-

ferent voltages can be used to cali-
brate the meter. You should be careful
when using this meter because the
voltages used can cause a bad shock.
When measuring voltage, it is important to avoid coming in contact with
the terminals. Using a 90-volt B battery connect the two meter leads across
the terminals of the battery. Turn the
potentiometer to where the neon bulb
just starts to glow. If the bulb is already glowing when the leads are connected, turn the potentiometer until
the glow is almost out. At this point
(where the glow starts to go out) place
a mark on the end of the tubing. Label
this mark "90 volts." The two test
leads can be placed in a wall outlet
and this voltage marked on the dial.
The wall outlet voltage is usually
about 117 volts. As in the B battery
voltage, the dial should be turned to
the point when the glow starts to go
out. Other known voltages can be
marked on the dial. The meter will

PICTORIAL DRAWING OF A NEON BULB VOLTMETER

SCHEMATIC DIAGRAM

◆ 18. Pictorial and schematic diagrams of a neon voltmeter.

read up to 650 volts and as low as 70
volts.

REVIEW QUESTIONS

1. What is voltage?

2. Give another name for voltage.

3. List several devices that can produce a voltage.

4. What are the common voltages
found in the home?

5. Draw a circuit showing where
a voltmeter is placed in a circuit to
measure the voltage or electromotive
force.

6. When using alternating current
voltmeters, why is it not necessary to
have polarity markings on the meters?

7. What is the meter called that can
measure both alternating and direct

current as well as various voltages?

8. List the important parts of a
moving coil meter.

9. Why is it necessary to damp a
moving coil meter?

10. Why is a resistor used in series
with a moving coil voltmeter?

11. What device is used with a moving coil meter when it is used to measure alternating current?

12. If the peak voltage of alternating current is 20 volts what is the effective voltage?

13. List the principle parts of a
moving iron vane meter.

UNIT 11
MEASURING CURRENT

Current and Electron Flow

The flow of electricity is the movement of electrons in a circuit. This electron flow in a circuit is called *current* and if the electrons are always going in the same direction it is called *direct current*. *Alternating current* is a flow of electrons that is continuously changing directions.

To have a flow of electrons it is necessary to have a source of electricity, such as a generator, to provide the pressure or voltage to push the electrons through the circuit. These electrons go from the negative pole of the generator through the circuit and return to the positive pole of the generator.

Moving electrons might be compared to a bucket brigade used in putting out a fire. The source of water

is a well and after the bucket is filled, the people in the brigade pass it from one person to the next. The last person in line receives the bucket and pours the water on the fire. He then passes the bucket to another line of people who return it to the well to be filled again. Buckets are continuously being passed from one person to the next from the well to the fire and from the fire back to the well. This continuous movement of the buckets is like the flow of electrons which leave the source of electricity and flow through the circuit.

Electron Flow Measured in Amperes

In a city water system it is very common to measure the amount of water that is flowing through a pipe by determining the number of gal-

◆ 19. The small steel balls in the photograph represent electrons. The glass jar represents a battery with the negative side of the battery holding a large quantity of electrons (steel balls). The electrons leave the negative terminal of the battery, flow through the plastic tube and light bulb and return through the tube to the positive side of the battery. This flow of electrons from the negative terminal through the light bulb and back to the positive terminal produces light in the bulb. The flow of electrons is called *current*.

DRY CELL
1 1/2 VOLTS

◆ 20. This drawing indicates with arrows the flow of electrons from the negative terminal of the dry cell through the wire and light bulb back to the positive terminal. The circuit drawn here shows the same type of circuit that is illustrated with the steel balls in Photograph 19.

♦ 21. A heater element is plugged into a 115-volt alternating current wall outlet. Notice that one side of the wire going to the heater has been cut so that the ammeter can be connected in the circuit. The ammeter shows that a little more than 5 amperes of current is flowing through the element.

♦ 22. The drawing at the top shows the complete electrical circuit of Photograph 21. The generator is providing the voltage that is delivered by the two wires to the wall outlet. When the heater is connected to the outlet by an attachment plug, current flows in the circuit. The ammeter is connected in one side of the line to measure the current flow. The bottom drawing is a schematic diagram of the entire circuit. Symbols are used to represent the generator, ammeter, and heater element.

Ions that is flowing through the pipe in an hour. In electricity the electron flow is measured in amperes, which indicate the number of electrons that pass through the circuit in one second. Electrons are so very small that it takes about six million, million, million of them to pass through a circuit in one second to equal one ampere. Since this is such a large figure the quantity of current flow is stated in amperes. *Ampere* is the unit of measurement for current, the abbreviations being *amp* or *amps*.

Using Ammeters

An ammeter is used to measure the electron flow in amperes. All ammeters are labeled as to whether they will read AC or DC. Just as in using a voltmeter it is important that the ammeter have the correct scale for the current to be measured.

To measure the current flow in a

The letter "A" in a symbol means ammeter.

◆ 23. The milliammeter indicates that 185 milliamperes is the amount of current flowing through the 1½-volt light bulb when it is connected to a flashlight cell. The 185 milliamperes are equal to .185 ampere.

circuit the ammeter is connected in one wire of the line so that the electrons must flow through the meter as well as all of the rest of the circuit. Extreme care must be used to be sure that the voltage is not on when the meter is being connected.

Most direct current meters have a + marked on the positive connection. The other terminal is negative and should be connected to the negative side of the circuit. Alternating current ammeters do not have a polarity marking as they are made so that the electrons can flow through the meter in either direction.

When measuring current it is usually advisable to start with a meter that has a high ampere range. If the current is not enough to move the pointer so an accurate reading can be made, a smaller range meter can be used. Starting with a large range meter and then replacing with small range meter will avoid burning out the meter.

A common use of an ammeter is on the dashboard of some automobiles. The ammeter is used to show the driver whether the generator is charging or not. The meter is a center scale meter and indicates that no current is flowing through it when the pointer is in the center of the dial. As the generator charges the battery of the automobile the pointer moves to the right, showing that current is being supplied by the generator. When the generator is not charging the pointer moves to the left. This shows the driver that the battery is providing the electricity and usually indicates that the automobile generator is not working.

In some circuits, such as a radio circuit, very small amounts of current flow and meters must be used that will read thousandths of an ampere. Meters which read current in thousandths of an ampere are called *milliammeters* (Photograph 23). *Milli* means one-thousandth. If a milliammeter has a scale of 0 to 300 this means that the meter will read from zero to three-hundred thousandths of an ampere. Three-hundred thousandths of an ampere is equal to three-tenths of an ampere.

TYPICAL CURRENT CONSUMPTION

Approximate currents used by some common home appliances are listed below:

Sewing machine	.80 ampere
Lamp bulbs (100-watt)	.83 ampere
Radio (small)	.85 ampere
Refrigerator	2.00 amperes
Television	2.00 amperes
Washing machine	2.50 amperes
Iron	6.60 amperes
¾ hp home air conditioning unit	12.00 amperes

Daystrom Inc., Weston Instrument Div.

◆ 24. A view of a typical moving coil meter movement. The permanent magnet used is made in a U shape and is referred to as an "outside" magnet. The moving coil is the same as the one shown in Figure 11 on page 75.

Daystrom Inc., Weston Instrument Div.

◆ 25. An ammeter with the front of the case removed to show details of the movement. The movement for this meter uses a magnet which fits closely around the coil and is known as a core magnet.

Construction of the Ammeter

The basic construction of the ammeter is the same as that of the voltmeter described in the previous section. A moving coil movement is generally used and the amount of current flowing through it determines the amount of pointer deflection. Moving vane movements may also be used in some instruments. Figure 24 and 25 show details of typical meters.

An ammeter measures electron flow and must be connected in series with the circuit so that the total current to be measured will flow through it. In order that an accurate reading be obtained, it is important that the *meter* present as little resistance to the current flow as possible. If the meter presents opposition to the electron flow, the amount of current flowing would not be the same as when the meter is out of the circuit and an inaccurate reading would result.

The coil in most meters has very little resistance and can be used only for measuring small amounts of current as heavier currents would burn out the coil. A resistor cannot be connected in series with the movement to reduce the current since this would result in an inaccurate reading of the meter.

G.M. Laboratories Inc.

◆ 26. A cutaway view of a coil movement used in a galvanometer. This is a meter used to measure very small amounts of current.

◆ 27. In an ammeter, a shunt is connected in parallel with the moving coil. A small amount of current flows through the meter coil and a large amount of current flows through the shunt.

◆ 28. A meter with a one milliampere movement is placed in a circuit with 100 milliamps flowing through it. A full scale reading is obtained if the shunt carries 99 milliamps and only one milliamp goes through the meter coil.

Changing Meter Current Ranges

To avoid burning up the coil and to increase the range of the meter, a resistor called a *shunt* is connected across the meter coil. The shunt allows a small amount of the current to flow through the meter coil and a large amount of current flows through the shunt (Figure 27). Thus, the ammeter with the shunt provides very little opposition to current flow in the circuit and makes it possible to have a true reading of the current.

The shunt which is placed across the meter coil is said to be in parallel with the coil. Different ranges or maximum scale readings of ammeters may be obtained by changing the size of the shunt. To read large amounts of current a very low resistance shunt is placed across or in parallel with the coil. This light shunt allows most of the current to flow through the shunt and only a small amount through the coil. Since only a small amount of current flows through the coil it takes a larger current flow to

effect the movement of the pointer and thus the range of the meter is extended.

To read small amounts of current a larger resistance is used for the shunt. The larger resistance shunt forces more current to flow through the coil. As more current flows through the coil, the meter reacts to smaller amounts of current.

If, for example, a meter with a one milliampere (.001 amps) full scale deflection is placed in a circuit with 100 milliamperes (.1 amp) flowing through it, the pointer would be driven completely off scale and the coil could be burned out. (Full scale deflection means the amount of current that it takes to make the pointer move to the extreme end of the scale). To make such a meter read the correct current flow a shunt must be placed across the meter terminals, Fig. 28. The shunt must be designed so that the maximum current that can go through the meter coil is the amount needed for full scale reading. The rest goes through the shunt.

Electroplating

Electrons will flow through certain chemical solutions the same as through wire conductors. This principle of current flow in solutions is used in *electroplating*. Electroplating is a very valuable commercial process used when metals need to be coated to prevent rust or to improve their appearance. Copper, nickel, silver, chromium, zinc, cadmium, and gold are the materials most often used in electroplating. The shiny chromium finish found on many automobile accessories is electroplated onto steel.

Electroplating solutions are usually made of a metallic salt solution such as copper sulfate for copper-plating, or nickel sulfate for nickel-plating. A direct current is always used in the plating process.

The object to be plated is placed in the electrolyte solution and is connected to the negative terminal of the direct current electricity. The positive terminal of the electricity is usually connected to a metal such as copper, nickel, or silver that is being used for the plating process. The object to be

◆ 29. With a brass key and copper strip connected as shown, the positive copper particles dissolve and are then attracted by the negatively charged key. As the key is plated, the copper strip is worn away.

plated and the metal used for the plating are placed in the solution as shown in Illustration 29.

When direct current electricity is connected to the two metals, a current starts to flow through the metallic salt solution. The plating metal is dissolved into the solution. This makes the solution have an excess of metal particles which are pulled toward the material to be plated. As the metal particles reach the object a thin plating of the metal is placed on the object.

INTERESTING THINGS TO DO

NEON LAMP

This symbol is used for an alternating current neon lamp.

1. Using a Neon Bulb as an Alternating or Direct Current Indicator.

Obtain a 105-125–volt neon lamp and socket for the lamp. Connect two wires from terminals on the socket to a 115-volt alternating current outlet. The lamp will light up immediately and both elements will appear to be lighted. Notice that there is a slight flickering glow from the elements. This flickering is due to the fluctuations of the alternating current.

Now connect the two socket leads of the neon lamp to a direct current source of electricity. This can be obtained from a 90-volt B battery. Notice that only one element of the lamp glows. Reverse the connections to the socket. What happens? How can we determine whether the current is alternating or direct with this neon bulb?

2. Constructing an Experimental Ammeter.

Material needed to construct the ammeter:

50' No. 26 magnet wire
Two washers (fiber or masonite), ¾" diameter
Tubing (cardboard, fiber, hard rubber), with hollow center, about ³⁄₁₆" to ¼" diameter x 1½" long
Pointer of tin, 2¾" x 3¼"
Back of plywood (or masonite), ¼" x 4½" x 7"
Base of pine, ¾" x 3" x 4½"
Plunger—round soft iron, ³⁄₁₆" x 2¼" (a 20-penny or 40-penny common nail can be used). Plunger must slide freely through the tubing.

Terminals—roundhead (RH) ½", No. 6 wood screws and soldering lugs or washers.

Construction. Drill holes in the two washers so that they will fit snugly over the tubing. Glue the washers to each end of the tubing. Wind the 50' of No. 26 magnet wire on the tubing. Even layers of wire will make a much nicer looking coil.

Make the meter holder by nailing the pine base to the plywood back. Refer to Drawing 31 for placement of the parts.

Cut the tin pointer as shown in the drawing. Punch a hole in the center with a shingle nail. To keep it from tilting, it is necessary to solder a small piece of tin to the back of the pointer. This tin strip is about ¼" wide and 1" long. It is soldered just below the center hole of the pointer and is bent as shown in the drawing. A small hole the same size as the pointer is punched in it so that the center nail must go through the pointer and the small tin strip. A shingle nail acts as the pivot and holds the pointer on to the back. The coil is held to the back by two

◆ **30. Experimental Ammeter for measuring the current of a light bulb.**

small pieces of wire at the top and bottom of the coil. Four small holes are drilled through the plywood back so that the wires can be tightened in the rear of the plywood. Solder the two leads from the coil to two terminals on the baseboard.

Check to be sure that the plunger ($\frac{3}{16}$″ x 2$\frac{1}{4}$″ long) will slide freely through the center of the coil. Make a small hookeye on the top of the plunger by soldering a piece of copper wire to it. A thread is tied to the pointer and to the plunger so that when the pointer is centered the plunger will be about $\frac{1}{4}$″ inside the coil. Another piece of thread is tied to the other side of the pointer and the plunger is balanced by placing small pieces of solder through the thread loop.

Calibrating the Meter. The experimental meter may be calibrated by using a group of light bulbs of a known wattage.

Wire three light bulb sockets in parallel. The terminals on the meter should be connected in one side of a pair of leads that can be plugged into a 115-volt outlet.

Obtain three electric light bulbs—two 25-watt bulbs and one 50-watt bulb.

Screw in the 50-watt bulb. The bulb will burn and the pointer of the meter will move toward the left. Place a mark at that point. This mark shows about .41 ampere of current. With the 50-watt bulb still burning, screw in a 25-watt bulb in the second socket. The pointer will move farther to the left. The meter is now reading about .62 ampere and the dial should again

◆ 31. Drawing of the Experimental Ammeter.

be labeled. Now screw in the other 25-watt bulb. The pointer will again move and the current flow will be about .82 ampere. The ammeter is now calibrated and can be used to make other measurements.

3. Copper-Plating an Object.

Fill a glass jar (pint size) with a solution of copper sulfate. Place a strip of sheet copper about 1″ wide and 4″ long in one side of the jar. In the other side of the jar place the object to be plated such as a piece of brass, or other non-ferrous metal. Using a dry cell connect the positive terminal to the copper strip and the negative terminal to the object to be plated. Current will flow in the circuit and the plating process will start. After about 15 minutes remove the object from the solution. What has happened?

REVIEW QUESTIONS

1. What is the unit of measurement of electron flow?

2. Explain the difference between alternating current and direct current.

3. Give the name of the meter used to measure current.

4. Draw a circuit of a dry cell connected to a light bulb and show where the ammeter should be connected.

5. Why is it important to have the voltage off when connecting meters?

6. What does the term *milli* mean?

7. If a circuit has a .150 ampere of current flowing in it, how many milliamperes is that?

8. What type of current is used for electroplating?

9. Why is electroplating a very valuable process to many manufacturers of metal objects?

UNIT 12
MEASURING RESISTANCE

Meaning of Resistance

Every complete electrical circuit includes wire and a device that consumes current. The voltage forces the current through the circuit. The wire and the current-consuming device, such as a lamp, provide what is called *resistance*. Resistance is the opposition to electron flow that is found in every circuit.

Electrical resistance can be called friction. Electrical friction might be compared to friction which tends to keep things in motion from moving freely. Automobiles traveling on a

FIXED
RESISTOR

The resistor symbol begins with an up-stroke.

highway have friction between the pavement and the tires, boats have friction when moving in water, and friction is developed when an airplane flies through the air. In all of these examples, friction is slowing down the object.

In electricity, the friction or resistance developed by the flow of electrons in a circuit tends to reduce the amount of current flow. The greater the resistance in a circuit, the less the current flow, just as the increased friction developed when an automobile drives off a paved highway onto a dirt road tends to slow it down. The resistance in a circuit can be increased if the length of the wire used in the circuit is made longer, since this will lengthen the path over which the electrons must flow. If the wire is made smaller this too will increase the resistance since it will provide a smaller path for the electrons to flow through.

How Resistance Produces Heat

Electrical resistance has many uses. One of the most important uses of resistance is its ability to make electricity produce heat. Heat is produced by friction. This can be demonstrated if we rub two wooden blocks together very rapidly. The blocks will become warm owing to the friction caused by the rubbing. In electricity, the electrons that are flowing through the wires hit each other, and this collision of electrons results in heat being developed the same as by the rubbing of the blocks together.

We can increase the heating effect of electricity if we can increase the amount of current flow. Current flow can be increased by adding additional voltage or pressure to the circuit. The greater the electron flow the greater the friction from the electrons coming in contact with each other and thus the greater the heat developed.

We are all familiar with the use of electricity in many types of heating appliances such as electric stoves, hot water heaters, flat irons, waffle irons, toasters, and electric blankets. In these appliances (Photograph 32) a special

◆ 32. Examples of three types of heating elements. The large element on the left is used in a wall heater; the small element in the center is used to heat a coffee percolator; the element on the right is used in a portable room heater. All of these elements use coiled nichrome mounted on a ceramic base.

resistance wire called *nichrome* is used to produce heat. Nichrome is an alloy of nickel and chromium and has a high resistance to electron flow. This high resistance plus its ability to be very hot without melting makes it ideal for use as a heater element.

The light bulb, called an *incandescent lamp* (Illustration 33), also uses the heating effect of electricity to produce light. The lamp has a wire

RHEOSTAT

The arrow across the symbol indicates that the resistor is variable.

OHM

OHMMETER

This is how to indicate the instrument for measuring resistance in ohms.

Filament
The filament material usually
used is tungsten. The filament
may be a straight wire, a coil
or a coiled coil.

Bulb
Soft glass is generally used.
Hard glass used for some
lamps to withstand higher
bulb temperatures and for
protection against the weather.
Bulbs are made in various
shapes and finishes.

Gas
Usually a mixture of
nitrogen and argon is used
in most lamps of 40 watts
or larger to retard evaporation of the filament.

Support Wires
Molybdenum wires support
the filament.

Lead-in Wires
Made of copper from base
to stem press and nickel
from stem press to fila-
ment; carry the current
to and from the filament.

Button
Glass is heated during
manufacture and support
wires stuck into it.

Button Rod
Glass rod supports button.

Stem Press
The lead-in wires in the glass
have an airtight seal here and
are made of a combination of a
nickel-iron alloy core and a
copper sleeve (Dumet wire) to
assure about the same coefficient
of expansion as the glass.

Mica Disk
Used in higher wattage
general service lamps and
other types when needed to
reduce circulation of hot
gasses into neck of bulb.

Exhaust Tube
Air is exhausted through this
tube during manufacture and
inert gasses introduced into
the bulb. The tube, which
originally projects beyond the
bulb, is then sealed off short
enough to be capped by the base.

Fuse
Protects the lamp and
circuit by blowing if the
filament arcs.

Base
Typical screw base is shown.
One lead-in wire is soldered to
the center contact and the other
to the upper rim of the base
shell. Made of brass.

Courtesy Sylvania Electric Products, Inc.

◆ **33. In the incandescent lamp, light results from the heating effect of electrical resistance.**

inside of the glass bulb called a *filament.* This filament is made of a high
resistance wire made of tungsten. As
the electrons flow through the tungsten the friction of the electrons produces heat. This heat is so great that
the filament becomes white hot and
gives off light. To keep the tungsten
filament from burning up because of
the oxygen in the air, it is placed in a
glass bulb. All of the air is then removed from the bulb and the filament
can get very hot without burning up.

Resistance Used to Control Current Flow and Reduce Voltage

Very often it is desirable to be able
to control the amount of electricity
used by a device. A good example of
this is stage lighting where it is neces-

sary to dim the lights. If the amount of current flowing through the lights can be reduced then the lights will become dimmer. We can reduce the current flow by putting more resistance in the circuit. The resistance can be a specially constructed resistor of nichrome wire. The resistor is connected in the circuit as shown in Illustration 34, so that the current must flow through the resistor and the light bulb. In this way the quantity of electrons flowing through the lamp is reduced by the resistor. The light is dimmed because part of the voltage delivered by the wall outlet is being reduced by the resistor. If we want to vary the brightness of the light a variable resistor called a *rheostat* must be used.

A rheostat has a movable contact arm that makes it possible to change the amount of resistance in the circuit (Photographs 35 and 36). When the contact arm is moved to the extreme left the entire voltage is available for the lamp and it burns brightly. As the contact arm moves to the right (clockwise) more resistance is placed in the circuit and the lamp becomes dimmer. The increased resistance lowers the current flow and the resistor reduces the voltage.

Rheostats are used to control the speed of motors. The speed of electric sewing machines is controlled through the use of a variable resistor that can be moved with the knee or foot. As the rheostat is pushed down it decreases the amount of resistance and allows more voltage to be used to speed up the sewing machine motor.

Resistance Measurement

The unit of measurement of resistance is the *ohm*. Some circuits have a very few ohms resistance whereas others may have a million ohms resistance. All circuits have resistance in the wire and in the device using the electricity.

◆ 34. (A) The fixed resistor in the circuit reduces the current flow through the lamp bulb. The light from the lamp is dimmer because part of the voltage is used by the fixed resistor. (B) A wiring diagram using electrical symbols to represent the circuit shown in *A*. (C) This schematic diagram shows how a rheostat is used in a circuit to vary the brightness of a lamp bulb.

◆ 35. The lamp is burning brightly as the contact arm of the rheostat is allowing all of the current to flow directly to the lamp. The voltmeter connected across the lamp reads about 117 volts.

Where fairly heavy current is flowing fixed resistors are made of nichrome wire. If small amounts of current are flowing through the circuit, such as in many radio circuits, fixed resistors made of carbon can be used.

◆ 36. The contact or arm has been moved so that the current must flow through part of the rheostat before going to the lamp. The rheostat has provided enough resistance to reduce the voltage across the lamp to about 60 volts. The light from the lamp is dimmer.

Variable resistors are also made of nichrome wire or carbon, depending upon the amount of current to be controlled.

Resistance can be measured directly by the use of a meter called an *ohmmeter*. Some multimeters used to measure voltage and current are also used as ohmmeters. A very accurate device used to measure resistance is called a *Wheatstone bridge*.

Care must be used in measuring resistance with an ohmmeter to be sure that the voltage has been disconnected from the circuit. Leaving the voltage on when measuring the resistance will damage the ohmmeter.

In circuits where heat is developed the true resistance cannot be measured with an ohmmeter. As wires heat they increase their opposition to electron flow and the resistance in the circuit is increased. To determine the resistance of circuits where heat is being developed Ohm's law, which will be explained in Unit 14, must be used.

Using the Color Code

The value of the stripes or bands used for color coding composition resistors is shown in Figure 37. To find the size of a particular resistor we must first look at the color bands and by using the color code chart we can de-

Resistor Color Code

COLOR	SIGNIFICANT FIGURE	DECIMAL MULTIPLIER
Black	0	1
Brown	1	10
Red	2	100
Orange	3	1000
Yellow	4	10,000
Green	5	100,000
Blue	6	1,000,000
Violet	7	10,000,000
Gray	8	100,000,000
White	9	1,000,000,000

TOLERANCE
No band = 20%
Silver   = 10%
Gold   = 5%

4 TOLERANCE
3 DECIMAL MULTIPLIER
2 SECOND FIGURE
1 FIRST FIGURE

◆ **37. Composition resistor color-coding**

termine its resistance. For example, a resistor has as its first band the color red, the second color yellow, the third color orange, and no fourth color band. The first figure (red) is 2, the second figure (yellow) is 4, and the decimal multiplier (orange) is 1000. The value of the resistance is 24,000 ohms and since there is no fourth color band the tolerance is plus or minus 20%.

INTERESTING THINGS TO DO

Constructing an Experimental Ohmmeter.

Materials needed to construct the ohmmeter:

85' No. 32 magnet wire

Cardboard tubing, $1\frac{1}{2}$" inside diameter x 2" long
Wood base, $\frac{1}{2}$" x 3" x 5"
Pointer of sheet brass, $2\frac{5}{8}$" x $\frac{1}{8}$"
Piece of hacksaw blade, $\frac{3}{16}$" x $1\frac{3}{8}$"
Sheet brass, $\frac{1}{2}$" x $1\frac{3}{4}$" (2 required)
Sheet brass, $\frac{5}{8}$" x $1\frac{1}{2}$" (2 required)

◆ **38. An experimental ohmmeter**

◆ **39. Drawing of the experimental ohmmeter**

Construction. Shape the two brass pointer bearings as shown in Drawing 39. Center-punch the upper ends of the bearings and secure them to the wood base with wood screws ½" apart. Cut the meter pointer to the shape shown in the drawing. Cut a small steel brad and sharpen the ends so that it will turn freely between the pointer bearings. Drill a hole the size of the steel brad through the brass pointer ¾" from the square end. Drill a similar hole through the center of the piece of hacksaw blade. Harden the piece of hacksaw blade by heating it to a cherry red over a flame, then plunging it into cold water. Solder the meter pointer and piece of hacksaw blade to the steel brad so that the two pieces will be at a right angle to each other. Secure a loop of solder to the lower end of the meter pointer, place the pointer between the bearings and test it for balance. The pointer should swing freely between the bearings and come to rest in an exact upright position. If it is neces-

sary to lighten either end of the piece of hacksaw blade it may be done with a grinder or file, but care must be used because the hardened steel may break easily. After the pointer has been checked for balance, the piece of hacksaw blade may be magnetized by stroking it with a magnet as described in another part of this book.

Wind about 200 turns of magnet wire around the center of the cardboard tubing. Drill two small holes through the wood base through which to pass the coil ends and glue the coil to the wood base. Make certain that the coil does not touch the ends of the piece of hacksaw blade.

Shape two pieces of sheet brass to hold a flashlight cell and secure them to the wood base as shown in the drawing. Secure two machine screws at the end of the wood base to serve as terminal screws. Connect a piece of magnet wire on the bottom of the wood base between one of the flashlight cell holders and one end of the coil. Connect the other flashlight support to a screw terminal. Connect the other end of the coil to the other screw terminal. Secure a piece of white cardboard to the top of the coil to serve as a meter scale. Secure two pieces of flexible wire to the meter terminals to serve as test leads. The meter is now ready to be calibrated.

Calibrating the Ohmmeter. Place a flashlight cell in the holder and touch the two ends of the flexible leads together. The meter pointer will now swing to an extreme right or left position, depending upon which way the flashlight cell was placed in its holder. This is called the "zero" position and should be marked on the cardboard scale with the figure "0". Secure a 60-watt mazda lamp and touch the ends of the meter test leads to the contacts at the base of the lamp. The meter pointer will swing away from its center position and come to rest at a point toward the "0" position. Since the cold resistance of the 60-watt lamp is 20 ohms, write the figure "20" on the meter scale directly above the meter pointer. Other figures for calibrating the meter may be obtained from other size lamps and household electrical appliances. A 25-watt lamp has a cold resistance of about 50 ohms, while a 100-watt lamp has a cold resistance of only 10 ohms. A spiral heating element such as is used in an electric heater has a cold resistance of about 20 ohms.

REVIEW QUESTIONS

1. What is resistance?

2. What happens to the resistance of a circuit if a large diameter wire is replaced with a smaller diameter wire?

3. How does resistance produce heat?

4. Name the material used for heater elements.

5. Why is it necessary to keep the air away from the filament of an incandescent lamp?

6. What is a variable resistor called?

7. What is the unit of measurement of resistance called?

8. Explain what happens to the resistance of a heater element when the current is turned on.

UNIT 13
USING CONDUCTORS AND INSULATORS

Common Conductors

We have stated that wires are used to provide a path through which electrons flow. These wires are called *conductors* because they conduct the electricity to the various parts of the circuit. Conductors are usually made of metal since most metals permit electrons to flow through them easily. Some liquids are conductors of electricity but are used only for special purposes such as the electrolyte in storage batteries and electroplating.

All metals are conductors of electricity but some have more resistance than others. Copper is one of the metals which has a low resistance. Silver has a slightly lower resistance than copper but because it is more expensive than copper it is used only in special types of circuits. Almost all circuits use copper wire for conductors, as it is an excellent conductor that is fairly plentiful and not too expensive.

Aluminum has a higher resistance than copper but is occasionally used when extremely light weight is needed. Long power transmission lines are sometimes made of aluminum to reduce the weight of the wire.

Since all metals are conductors, different metals are sometimes used where they can supply special needs. These metals and some of their uses are listed above. They are listed according to their resistance with the first, silver, having the lowest resist-ance and the last, carbon, having the highest resistance.

CONDUCTORS	TYPICAL APPLICATIONS
Silver	Circuit breaker contacts, electronic circuits
Copper	All types of electrical conductors
Gold	Electroscope leaves
Aluminum	Lightweight conductors
Tungsten	Radio and lamp filaments
Zinc	Fuses and dry cells
Brass	Wall plugs and other types of exposed electrical connections
Nickel	Radio tubes
Tin	Solder
Steel	Telephone and telegraph lines
Lead	Solder and storage battery plates
Mercury	Switches
Nichrome	Heater elements
Carbon	Arc lamps and motor brushes

Measuring Wire Sizes

All conductors have resistance. Large conductors have less resistance than small conductors because the electrons have more freedom to move in the large conductors. Long conductors have more resistance than short conductors (of the same size) because the electrons have a longer path to flow through in the long conductor.

Since resistance can reduce the amount of electricity that flows in a circuit, it is often necessary to have conductors which will provide very little opposition to electron flow. To help in selecting the correct conductor all wires are designated according to number size. The smaller the number the larger the wire. A No. 8 wire is about $\frac{1}{8}''$ in diameter and is much larger than a No. 14 wire which is about $\frac{1}{16}''$ in diameter. A No. 36 wire

WIRE - ALUMINUM
336,400 CM. 18/1 ACSR
BARE STRANDED - COND.
FILLED WITH CALOL
WHITE GREASE

WIRE - ALUMINUM
BARE #4/0 - 7 STRAND

CABLE - LEAD COVERED
#6 - 1 COND. 1-KV
PAPER INSULATED

WIRE - COPPER
#6 - 5 KV, 1/C 19 STRAND
WITH 10/64'' OIL BASE
COMPOUND INSULATION AND
2/64'' NEOPRENE JACKET

WIRE - WEATHERPROOF
#2 - 7 STRAND, 2 BRAID
MEDIUM HARD DRAWN COPPER

WIRE - WEATHERPROOF
#8 SOLID, 2 BRAID, MEDIUM
HARD DRAWN COPPER

CABLE - LEAD COVERED
500 MCM, 3/C, 15 KV COMPACT
SECTOR, PAPER INSULATED,
METALLIZED PAPER STRAND
SHIELDING, .175 MILS WOOD
PULP PAPER, NON-MAGNETIC
METALLIC SHIELDING TAPE
INTERCALATED WITH A PAPER
TAPE, CONDUCTORS CABLED
WITH PAPER FILLERS, NON-
MAGNETIC BINDER INTER-
CALATED WITH A PAPER TAPE,
.085 MILS GENCALLOY 'A'
LEAD SHEATH .115 MILS
REINFORCED NEOPRENE JACKET

WIRE - ALUMINUM
#6 SOLID, 3 BRAID
HARD DRAWN

WIRE - ALUMINUM
#6 SOLID NEOPRENE
COVERED HARD DRAWN

WIRE - BARE COPPER
250,000 CM, 18 STRAND
HOLLOW CONDUCTOR

WIRE - BARE COPPER
250,000 CM, 19 STRAND

WIRE - BARE COPPER
#4/0 - 7 STRAND

CABLE - RED JUMPER
#1/0 - 7500 V, 1/C 259 STRAND,
WITH 16/64'' OKOLITE AND
5/64'' OKOPRENE INSULATION

CABLE - SUPERVISORY CONTROL
#19 - 10 PR. (20 COND.) PAPER
INSULATED LEAD COVERED

CABLE - SUPERVISORY CONTROL
#19 - 11 PR. (10 PR. GUARANTEED)
HAZAPRENE - WITH 5/16'' - 30½
EHS COPPERWELD STRD. MESSENGER

CABLE - SELF-SUPPORTING SERVICE
#6 - 3 CONDUCTOR
2 - #6 - 7 STRD. COPPER CONDUCTORS
WITH 4/64'' ROPRENE INSULATION
1 - #6- 3 STRD. BARE
COPPERWELD NEUTRAL

◆ 40. Conductors used for power distribution are made to meet the requirements of different conditions.

◆ 41. Using a wire gage to determine the size of a wire. The size of wire is found by placing the wire between the slots on the outside edge of the gage. The slot in which the wire fits snugly indicates the gage of the wire. The round hole at the bottom of the slot makes it easier to remove the wire after checking for size.

is extremely small and is about the diameter of a human hair.

Wire sizes may be measured by a gage called a *wire gage* (Photograph 41). Gages used in the United States are called *American Standard Wire Gages*.

Use of the correct wire size for different circuits is necessary to prevent loss due to resistance and to keep the wire from heating. If the wire used is too small for the amount of current flowing in the circuit, heat will be produced. This heat from excess current in wires can produce a fire and has been the cause of many houses burning down. Each electrical device and every circuit in the home uses a size wire that will carry the current safely. It is important to know how much current each circuit will be using in order to select the proper size wire.

The National Board of Fire Underwriters has adopted regulations which state the maximum amount of current that can be carried by conductors used in home and industrial wiring. These regulations are part of what is known as the *National Electrical Code*. Current carrying values for conductors commonly used in home wiring are listed in the table below:

A. W. G.	AMPERES	
16	7	
14	15	
12	20	ROOM TEMP. 86°F.
10	30	
8	40	
6	55	

Since the amount of current that a conductor can carry safely depends upon its cross-sectional area, a unit known as a *"circular-mil,"* abbreviated, C. M., has been selected to give us this information. A mil is equal to 0.001 inch and an area with a dimension of 1 mil on each side, such as Figure 42, would have an area of one square mil. Since most conductors, except those used in special applications, are round we need a unit to express circular area. If we square the diameter of the circle shown in Figure 42, we will get the same answer as we would with the square figure, but it will be in terms of circular mils rather than square mils. Thus, we can

1 CIRCULAR MIL AREA   .001   1 SQUARE MIL. AREA

◆ 42. Circular and square mil area.

see that a circular mil bears the same relationship to a square mil as the area of a circle does to a square, which is 0.7854, and all we have to do to get the circular mil area of a conductor is to square its diameter in mils.

The column under "Circular-Mil Area" in the wire table shows the relationship between conductors of different number sizes. If we divide the circular-mil area of one conductor by the area of the next smaller conductor, for example, 10,380 cir-mils (No. 10), by 8234 cir-mils (No. 11) the an-

swer will be 1.26. This ratio holds true throughout the whole scale for any two adjacent wire sizes.

Wire may be obtained either solid or stranded. Solid wire is usually used for wiring homes and in places where the wires do not need to be moved. Stranded wire is made up of several small wires twisted together. By using several small wires together it is possible to have a very flexible wire that can be moved easily. All large cables used for transmission lines are stranded. Cords used on home appliances and extension cords are stranded

COPPER-WIRE TABLE

Gauge No. A.W.G.[1]	Diam. in Mils	Circular Mil Area	Turns per Linear Inch	Turns per Square Inch	Feet per Lb.	Ohms per 1000 ft. 25° C.	Current Carrying Capacity at 1500 C.M. per Amp.
			Enamel	Enamel	Bare		
1	289.3	83690	—	—	3.947	.1264	55.7
2	257.6	66370	—	—	4.977	.1593	44.1
3	229.4	52640	—	—	6.276	.2009	35.0
4	204.3	41740	—	—	7.914	.2533	27.7
5	181.9	33100	—	—	9.980	.3195	22.0
6	162.0	26250	—	—	12.58	.4028	17.5
7	144.3	20820	—	—	15.87	.5080	13.8
8	128.5	16510	7.6	—	20.01	.6405	11.0
9	114.4	13090	8.6	—	25.23	.8077	8.7
10	101.9	10380	9.6	84.8	31.82	1.018	6.9
11	90.74	8234	10.7	105	40.12	1.284	5.5
12	80.81	6530	12.0	131	50.59	1.619	4.4
13	71.96	5178	13.5	162	63.80	2.042	3.5
14	64.08	4107	15.0	198	80.44	2.575	2.7
15	57.07	3257	16.8	250	101.4	3.247	2.2
16	50.82	2583	18.9	306	127.9	4.094	1.7
17	45.26	2048	21.2	372	161.3	5.163	1.3
18	40.30	1624	23.6	454	203.4	6.510	1.1
19	35.89	1288	26.4	553	256.5	8.210	.86
20	31.96	1022	29.4	725	323.4	10.35	.68
21	28.46	810.1	33.1	895	407.8	13.05	.54
22	25.35	642.4	37.0	1070	514.2	16.46	.43
23	22.57	509.5	41.3	1300	648.4	20.76	.34
24	20.10	404.0	46.3	1570	817.7	26.17	.27
25	17.90	320.4	51.7	1910	1031	33.00	.21
26	15.94	254.1	58.0	2300	1300	41.62	.17
27	14.20	201.5	64.9	2780	1639	52.48	.13
28	12.64	159.8	72.7	3350	2067	66.17	.11
29	11.26	126.7	81.6	3900	2607	83.44	.084
30	10.03	100.5	90.5	4660	3287	105.2	.067
31	8.928	79.70	101	5280	4145	132.7	.053
32	7.950	63.21	113	6250	5227	167.3	.042
33	7.080	50.13	127	7360	6591	211.0	.033
34	6.305	39.75	143	8310	8310	266.0	.026
35	5.615	31.52	158	8700	10480	335.0	.021
36	5.000	25.00	175	10700	13210	423.0	.017
37	4.453	19.83	198	—	16660	533.4	.013
38	3.965	15.72	224	—	21010	672.6	.010
39	3.531	12.47	248	—	26500	848.1	.008
40	3.145	9.88	282	—	33410	1069	.006

1. American Wire Gauge

◆ 43. Insulators are designed for special purposes; without them, electricity could not be used.

so that the cords can be moved and coiled readily.

The following table shows several wire sizes and gives some common uses for these sizes.

Size of Wire	Common Use
6 to 10	Service leads for light and power to homes
12 to 14	Interior house wiring
16 to 18	Lighting fixtures
18 to 20	Bell wire, radio circuits
20 to 24	Motors, door chimes
24 to 30	Radio coils, small motors

Purpose of Insulators

Materials which do not permit electrons to flow through them are called *nonconductors* or *insulators*. These insulators are nonmetallic. In electrical circuits insulators are just as important as conductors. Conductors provide a definite path through which electrons will flow; insulators are used to prevent the electrons from flowing where they are not wanted.

Insulation is necessary in most electrical wiring to avoid short circuits. Short circuits occur when wires or bare electrical contacts touch each other so that an unwanted path is made through which current can flow. These unwanted paths allow the current to flow through them instead of through the regular circuit. The wires used in electrical circuits in the home are covered with insulation so that they can be placed next to each other without causing a "short circuit." Should the bare copper wires touch each other the electrons would stop flowing through the necessary parts of the circuit. Most wires are covered with enamel, cotton, rubber, or plastic materials. The type of material selected for wire insulation depends upon where the wire is going to be used. Heavy insulation is needed on wires that may contact other objects or where high voltages are used.

WRAP ASBESTOS COVERING WITH THREAD

TWIST WIRES TOGETHER

STRANDED WIRE

ASBESTOS

FABRIC COVERING

RUBBER

◆ 44. A drawing showing asbestos insulation in a heater cord. Each wire is wrapped in asbestos which will not burn. The drawing illustrates the method used to repair this type of cord.

Insulation is needed to protect people from coming into contact with electrical circuits. All switches must be insulated so that people may turn them off and on without receiving a shock from the electricity. Wall outlets are insulated so that they will not shock anyone that touches them.

Types of Insulators

There are many types of insulators. Each is used for a specific purpose. Air is a good insulator and is used where space is not a problem and where people cannot touch the circuit. Air is actually the insulation between the wires that are strung on high power transmission lines.

Circuits carrying very high voltages require extremely good insulators. The pressure from high voltages can make the electrons jump from one part of the circuit to another the same as lightning jumps between the sky and the ground. High-voltage transmission lines use large glass or ceramic insulators on the power poles. These insulators prevent the electricity from flowing through the poles to the ground. Power poles made of wood become very good conductors of electricity when wet.

In circuits where heat is involved asbestos, ceramic, and mica are used for insulation. Wire cords connected to heater elements, such as in flat irons, are usually covered with asbestos and cotton. The asbestos will not burn and is a very good insulator for electricity. See Photograph 44. Mica and ceramic materials are used as a base to hold the heater elements made of nichrome wire in toasters, flat irons, and all types of electrical heaters. Both materials are good insulators and can withstand tremendous heat without burning or melting.

Special types of insulators are needed in high-frequency radio circuits. These high-frequency waves have the ability to make electrons flow through some types of insulation. Materials such as steatite and polystyrene are often used in high-frequency circuits since they are good insulators for this purpose.

The following are some common insulators and their uses:

INSULATOR	COMMON USE
Air	Between transmission lines
Paper	To separate windings in transformers and motors
Enamel	Covering on magnet wire
Fiber	Motors, solenoids
Mica	Toasters, separation for radio capacitors
Rubber	Wire covering
Bakelite	Electrical outlets and switches
Ceramics	Heater element bases, transmission lines
Plastic	Wire covering
Steatite	Television, radio
Oil	Transformers and capacitors

INTERESTING THINGS TO DO

1. Making a Pigtail Splice.

Skin the wire ends about 2", as shown at *A*, Illustration 47. Cross the cleaned bare ends just below the end

◆ 45. When removing insulation with a knife, use a fairly sharp knife and cut the insulation at an angle of about 30 degrees. Do not circle the wire with the blade at right angles to it. Usually, this produces a groove or nick in the wire which will cause it to break easily when bent at this point. Also a nick in the wire may reduce its capacity to carry current. Use a wire stripper to remove insulation whenever possible.

◆ 46. Pigtail splices are used where wires are to be joined together. The splice is usually placed in a junction box. The joint is always soldered and taped before the cover is placed on the box.

of the insulation, *B*. Hold the ends with the fingers and thumb of one hand, and twisting them together with the other hand, make about six turns, *C*. Trim the ends, as shown at *D*. Solder the splice, *E* and *F*. After the wire has cooled, wipe it with a damp cloth and insulate the splice with Scotch Electrical Tape.

◆ 47. This is how to make a pigtail splice.

◆ 48. A tee-tap splice is used where it is necessary to connect onto an existing circuit. The tee-tap makes it possible to splice onto the wire without cutting it.

2. Making a Tee-Tap Splice.

Remove the insulation from the wires, *A,* Illustration 49. Cross the wires, as shown at *B.* Wrap the branch wire around the main wire, *C.* Wind the wire tightly with pliers, *D.* Cut off the projecting end of the wire, leaving no sharp projection, *E.* Solder the splice, as shown at *F* and *G.* After the wire has cooled, wipe it with a damp cloth and insulate the splice with Scotch Electrical Tape.

◆ 49. This is how to make a tee-tap splice.

◆ 50. A Western Union splice is used where wire needs to be lengthened.

3. Making a Western Union Splice.

Remove the insulation from the ends of the wires for a distance of about 3", *A*, Illustration 51. Cross the two wires, as shown at *B*. Twist the wires around each other, so as to make two complete turns, *C*. Wrap the projecting ends around the straight sections of the wires so as to make three close turns, *D*. Wind the wire tightly with pliers and cut off the remaining ends. Solder the splice, as shown at *E*. After the wire has cooled, wipe it with a damp cloth and insulate the splice with Scotch Electrical Tape.

◆ 51. These are the steps to follow in making a Western Union splice.

REVIEW QUESTIONS

1. Why is copper used most often as a conductor?

2. Where is aluminum used as a conductor?

3. What metal has the lowest resistance?

4. In wire sizes, which is larger in diameter, a No. 10 wire or a No. 12?

5. Why is it important to use the correct size wire when wiring a home?

6. What is the resistance of 50' of No. 30 wire?

7. Give the purpose of insulators in a circuit.

8. List several commercial-type insulating materials.

9. What is the difference between conductors and insulators?

UNIT 14
SHOWING THE RELATIONSHIP OF VOLTAGE, CURRENT, AND RESISTANCE

Importance of Ohm's Law

In every electrical circuit we have three basic measurements:

1. *Voltage* —The pressure that forces electrons through the circuit.

2. *Current* —The amount of electrons flowing.

3. *Resistance*—The opposition to electron flow.

Before connecting a circuit it is often important to know what each of these measurements will be. By knowing what the current flow is we can select the proper size wire. By knowing what the voltage is we can select the correct size device that will work from the known voltage. It would be very time-consuming if every electrical circuit had to be tried out experimentally before it was possible to determine the amount of voltage, current, or resistance in the circuit. If we are to work efficiently with electricity we must be able to calculate the electrical measurements of the circuit before we hook them up.

There is a definite relationship between the voltage, current, and resistance in every circuit. When the voltage is increased the current will also be increased since more voltage will provide more pressure to push electrons through the circuit. If more resistance is added to a circuit this will reduce the amount of current, as

3 OHM BULB

6 VOLT STORAGE BATTERY

3 OHM RESISTANCE

6 VOLTS

SCHEMATIC DIAGRAM

◆ 52. **Six-volt storage battery connected to a light bulb with 3 ohms resistance.**

there will be more opposition to electron flow. Whenever any change is made in either the voltage or resistance this changes the current flow.

This relationship that exists between the three electrical measurements can be calculated mathematically by a law called *Ohm's law*. Ohm's law is a mathematical formula that is used to calculate the current flow if the voltage and resistance of the circuit are known; it is used to determine the voltage if the current and resistance are known; and it is used to calculate the resistance if the voltage and current are known. From this we can see that if any two measurements are known the third measurement can be determined.

Calculating Current Flow

Ohm's law states that the *current is equal to the voltage divided by the resistance*. This can be shown mathematically as

Current (in amperes) =

$$\frac{\text{Voltage (in volts)}}{\text{Resistance (in ohms)}}$$

In the circuit in Illustration 52 the voltage of the storage battery is 6 volts. The resistance of the bulb is 3 ohms. How much current will flow in the circuit? Using the formula

$$\text{Current} = \frac{\text{Voltage}}{\text{Resistance}}$$

Voltage is 6 volts

Resistance is 3 ohms

Placing the numbers in the formula:

$$\text{Current} = \frac{6}{3}$$

Current = 2 amperes

In Ohm's law as in most mathematical formulas symbols are used for each of the measurements.

The letter I is used for current in amperes.

The letter E is used for voltage in volts.

The letter R is used for resistance in ohms.

Ohm's law formula:

$$\text{Current} = \frac{\text{Voltage}}{\text{Resistance}}$$

Ohm's law formula with symbols:

$$I = \frac{E}{R}$$

Devices connected to a source of voltage are often shown in a diagram as being a resistor. The pictorial drawing in Illustration 53 shows a generator connected to a searchlight. The line drawing using symbols is called a *schematic diagram* and shows the searchlight as a resistor.

If the generator is producing 50 volts and the resistance of the searchlight is 5 ohms how much current would be flowing in the circuit?

PICTORIAL

SCHEMATIC

◆ **53. The generator supplies current to the searchlight, which acts as a resistor.**

◆ 54. A current of 5 amperes is flowing through a resistance of 6 ohms.

Ohm's law formula $I = \dfrac{E}{R}$

Placing numbers in the formula

$$I = \dfrac{50}{5}$$

$$I = 10 \text{ amperes}$$

The current flowing in the circuit would be 10 amperes.

Calculating Voltage

Ohm's law can be used to determine the voltage being applied to a circuit provided the current and resistance are known. The formula for determining the voltage is:

Voltage = Current × Resistance

Using symbols $E = I \times R$

In the circuit in Illustration 54 the current is 5 amperes. The resistance is 6 ohms. What is the voltage of the generator?

$$E = I \times R$$
$$E = 5 \times 6$$
$$E = 30 \text{ volts}$$

The voltage of the generator is 30 volts.

Calculating Resistance

Ohm's law can be used to calculate the resistance in a circuit if the voltage and the current are known. The formula for calculating resistance is:

Resistance is equal to voltage divided by the current.

$$\text{Resistance (ohms)} = \frac{\text{Voltage (volts)}}{\text{Current (amperes)}}$$

Using symbols $R = \dfrac{E}{I}$

◆ 55. The generator is producing 100 volts and 2 amperes of current is flowing through the resistor.

In the circuit in Illustration 55 the voltage is 100 volts. The current is 2 amperes. The circuit resistance is the circuit?

$$R = \frac{E}{I}$$

$$R = \frac{100}{2}$$

$$R = 50 \text{ ohms}$$

The resistance of the circuit is 50 ohms.

The Three Forms of Ohm's Law

Ohm's law can be used for three different purposes:

To find the current $I = \dfrac{E}{R}$

To find the voltage $E = I \times R$

To find the resistance $R = \dfrac{E}{I}$

If any two of the electrical measurements are known the third measurement can be determined.

Measuring Electrical Power

The amount of electrical energy required to produce heat, light, or motion is often stated in watts.

The *watt* is the electrical unit of power. Power means the ability to do

WATTMETER

This symbol indicates an instrument for measuring power.

work. We are all familiar with the unit of work called *horsepower* used with automobiles. In automobiles it is customary to state the amount of horsepower that the engine will produce. A 175-horsepower engine is more powerful and will do more work than a 100-horsepower engine. In electricity the wattage indicates the power being used by the electrical device.

Electric light bulbs are marked according to the number of watts of electricity they use. The greater the wattage of the bulb the greater the amount of light produced. A 25-watt electric light bulb will not burn as brightly nor will it use as much electricity as a 100-watt bulb. A 75-watt electric soldering iron will not get as hot as a 100-watt soldering iron. A 600-watt electric wall heater will not heat a room as fast as a 1,000-watt heater. In each of these items the lower wattage produces less power in the form of heat or light, and uses less electricity. From this we can see that it is important to look at the wattage rating on all electrical equipment that we plan to buy or use.

Calculating Wattage

The power or wattage used by electrical circuits can be calculated mathematically. The basic formula for determining wattage states that *the number of watts used equals the voltage across the circuit multiplied by the current flowing in the circuit.*

Basic watt formula

Watts = Voltage × Current

Using symbols

$$W = E \times I$$

◆ **56. The amount of electricity used is measured in watts.**

In the circuit in Illustration 56 the toaster has 9 amperes of current flowing through it and the voltage at the electrical outlet is 120 volts. What is the wattage of the toaster?

Basic formula

Watts = Voltage × Current

$$W = E \times I$$

(Placing numbers in the formula)

Volts = 120

Amperes = 9

$$W = 120 \times 9$$

$$W = 1080 \text{ Watts}$$

The toaster is using 1,080 watts of electricity.

The instruments used to calculate the wattage are a voltmeter and an ammeter. A single meter called a watt-meter which is a combination volt-

◆ **57. The wattmeter on the left shows that the heater element is using a little more than 600 watts of electricity. If a wattmeter is not available a voltmeter and an ammeter may be used to determine the wattage of the circuit. The voltmeter reads about 120 volts. The** ammeter reads about 5 amperes. Using the watt formula the power can be calculated by multiplying the voltage times the current. Thus, 120 volts times 5 amperes equals 600 watts.

meter and ammeter can be used to measure the wattage of a circuit. With this meter it is not necessary to use the watt formula. When connected in the circuit a wattmeter scale reading shows the amount of wattage being used by the circuit.

Meaning of Kilowatt

The term *kilowatt* is sometimes used to express power used by electrical equipment. *Kilo* means 1,000. One kilowatt equals 1,000 watts. Ten kilowatts equals 10,000 watts. If an electrical heater has a name plate that states that the heater uses 3 kilowatts of electricity this means that it uses 3,000 watts of electricity.

Using Watt-Hour Meters

The power company that delivers electricity to homes and businesses

Courtesy General Electric Co.

◆ 58. This watt-hour meter records the amount of electricity used.

throughout a community uses a meter called a *kilowatt-hour* meter at each location. The meter is connected so that all the electricity goes through it

◆ 59. This is how to read a watt-hour meter. Record the figure which the pointer on the right-hand dial has last passed and proceed to the left, recording in like manner the respective figure indicated on each successive dial. Thus, the top meter would read, 23,920 (setting numbers down right to left —20, —920, -3,920, —23,920) and the bottom one 2,176.

before going into the building. Each meter is so constructed that it measures the wattage and also operates like a stop watch that runs only when the current is being used. Thus the meter is keeping a record of the amount of time that it is being used. The dials on the face of the meter record the number of kilowatt-hours flowing into the building. The exact number of kilowatt-hours of electricity consumed can be determined at any time by reading the meter. Power companies have a rate that they charge for each kilowatt-hour of electricity. Electric bills are figured by determining the number of kilowatt-hours consumed and multiplying this by the rate charged.

INTERESTING THINGS TO DO

1. Determining the Hot Resistance of an Electric Light Bulb.

Materials needed are a 100-watt light bulb, lamp socket, attachment plug, insulated wire, AC voltmeter and an AC ammeter.

Connect the circuit as shown in Illustration 60. The voltmeter and ammeter constructed in Units 10 and 11 may be used. After measuring the voltage and the current use Ohm's law to calculate the resistance of the lamp bulb. How will this resistance differ from the cold resistance of the lamp?

2. Determining the Current Used by a Heater Element.

Materials needed are a lamp socket, a screw-base type 600-watt heater element, attachment plug, AC voltmeter, and AC ammeter.

Wire the circuit as shown in Illustration 61. The resistance of the heater element is approximately 20 ohms. After measuring the voltage calculate the current flow using Ohm's law. Prove your answer by using an AC ammeter to measure the current.

◆ 61. Current used by heater element

3. Determining the Wattage of a Household Appliance.

Materials needed are an AC voltmeter, AC ammeter, attachment plug, insulated wire, outlet box, and some type of household appliance such as waffle iron, toaster, heater, radio, or flat iron.

◆ 60. Hot resistance of light bulb

◆ **62. Wattage of an appliance**

Wire a circuit as shown in Illustration 62. Plug the household appliance attachment plug into the outlet box. After measuring the voltage and the current use the watt formula to determine the wattage of the appliance.

4. Constructing a Soldering Iron.
Materials needed:

1 Wood handle (a file handle is satisfactory)
1 Piece of pipe (steel or brass), ½″ outside diameter, 7″ long
1 Piece of round copper rod, ½″ x 1¾″
1 Heating element (Eagle soldering iron element Catalog No. 407, Eagle Electric Mfg. Co. Inc., 23-10 Bridge Plaza So., Long Island City 1, New York)
6′ of No. 18 heater cord
1 Metal ring (diameter and width to fit handle)

◆ **63. Electric soldering iron**

◆ **64. Drawing of soldering iron**

Drill the handle as shown in Drawing 64. Drill a series of $\frac{1}{8}''$ ventilating holes in pipe. Drill and tap 6–32 threads in each end of pipe for setscrews. Drill a $\frac{11}{32}''$ hole in one end of the copper rod 1" deep. File or turn shoulder on copper tip so that it will fit snugly into the pipe. File a four-sided point on the tip.

Insert the pipe into the handle and secure with the setscrew. Push heater cord through both the handle and the pipe. Connect the heating element leads to the heater cord extending out from the pipe. Solder and tape the connections. With the heater element extending $\frac{3}{4}''$ beyond the end of the pipe determine where the cord will enter the wood handle. At this point wrap the cord with several layers of tape so that the cord cannot be pulled out of the iron.

Place the tip in the pipe and secure with the setscrew. Drill $\frac{5}{32}''$ holes through the metal ring and into the handle. Slip the ring on the handle and fasten it in place with a round-head wood screw. Connect the attachment plug cap to the end of the cord. The iron is now ready to try out. Using an AC ammeter and a voltmeter determine how much wattage the iron is consuming.

REVIEW QUESTIONS

1. How can a knowledge of Ohm's law help us in making electrical calculations?

2. Explain what is meant by "hot" resistance in an electrical circuit.

3. How can we overcome the effect of high resistance in an electrical circuit?

4. If we increase the voltage in an electrical circuit containing a light bulb what might happen? Why?

5. Explain with a diagram how you would connect a voltmeter and an ammeter in a circuit to determine the "hot" resistance of a light bulb.

6. In what ways could you increase the amount of current flowing in an electrical circuit?

7. What are the three basic measurements usually made in an electrical circuit?

8. An electrical circuit has a voltage of 10 volts and the current flowing through it is 2 amperes. What is the resistance of the circuit?

9. Calculate the current flowing through a circuit that has a voltage of 50 volts and a resistance of 10 ohms.

10. If an electrical circuit has a resistance of 50 ohms and current of 3 amperes flowing through it, what is the voltage being applied to the current?

11. Name the unit used to express electrical power.

12. State the basic formula for calculating electrical power.

13. What is the unit used to measure the amount of electricity used?

14. How are home electric bills figured?

UNIT 15
CONNECTING ELECTRICAL CIRCUITS

Series Battery Connections

We know that a single dry cell will deliver 1½ volts and that one cell of a storage battery delivers about 2 volts. We also know that batteries, which are made up of more than one cell, deliver more voltage than a single cell. These batteries have the cells connected so that the voltage of all of the cells can be added together to make the total voltage of the battery.

When cells are connected so that the voltage or pressure is increased the cells are said **to be** connected in

series. In a series connection of cells the positive terminal of one cell is connected to the negative terminal of the next cell. In this way each cell adds its voltage to that of the other cells. The total voltage produced by all cells connected in series is equal to the sum of the voltages of all the cells. See Illustration 65.

When connecting cells in series it is important to watch the polarity of the cells so that the positive terminal of one cell always connects to the negative terminal of the next cell. The two remaining terminals, one positive and one negative, make up the total voltage of the battery and must not be connected together. These two terminals are connected across the

FOUR DRY CELLS CONNECTED IN SERIES
DELIVER 6 VOLTS TO A LIGHT BULB

◆ 65. The voltage of cells connected in series is found by adding the voltages of the individual cells.

◆ 66. This flashlight uses two dry cells connected in series to produce 3 volts to light the bulb. The positive terminal of the first cell makes contact with the bulb at point *A*. Flashlight cells always use the bottom of the cell as the negative terminal. The negative terminal of the first cell connects to the positive terminal of the second cell at *B*. At *C* the negative terminal of the second cell makes contact with the spring attached to the frame of the flashlight. When the switch is closed the lead connected to the bulb at point *D* completes the circuit.

SIX VOLTS

SIX VOLTS

TWELVE VOLTS

TWELVE VOLTS

◆ 67. These are typical cell arrangements for automobile storage batteries.

electrical device called the electrical *load*.

Six-volt storage batteries have three 2-volt cells connected in series. Storage batteries producing 12 volts have six cells connected in series. See Illustration 67. Radio B batteries that deliver 45 volts have 30 dry cells connected in series, each delivering 1½ volts.

Parallel Battery Connections

Dry cells which are very small will not last as long as dry cells which are

larger. Even though the voltage of the two cells is the same the large cell will be able to deliver more current.

Sometimes the cells or batteries that are available are not large enough to supply the amount of current needed in a circuit. When this happens the cells or batteries can be connected together so that they each help provide current for the circuit.

Cells are said to be connected in *parallel* (Illustration 68) when they help each other by providing an increase in the amount of current available. When connecting cells in parallel the negative terminals of all the cells are connected together and all

1 1/2-VOLT BULB

1 1/2 VOLTS

1 1/2 VOLTS

FOUR DRY CELLS CONNECTED IN PARALLEL DELIVER 1 1/2 VOLTS TO A LIGHT BULB. THE FOUR CELLS CAN PRODUCE FOUR TIMES THE CURRENT OF A SINGLE CELL.

1 1/2 VOLTS

SCHEMATIC DIAGRAM OF FOUR CELLS IN PARALLEL CONNECTED TO A LOAD

◆ 68. Current capacity is increased when cells are connected in parallel.

LIGHT BULB

METAL KNIFE BLADE

1 1/2-VOLT DRY CELL   METAL CLIP CONTACT   SWITCH

1 1/2-VOLT DRY CELL

CURRENT IS FLOWING IN THE CIRCUIT
AS THE SWITCH IS CLOSED
TO COMPLETE THE CIRCUIT

DRY CELL   LOAD RESISTOR

SWITCH

SCHEMATIC DIAGRAM SHOWING A SWITCH
TO OPEN CIRCUIT

◆ 69. A switch enables us to start and stop
the flow of current.

Opening and Closing Circuits

When two wires are connected to the terminals of a dry cell and then connected to a light bulb the light will burn. The light can be turned off by disconnecting one wire from either of the battery terminals or from either of the connections to the lamp socket. When the light is burning this is called a complete or *closed circuit* and when one of the wires is disconnected the current stops and it is called an *open circuit*.

Practically every circuit needs some method of opening and closing. When the circuit is closed electrons start to flow and electricity is able to do its work. When the circuit is open the electrons are no longer flowing. The device used to open and close circuits is called a *switch*.

The switch is always placed in one side of the line so that the circuit can

CASE   BUTTON

PUSH-BUTTON
SYMBOL
(PB)

the positive terminals are connected together. Each cell delivers current to the circuit without an increase in the voltage.

If batteries are not large enough to provide the amount of current needed they too may be connected in parallel. When batteries are connected in parallel it is necessary that each of them deliver the same voltage.

A

BASE

B

TERMINAL

◆ 70. A push button is used as a switch when the circuit needs to be closed for very short intervals. When the button is pushed, contact *A* touches contact *B*, making a complete circuit.

◆ 72. Schematic symbols of several switches.
A—Single Pole Single Throw Switch
B—Single Pole Double Throw Switch
C—Double Pole Single Throw Switch
D—Double Pole Double Throw Switch
E—Multipoint Switch. A variety of
contacts can be obtained through
the use of rotary switches.

◆ 71. The push button closes the circuit, allowing current to flow from the cell to the bell.

be opened or closed. As the switch is closed the two contacts in the switch come together and the electrons flow through the switch to the rest of the circuit. Opening the switch breaks the contact points on the switch and the electrons are stopped from flowing.

Types of Switches

There are many different types of switches that are used to open and close circuits. One of the most familiar switches is the wall type tumbler switch used in the home to turn lights off and on. When a single circuit is opened and closed as in Figure 69 the switch is known as a *single pole-single throw* switch. The single pole means that it has one lever and single throw means that it will operate in only one direction. This type switch is often abbreviated as SPST.

Circuits have different requirements for controlling the electron flow and thus a variety of switches are manufactured. Symbols of some common switches are illustrated in Figure 72. A double pole, single throw (DPST) switch makes or breaks two circuits simultaneously. The double pole, double throw (DPDT) switch is used where two contacts are simultaneously connected first to one set of circuits and then to another.

The two types of switches most often used in electronic circuits are the toggle and the rotary. The toggle switch is operated by a lever or toggle with an up and down motion, and the rotary switch, operated by a rotating knob or dial, Figure 73. Toggle switches are rated by their current carrying ability and the voltage with which they may safely be used. Radio receivers and television sets use switches with about 3 ampere and 125 volt ratings.

◆ 73. Two types of switches used in electronics work. A toggle on the left and a rotary switch on the right.

The parallel circuit is probably the most common type of circuit and is used in the wiring of all circuits for the home. Each electrical device in a parallel circuit is connected directly across the two wires used to carry the current flow. All devices must have the same voltage rating as the full voltage of the source of electricity that is connected to them.

In parallel circuits, each device provides a separate electron path and each

In the rotary switch, the moving arm rotates in a circle, making contact with taps located on the outside edge. The contacts are usually arranged in a circle on a wafer, or deck of bakelite or ceramic material. The moving arm is rotated by means of a shaft running through the center so that the arm makes contact with each tap as the shaft is rotated. In some switches a number of decks are placed next to each other so that a single shaft can rotate the contact arm in each deck. Such a switch makes it possible to obtain a great number of different combinations of circuits. A good example of a multiple rotary switch is the channel selector used in some television sets.

Parallel Electrical Circuits

If we wish to have three bulbs burn off the same dry cell they should be connected directly across the two terminals as shown in Illustration 74. These bulbs are said to be connected in parallel because each bulb provides a separate parallel path through which the current must flow.

THREE BULBS CONNECTED IN PARALLEL. ARROWS SHOW THREE SEPARATE PATHS FOR CURRENT FLOW.

SCHEMATIC DIAGRAM OF THREE BULBS IN PARALLEL

◆ 74. The voltage across each bulb connected in parallel is the same as that of the source of electricity.

path may have a different amount of current flowing through it. The amount of current flowing through each path is determined by the resistance of the device since the voltage across every item is the same. Through the use of parallel circuits it is possible to have a separate switch on each appliance so that they can be turned on or off individually.

Calculating Resistances Connected In Parallel

If two resistors of the same value are connected in parallel as in Figure 75 the total resistance in the circuit is half as much resistance as for the single resistor. In such a circuit the current has two paths to flow through with both paths having an equal amount of resistance. Since the two paths reduce the resistance to electron flow the total resistance is cut in half.

When resistance of equal value are connected in parallel, the total resistance can be calculated by dividing the resistance of a single resistor by the number of resistors in parallel. For example, if four resistors of 100 ohms are connected in parallel the total resistance would be one fourth of the 100 ohms or the resistance would be 25 ohms.

Many times resistors of unequal value are connected in parallel and then it is necessary to use the formula for parallel resistance. This formula is written:

$$\frac{1}{R_{Total}} = \frac{1}{R_1} + \frac{1}{R_2} + \frac{1}{R_3} + \ldots$$

◆ 75. In this circuit the two parallel resistors have equal resistance and the current flow through each resistor will be the same. Since parallel resistance reduces the opposition to electron flow the total resistance in the circuit will be 5 ohms.

If resistors of 50 ohms, 100 ohms, and 50 ohms are connected in parallel as in Figure 76 the total resistance can be calculated as follows:

$$\frac{1}{R_{Total}} = \frac{1}{50} + \frac{1}{100} + \frac{1}{50}$$

$$\frac{1}{R_T} = \frac{2}{100} + \frac{1}{100} + \frac{2}{100}$$

$$\frac{1}{R_T} = \frac{5}{100}$$

$$5R_T = 100 \quad R_{Total} = \frac{100}{5}$$

$$R_{Total} = 20\,ohms$$

In the above problem it should be noted that the total resistance of 20 ohms is less than the resistance of any of the resistors connected in the circuit. One important factor to remember

◆ 76. In this parallel circuit the total resistance is 20 ohms.

◆ **77. In a parallel circuit the total current flow (I_T) is equal to the sum of the current flow through each of the resistors. The total resistance in the circuit is 7.5 ohms.**

about parallel resistance is that the total resistance will always be less than the smallest resistor in the circuit.

Current Flow In Parallel Circuits

In a parallel circuit each resistor may be of a different value and thus the current flow in each resistor will be different. The total current flowing in the entire circuit will be equal to the sum of the current flowing through each resistor.

Three resistors of 15 ohms, 30 ohms, and 30 ohms in Figure 77 are in parallel and connected to a 6 volt battery. By using Ohm's law we can calculate the current flow through each resistor:

$$I = \frac{E}{R}$$

$$I_1 = \frac{6}{15} = .4 \text{ amperes}$$

$$I_2 = \frac{6}{30} = .2 \text{ amperes}$$

$$I_3 = \frac{6}{30} = .2 \text{ amperes}$$

The total current flow in the entire circuit is equal to the sum of the current flowing through each of the resistors.

$$I_{Total} = I_1 + I_2 + I_3$$
$$I_{Total} = .4 + .2 + .2$$
$$I_{Total} = .8 \text{ amperes}$$

Another method can be used to find the total current flow in the circuit if the total resistance of the circuit is determined. By using the parallel resistance formula the total resistance is calculated as follows:

$$\frac{1}{R_T} = \frac{1}{R_1} + \frac{1}{R_2} + \frac{1}{R_3}$$

$$\frac{1}{R_T} = \frac{1}{15} + \frac{1}{30} + \frac{1}{30}$$

$$\frac{1}{R_T} = \frac{2}{30} + \frac{1}{30} + \frac{1}{30}$$

$$\frac{1}{R_T} = \frac{4}{30} \qquad R_T = \frac{30}{4}$$

$$R_T = 7.5 \text{ ohms}$$

The total resistance of the circuit is 7.5 ohms. Now the total current can be calculated.

$$I_{Total} = \frac{E}{R_{Total}}$$

$$I_T = \frac{6 \text{ volts}}{7.5 \text{ ohms}}$$

$$I_{Total} = .8 \text{ amperes}$$

It should be noted that the current flow of .8 amperes calculated by determining the total resistance is the same as when the total current flow was calculated by finding the current flow through each resistor.

♦ 78. The wiring installed in the basement of this home is a practical example of parallel circuits.

Series Electrical Circuits

In a series circuit the electrons must flow through each device before the circuit is completed. If a number of devices are connected in series the voltage is divided among them. See Fig. 79. Should any device be disconnected from a series circuit, the entire electron flow is stopped.

Some small radio receivers often called AC-DC receivers also have the radio tube filaments connected in series. When one of the tubes burns out it is necessary to test all of the tubes to determine which one must be replaced to get the set back into operation.

Resistors Connected in Series

When two or more resistors are connected in series the same current flows

ELECTRONS FLOW FROM THE NEGATIVE POLE
OF THE BATTERY THROUGH ONE BULB
AND THEN THROUGH THE SECOND BULB

SCHEMATIC DIAGRAM SHOWING HOW VOLTAGE
IS DIVIDED ACROSS EACH BULB

◆ 79. When bulbs are connected in series, the
voltage is divided between them.

through each resistor. In Figure 80
four light bulbs, requiring 3 volts to
light them properly, are connected in
series and the bulbs are connected to
a twelve volt storage battery. If a single
bulb was connected to the twelve volts
it would burn out, but since the bulbs
are in series they divide the 12 volts

◆ 80. In a series circuit the same current
flows through each resistor. The total resistance of this circuit is 12 ohms.

between them. Thus each bulb has a
required 3 volts.

When two or more resistors are connected in series their total resistance is
equal to the sum of all of the resistors.
The formula for series resistance is
written as:

$$R_{Total} = R_1 + R_2 + R_3 + \ldots.$$

If each bulb in Figure 80 has 3 ohms
resistance the total resistance in the circuit can be calculated using the series
formula:

$$R_{Total} + R_1 + R_2 + R_3 + R_4$$
$$R_1 = 3 \text{ ohms} \qquad R_3 = 3 \text{ ohms}$$
$$R_2 = 3 \text{ ohms} \qquad R_4 = 3 \text{ ohms}$$
$$R_{Total} = 3 + 3 + 3 + 3$$
$$R_{Total} = 12 \text{ ohms}$$

The current flow in this circuit can
be calculated after the total resistance
in the circuit has been determined.

$$I = \frac{E}{R}$$
$$E = 12 \text{ volts}$$
$$R_{Total} = 12 \text{ ohms}$$
$$I = \frac{12}{12}$$
$$I = 1 \text{ ampere}$$

INTERESTING THINGS TO DO

1. Constructing a Buzzer.

Material needed:

◆ 81. Buzzer

1 Wood base, ½" x 2½" x 2½"
1 Piece soft steel, round, ¼" x 1 1/16"
2 Fiber washers, ⅛" x ¾"
1 Piece of spring brass, 26 gage, ⅞" x 1¼"
1 Piece of soft steel, round, ¼" diameter,
  ⅛" thick
1 Piece of 20 gage sheet steel, ⅞" x ⅞"
20' of No. 22 magnet wire
1 Piece of tin ¾" wide by 2" long
2 Terminal screws

Bevel edges of block as shown in Drawing 82. Drill ¼" holes in the center of the washers. Drill two 1/16" holes in one of the washers. One of the holes should be near the inside edge of the

TIN STRIP FOR HOLDING COIL IN PLACE

TERMINAL SCREWS

2 1/2"

2 1/2"

CONTACT SCREW

VIBRATOR

WIND WITH 20 FT. OF #22 MAGNET WIRE

3/4"

COIL FORM

1 1/4"   1/8"

1/2"   BEND   1/4"

3/8"

SOLDER PIECE OF STEEL TO VIBRATOR

26 GAGE SPRING BRASS   5/32" DRILL   BEND

3/8"

VIBRATOR

20 GAGE SHEET STEEL

7/8"

5/8"

BEND   1/4"

SOLDER 6 - 32 NUT TO CONTACT SCREW SUPPORT

CONTACT SCREW SUPPORT

◆ 82. Buzzer details

washer and the other hole near the outside edge. Place the washers on each end of the 1/4" steel rod so that they will be 3/4" apart. Insert one end of the magnet wire through the inside hole in one of the washers allowing about 3" to extend beyond the washer. Wind eight layers of wire evenly on the steel core. The remaining end of the wire should then be pulled through the outside hole in the washer.

Cut the piece of spring brass to the shape shown in the drawing. This spring is the vibrator of the buzzer. Drill and bend the spring brass as shown in the drawing. Solder the small piece of 1/4" round steel to the vibrator.

Cut the piece of sheet steel to shape as illustrated in the drawing. Bend and drill this contact screw support. Solder a 6–32 brass nut to this support. File a blunt point on the end of a roundhead brass 6–32 machine screw. This will serve as the adjusting screw in the contact screw support.

Drill two holes at each end of the tin strap. Shape this strap so that it will hold the coil in place.

Mount all of the parts on the wood base as shown in the drawing. Make connections on the bottom of the wood block as indicated by dotted lines on the drawing. Place a 6–32 brass nut on the adjusting screw and insert the screw into the nut soldered on the contact screw support. The buzzer is now ready to test.

Connect the two terminal screws to 3 to 6 volts either AC or DC. Adjust the contact screw to the desired tone.

◆ 83. Push button and buzzer connected to a dry cell.

2. Connecting Dry Cells in Series to Operate a Buzzer.

Obtain four dry cells, a buzzer, a push button, and some wire for connections. Connect the dry cells in series as described in the text so that the center or positive terminal of one cell is connected to the outside or negative terminal of the next cell. See Diagram 84. When all of the cells have

◆ 84. Connecting dry cells in series to operate a buzzer

been connected together, a positive terminal of one cell and a negative terminal of another cell will be unconnected. Run a wire from one of those terminals to a terminal on the push button. Connect the other push button terminal to one of the buzzer terminals and connect the other buzzer terminal to the remaining dry cell terminal. Press the push button and if all connections have been made correctly the buzzer will operate.

When making an electrical connection by attaching a wire to a terminal screw, always wind the wire around the terminal in a clockwise direction. See Illustration 85. This will cause

◆ 85. **Wind wire clockwise around a terminal**

the wire to wrap more closely around the terminal screw and prevent a loose connection.

When the buzzer is operating, note the loudness of the sound produced by the four dry cells connected in series. The tone of a buzzer may be changed by adjusting the contact screw. If it does not have an adjustable contact screw, the fixed contact arm may be bent backward or forward to produce the same result.

3. Connecting Dry Cells in Parallel to Operate a Buzzer.

Connect the four negative terminals of the dry cells together. Connect the four positive terminals of the dry cells

◆ 86. **Dry cells in parallel to operate a buzzer**

together as shown in Diagram 86. Connect a wire from the negative terminal of one of the end cells to a push but-

ton terminal. Connect a wire from the other push button terminal to one of the buzzer terminals. Connect a wire from the other buzzer terminal to the positive terminal of the end cell. Press the push button and if all connections have been made correctly the buzzer will operate. Is the sound of the buzzer louder or softer than with the series connection? Why?

4. Connecting Dry Cells in Series with Light Bulbs in Parallel.

Obtain four dry cells, four 6-volt flashlight bulbs, four miniature receptacles, a single-pole switch, and some wire for connections. Connect the four dry cells in series. Connect the receptacles together by placing them in line and running a wire to each terminal on the same side as shown in Diagram 87. Connect the opposite sides of the

◆ 87. **Dry cells in series with light bulbs in parallel**

receptacles in the same manner. Connect a wire from the unconnected positive terminal of the dry cells to one of the receptacles. Connect the other terminal of the same receptacle to one of the switch terminals. Connect the other switch terminal to the negative terminal of the dry cell. Close the switch and if all connections have been made correctly, the light bulbs should light.

Unscrew one of the bulbs and notice whether the remaining bulbs get dimmer or brighter. Normally, when good dry cells are being used there will be no change in the brightness of the bulbs. When the dry cells are nearly worn out they cannot supply sufficient voltage to force the correct amount of current through the light bulbs. When one of the bulbs is removed from the parallel circuit the remaining bulbs are apt to burn brighter, because they will require less current from the dry cells.

5. Connecting Dry Cells and Flashlight Bulbs in Series.

Obtain four dry cells, four 1.5-volt flashlight bulbs, four miniature receptacles, a single-pole switch, and connecting wire. Connect four dry cells in series. Connect the four receptacles in series, as shown in Diagram 88. Run

◆ **88. Dry cells and flashlight bulbs in series**

connecting wires between the dry cells, receptacles, and switch so that they will all be in series. Close the switch and if all connections have been made correctly the bulbs will light. Unscrew one of the light bulbs. What happens? Where could this system of connections be used? Replace the 1.5-volt flashlight bulbs with 6-volt bulbs. What happens? Why?

6. Connecting Dry Cells in Series with Push Buttons and Buzzers in Parallel.

Obtain four dry cells, two push buttons, two buzzers, and connecting wire. When you worked with dry cells and buzzers before, you learned that increasing the number of dry cells caused the buzzer to make a louder sound. Although most buzzers will operate on voltage as low as 1.5, when they are used in noisy locations for signaling, a higher voltage is used. The circuit you are about to connect is like the ones used where it is necessary to operate two buzzers from two push buttons which are located at different points.

Connect four dry cells in series. Connect the two push buttons in parallel and the two buzzers in parallel as shown in Diagram 89. Connect one of

◆ **89. Dry cells in series with push buttons and buzzers in parallel**

the series dry cell terminals to one of the buzzer terminals. Connect the other buzzer terminal to one of the push button terminals. Connect the other push button terminal to the remaining series dry cell terminal. Press either push button and if the connections have been made correctly, both buzzers should operate. Place your hand against the armature of one of the buzzers, so that it will not operate and press a push button. Is the operation of the other buzzer affected? Why?

7. Connecting a Three-Wire Return Call Buzzer System.

Obtain four dry cells, two push buttons, two buzzers, and connecting wire. Connect the dry cells in series. Cut two pieces of wire the same length several feet long. Connect one end of each wire to a buzzer. Connect the other end of each wire to a push button. Arrange the wires so that a buzzer and a push button will be at the same ends of the wires. See Diagram 90. Connect a short piece of wire between the buzzer and the push button at both ends of the longer wire. Connect one terminal of the dry cells to the short piece of wire that connects a push button and a buzzer. Connect another wire from the remaining terminal of the dry cells to the short piece of wire that connects

♦ **90. Three-wire return call buzzer system**

the other push button and buzzer together. The connections should appear as shown in the diagram. If the connections have been made correctly a buzzer at the opposite end will sound when either push button is pressed. Draw a diagram showing how the system could be made to operate using four wires between the stations. What is the advantage of the three-wire system? Where could such a system be used?

REVIEW QUESTIONS

1. Draw a diagram showing how you would connect a group of dry cells to provide 7½ volts.

2. If we connect two No. 6 dry cells in series with two small flashlight cells, what voltage will we obtain?

3. List as many applications of cells connected in series as you can.

4. When would you connect dry cells in parallel?

5. Draw a diagram showing how you would connect four 1½-volt flashlight bulbs to a 6-volt storage battery.

6. Name as many applications of light bulbs connected in series as you can.

7. What is the disadvantage of connecting light bulbs in series?

8. Are the light bulbs in your home connected in series or in parallel?

9. What is the difference between a "short" circuit and an "open" circuit?

10. Make a list of the different types of switches that you know about.

11. Draw a schematic circuit showing how a single pole single throw switch can be used to control a 6 volt light bulb connected to a storage battery.

12. What is the total resistance in a circuit that has four 200 ohm resistors connected in parallel?

13. Calculate the total resistance of four resistors connected in parallel if the first resistor is 16 ohms, the second resistor is 32 ohms, the third resistor is 8 ohms, and the fourth is 32 ohms.

Electricity

for

Everyday Living

~~~~~~

UNIT 16
GENERATION AND TRANSMISSION OF ELECTRICITY

PERMANENT MAGNET

ARMATURE

N

S

SLIP RINGS

AC

◆ **1. This illustration shows the fundamental parts of an alternating current generator.**

Generating Electricity

We learned in Unit 8 that electricity could be generated when a coil of wire is rotated in a magnetic field. We also found that generators can be used to deliver either alternating current or direct current. An alternating current generator uses slip rings to deliver electricity to the brushes and direct current generators use a commutator. See Illustrations 1 and 2.

Most commercial alternating current generators used to provide electricity for the home produce a 60-cycle alternating current. This means that the direction of current flow is changing 120 times every second.

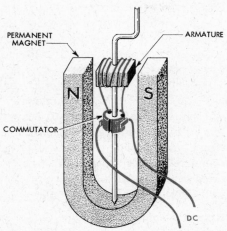

◆ 2. A direct current generator has these basic parts.

Rotating Generators

Every generator needs some method of rotating the armature or rotor. The large generators used to produce electricity for towns and industry are usually rotated by water power or by steam. These huge generators weighing many tons need a tremendous amount of power to turn them over.

The armature or rotor of these generators is usually coupled to a turbine. See Photograph 3.

A *turbine* is a device that might be compared to a windmill. A windmill has several blades or vanes that are pushed by the wind. As the blades rotate the center shaft connected to the blades turns so that it can be used to pump water or turn other devices.

When water power is used to turn over a generator it is necessary to have a rapid flow of water. This can be accomplished by a large waterfall such as the Niagara Falls or by having a dam that holds back a huge lake of water. As the water goes over the falls or out through the bottom of the dam it flows through a water turbine. This turbine has vanes called *blades* (or *buckets*) against which the water flows. The force of the water turns the turbine and the turbine rotates the generator.

Steam pressure is used to turn turbines on many commercial generators.

Courtesy General Electric Co.

◆ 3. In a modern turbine generator, the steam pushes against many blades to turn the rotor.

Courtesy General Electric Co.

◆ 4. How a steam turbine rotates a generator: 1. Steam is generated in a boiler. 2. Steam passes through a nozzle striking turbine blades. Blade wheel rotates. 3. Turbine turns rotor of generator and electricity is generated. 4. Exhaust steam from turbine is condensed and returned to boiler.

High-pressure steam is directed against the blades on a turbine at the rate of about 1,200 miles per hour. These steam turbines have a series of blade wheels arranged so that steam must pass through from 17 to 20 turbine wheels. The steam passes through the nozzle and strikes a row of blades on the first wheel, it loses some of its pressure, and then passes into another set of nozzles, then through another row of blades, and so on down the line. Sometimes the wheel that holds the last set of blades is 12' in diameter.

A large volume of water is needed for both the water turbine and the steam turbine. For this reason most commercial generating plants are located near lakes or other places where water is readily available.

Rotating Small Generators

Generators used to produce electricity where commercial electricity is not available usually are rotated by a diesel engine. Some small generators use a windmill to turn them over.

Large amounts of direct current are often needed for such purposes as electroplating and arc welding. These gen-

◆ 5. An old-type hand-operated generator used to ring telephone bells. Five horseshoe magnets were used to produce the magnetic field.

Courtesy Wincharger Corp.

◆ 6. A gasoline engine driven generator. The 10,000-watt generator will deliver either 115 volts or 230 volts.

Courtesy Katolight Corp.

◆ 7. A diesel-electric power unit. The 60,000-watt generator will deliver either 115 or 230 volts alternating current.

◆ 9. This small dynamotor is a combination motor and generator. It was used to provide power for radio equipment in a Navy airplane.

erators are usually rotated by electric motors. When an electric motor is used with a generator to produce electricity the combination is called a *motor-generator* (Photograph 8).

Transmission Line Losses

Commercial generating plants must be able to deliver tremendous amounts of electricity to serve the entire needs of a town or city. These generating plants sometimes supply electricity for several communities and often must be located many miles away from where the electricity is used. Power lines called *transmission lines* carry the electricity from the power plant to the towns.

The voltage of these transmission lines is usually very high. Voltages of 66,000 to 110,000 volts are very common. High voltages are used for two reasons: (1) to reduce the voltage loss that would result from the resistance of the wire; (2) to reduce the amount of heat that would result from the large amount of current that would have to flow in the wire.

Courtesy Westinghouse Electric Corp.

◆ 10. Large water-driven generators used by the Bureau of Reclamation on the Coulee Dam in the State of Washington.

◆ 8. A motor-generator set using an electric motor to rotate the generator.

◆ 11. This drawing shows how electricity might be produced and delivered to a city. A steam generating plant and a water power generator both produce electricity. After stepping up the voltage at both plants, the transmission lines deliver this very high voltage to a central station. Here the electrical power from each plant is brought together. Large step-down transformers reduce the voltage, for safer handling, as the electricity nears the city. The feeder lines deliver the electricity to a distribution substation where the voltage is again reduced. From this substation the distribution lines take the electricity to the homes.

TRANSFORMER

Courtesy Westinghouse Electric Corp.

◆ 12. Transmission lines deliver 287,000 volts to this substation. These large transformers reduce the voltage before the electricity is sent on to other distribution stations.

Loss Due to Resistance

We know that the circuits used in most homes are 115 volts. If the generator located many miles away from the homes delivered 115 volts to the transmission lines there would be a very large loss in voltage by the time it reached the homes. It would take several times the 115 volts to leave the generator so that the correct voltage would be available when it reached the town. The loss would be due to the resistance of the many miles of wire used to carry the electricity. To overcome this loss caused by the wire resistance, it is customary to use high voltages so that plenty of voltage will be available when the electricity reaches its destination.

Heavy Current Flow

If the generator produced only 115 volts of electricity the amount of current needed to supply all of the homes in a community would be very high. The amount of current would be so great that it would be impossible to build a generator with large enough wire to handle the current flow. It would be very difficult to have transmission wires large enough to take care of the current needs. By using high voltages it is possible to reduce the amount of current in the circuit.

We learned that electrical power

Courtesy General Electric Co.

◆ **13. Steel tower supporting electric transmission lines.**

voltage. We shall learn how transformers function in the next unit.

After the voltage has been stepped up it is carried by the transmission lines to local distributing stations called *substations.* There the voltage is reduced. The amount of voltage reduction varies according to the needs. Voltages of 2,200 volts to 6,000 volts are very common in substations.

From the substation the electricity is carried by power lines to the various sections of the community. Before bringing the electricity into the home it is necessary to again step the voltage down. Transformers located on top of power poles reduce the voltage to 115 or 230 volts. These 115- or 230-volt lines are then brought into the home.

was made up of the voltage multiplied by the current. From this we can see that large quantities of power can be made available if we have: (1) large voltage and a low current; or (2) a low voltage and a high current. Since high current would make the wire heat up it is necessary to reduce the current flow. Transmission lines must have a low current flow and a very high voltage.

Using High-Voltage Transmission Lines

Some commercial generators develop alternating current voltages up to 12,500 volts and higher. Even this is not enough to use on transmission lines that are hundreds of miles long. Voltages are stepped up to 66,000 or even higher after leaving the generator. A special device called a *transformer* is necessary to step up the

Transmission Line Construction

High-voltage transmission lines are made of several strands of heavy wire. Stranded wire makes the cable flexible so that it can swing between the poles without breaking. Also it makes it possible to coil the cable for easy handling. These cables use several strands of either copper or aluminum wire. Sometimes a kind of hollow tubing is used for transmission lines instead of solid wire. The hollow tubing makes a stronger cable than a solid wire of the same weight. The outside diameter of the entire cable may be as large as 2″.

Transmission poles are made of either steel or wood. Often the wire on top of the poles is a ground wire that serves as protection for the transmission wires in the event lightning strikes. If lightning strikes it usually hits the highest point. Since the ground wire is higher than the other wires the lightning is shorted to the ground.

Because of the extreme high voltage on transmission lines, it is necessary to use large insulators on the arms of the poles. These insulators prevent the electricity from shorting between the wires or from shorting to the power pole.

REVIEW QUESTIONS

1. What is the main difference between an alternating current generator and a direct current generator?

2. How are large commercial generators usually rotated?

3. What is the purpose of a turbine?

4. What effect do large transmission lines have on the voltage?

5. Why is it necessary to have a high voltage and a low current on transmission lines?

6. Give two reasons why high voltages are used on transmission lines.

7. What electrical measurements are needed to determine the electrical power in a circuit?

8. Name the device used to step up the voltage after it has been developed by a generator.

9. After delivering the electricity by a transmission line to a city why is it necessary to reduce the voltage?

10. What is the purpose of the ground wire on top of transmission poles?

UNIT 17
USING TRANSFORMERS TO INCREASE AND DECREASE VOLTAGE

Inducing Current in a Coil

We know that if a bar magnet is pushed into the center of a coil that electricity will be induced in the coil. Electricity can be induced only when the magnet is moving. This induced current was alternating current since each time the magnet was pushed in or out of the coil the direction of current flow changed.

Expanding and Collapsing of the Lines of Force

A magnetic field that is starting or stopping makes the lines of force build

LINES OF FORCE BUILDING UP

COIL WITH IRON CORE

KNIFE SWITCH JUST CLOSED

DRY CELL

◆ 14. As switch is closed the magnetic field expands.

♦ **15. As switch is opened the magnetic field collapses.**

up and then collapse around a coil. In Illustration 14 when the switch is first closed the lines of force build up or expand all around the coil. In just a fraction of a second all of the lines of force will have been completed and the coil becomes an electromagnet. When the switch is opened as in Illustration 15 the magnetic field starts to collapse. When all of the lines of force are gone the coil is no longer an electromagnet. Each time the switch is closed the lines of force build up and each time the switch is opened the lines of force collapse. The closing of the switch completes the circuit and at this time the lines of force start to move out all around the coil forming a path from one pole to the other. Just as soon as the circuit is opened all the lines of force start to move back toward the coil until they disappear.

Inducing Current in a Coil by the Current in Another Coil

A second coil is now placed near the first coil as shown in Illustration 16. The leads of this coil are connected to a galvanometer. When the switch is closed the galvanometer needle moves in one direction and then returns to the zero position. As long as the switch remains closed the galvanometer needle remains at zero. As soon as the switch is opened the needle moves in the opposite direction and then returns to zero as shown in Illustration 17.

From this we can see that current is induced in the second coil each time the switch is opened or closed. This is exactly the same as when a bar magnet is moving in or out of a coil. As long as the magnet is moving, current is induced in the coil.

♦ **16. Galvanometer connected to the secondary coil shows that current is induced by the primary coil when the switch is first closed.**

LINES OF FORCE COLLAPSING

KNIFE SWITCH JUST OPENED

◆ 17. When the current in the primary coil is stopped, the collapsing line of force induces a current in the secondary coil. The galvanometer shows that the current in the secondary coil flows in a direction opposite to that in which it flowed when the switch was closed.

Illustrations 16 and 17 show that current can be induced in a coil by current in another coil. To induce current it is necessary to stop and start the current in the first coil. When the current is started by closing the switch the magnetic lines of force start building up and move so that they cut through the second coil. As soon as all of the lines of force have been completed, the magnetic field is not moving and current is no longer induced in the second coil. When the switch is opened the lines of force start to collapse and again current is induced in the other coil. As soon as all of the lines of force collapse current stops flowing. Since the current flows first in one direction and then the other

direction, the induced current is alternating current.

Transformer Operation

Having one coil induce a current in another coil is the principle of the *transformer*. The first coil is called the *primary* winding. It must have a current that is starting and stopping to induce a current in the second coil. The second coil is called the *secondary* winding.

To improve the operation of a transformer the two windings are placed over a soft iron core as shown in Photograph 18. The iron core pro-

◆ 18. An iron core placed in the center of the primary coil and the secondary coil will improve the efficiency of the transformer.

vides a much better path for the magnetic lines of force to flow through. It also concentrates the lines of force so that they do not spread out but remain close to the coils of wire. By concentrating the lines of force the efficiency of the transformer is greatly improved. Most transformer cores are made of many soft iron strips called *laminations* (Illustration 19). These laminations help in improving the operation of the transformer.

PRIMARY WINDING

SECONDARY WINDING

LAMINATED IRON CORE

◆ 19. A drawing showing the construction of a transformer. The closed iron core provides a path for the magnetic field to flow through. The laminated core made of thin strips of soft iron improves its efficiency.

Using Transformers on Alternating Current

We have just learned that a transformer consists of a primary winding and a secondary winding surrounding an iron core. We also know that to induce a current in the secondary winding it is necessary to have the current in the primary continually starting and stopping.

A type of current that is continually starting and stopping by changing the direction of electron flow is alternating current. When alternating current is connected to the primary of a transformer the magnetic field will be expanding and collapsing each time the current starts and stops. This will induce a current in the secondary winding which will also be alternating current.

When direct current is connected to the primary of a transformer it is necessary to have some type of switch that will continually open and close the circuit to induce a current in the secondary winding.

Step-up Transformers

In the study of commercial generators we found that they produce alternating current. We also learned that it was necessary to step up the voltage of these generators so that high voltages would be available for the transmission lines. Transformers are used to step up the voltage. Generating stations use alternating current because the primary of the transformer can be connected directly to the output of the generator.

A transformer is a *step-up transformer* if the secondary winding has more turns than the primary winding. If the secondary has more turns than the primary, the lines of force cut through more turns of wire and the voltage is increased. In a transformer that has 100 turns of wire on the primary and 200 turns of wire on the secondary, the voltage across the secondary will be twice as much as the voltage connected to the primary. The relationship between the number of

Courtesy General Electric Co.
◆ 20. Large transformers are used in a power substation.

turns on a primary winding to the number on the secondary is often referred to as the *ratio* between them. In the transformer shown in Illustration 21, there is a 1 to 2 ratio.

Step-up transformers are used wherever it is necessary to increase the voltage. It is possible to increase the voltage a little or a great deal, depending upon the need. When it is desired to step up the voltage from 10 volts to 100 volts then the secondary winding must have ten times as many turns as the primary. Of course, there is some loss in a transformer. To take care of this loss a few extra turns of wire must be added to the secondary winding.

Step-down Transformers

After the high-voltage transmission lines bring the electricity into a town or city, a substation is used to reduce the voltage. These substations use *step-down transformers* to lower the voltage so that it will be safer to handle.

In a step-down transformer the primary has more turns than the secondary. Since the secondary winding has fewer turns than the primary winding the lines of force are cutting through fewer turns and the voltage is reduced.

If we wish to obtain 10 volts from a 100-volt alternating current source of electricity a transformer can be used. The secondary would have one-tenth as many turns as the primary. See Illustration 22.

Mutual Induction

We can see in Figures 16 and 17 how a varying magnetic field set up by a current flowing in a coil can induce current in another coil placed close to it. This effect is known as "mutual

PRIMARY COIL
100 TURNS

SECONDARY COIL
200 TURNS

100
VOLTS
AC

AC GENERATOR
50 VOLTS

STEP-UP TRANSFORMER

IRON CORE

PRIMARY

SECONDARY

SYMBOL FOR STEP-UP TRANSFORMER

◆ 21. A step-up transformer increases voltage.

AC
GENERATOR
100 VOLTS

PRIMARY COIL 2,000 TURNS
SECONDARY COIL

100 TURNS

5 VOLTS

5 VOLTS

200 TURNS

10
VOLTS

STEP-DOWN TRANSFORMER

SYMBOL FOR STEP-DOWN TRANSFORMER

◆ 22. The voltage from a step-down transformer may be divided as needed.

induction" and all power transformers operate on this principle.

Self-Induction

Another important principle governing the operation of transformers is that of self-induction. When an alternating current flows through the primary winding of a transformer, the varying magnetic field set up by the current will flow through the laminations and through the centers of the primary and secondary coils. This varying magnetic field will induce a voltage in the primary coil which is slightly less than the line voltage, but opposite in direction. Since this induced voltage opposes the line voltage it is referred to as a *counter electromotive force,* and usually abbreviated, *counter emf.* The characteristic of a coil which causes an opposing voltage to be induced in it is known as "self-induction." Self-induction plays an important part in regulating the primary current of a transformer, so that it will vary nearly in direct proportion to the current drawn from the secondary. Figure 23 shows how the self-induced current in a transformer primary opposes

— MAGNETIC FIELD SET UP BY SELF-INDUCED CURRENT

— MAGNETIC FIELD SET UP BY LINE CURRENT

LINE CURRENT

SELF-INDUCED CURRENT

◆ 23. In a transformer secondary winding the self induced current flows in the opposite direction to the line current.

the line current. To simplify the drawing the transformer core is not shown.

We learned above how a varying magnetic field causes a counter emf to be induced in transformer windings. Self-induction also occurs when a switch is opened in a direct current circuit which includes a coil with an iron core. This effect can be demonstrated by connecting a dry-cell, switch, iron-core coil, and 6-8 volt light bulb, as shown in Figure 24. When the switch is closed the bulb will light dimly. When it is opened the bulb will flash brilliantly. During the brief interval when the current through the coil is rising, the increasing magnetic field creates a counter emf in the coil which diminishes as the current reaches its maximum flow. When the switch is opened the magnetic field collapses so quickly without opposition from the dry cell that it induces a voltage in the coil many times higher than that of the dry cell.

Reactance

If we measure the resistance of the primary of a door chime transformer with an ohmmeter, we will find that it is about 250 ohms. With a line voltage of 117 volts and using Ohm's law, we learn that the apparent current that would flow through the primary would be about 0.47 ampere. On a 24 hour basis this would mean that approximately 1320 watts of electric power would be consumed, which would make the operating cost for a door bell or chime almost prohibitive. If we now connect an A. C. ammeter in series with the transformer primary and con-

◆ 24. Demonstrating the effect of counter-electromotive force.

nect the transformer to a 117 volt, A. C. line there will be little or no visible movement of the meter pointer. Only when we connect a load across the secondary of the transformer will we be able to detect a small movement of the meter pointer. Now, let us see how we can account for the difference between the calculated and measured values of the primary current. When we measured the resistance of the transformer primary with an ohmmeter, the value of 250 ohms was the same as it would be if the wire was stretched out in a straight line. Coiling a wire has no effect on its resistance. When we connected the transformer to a 117 volt, A. C. line the counter-emf developed opposed any increase or decrease of current with the result that very little current flowed in the winding. The ability of a coil to react against chang-

ing current is called "inductive reactance." The value of inductive reactance is expressed in ohms and it is represented by the symbol X_L. The letter, or subscript, L, has no value. It is used only to show that the reactance is due to a coil or inductance. Reactance is also a property of capacitance and we will learn about it when we study capacitors.

Impedance

We have learned how reactance can limit the flow of alternating current in a circuit. If we could make a coil that had no resistance, we could calculate the current that would flow through it by merely substituting X_L for R in ohm's law and saying that $I = \dfrac{E}{X_L}$. However, since all conductors have resistance, this value must be considered when calculating the current flow in A. C. circuits containing coils or inductances. The combined opposition of the resistance and the reactance to the flow of alternating current in a circuit is known as "impedance" and is represented by the letter Z. The value of impedance is expressed in ohms. The formula for determining impedance is:

$$Z = \sqrt{R^2 + X_L{}^2}$$

The Turns Ratio of the Transformer

The ratio between the voltage and the number of turns on the primary and the secondary windings of a transformer is called the turns ratio. By using the turns ratio formula, it is possible to determine either the output voltage or the turns needed on the secondary, providing the input voltage or the number of turns of the primary is known.

The turns ratio formula for a transformer is expressed as:

$$\frac{\text{Prim. Turns}}{\text{Sec. Turns}} = \frac{\text{Prim. Voltage}}{\text{Sec. Voltage}}$$

Using symbols for turns ratio

$$\frac{n_p}{n_s} = \frac{E_p}{E_s}$$

n_p = Number of turns on primary
n_s = Number of turns on secondary
E_p = Primary voltage
E_s = Secondary voltage

To determine how many turns are needed to make a power transformer that will produce 300 volts at the secondary if the primary with 500 turns is connected to 110 volts A.C., we can use

◆ **25. The turns ratio formula was used to calculate the number of turns needed on the secondary winding.**

the turns ratio formula:

$$\frac{500}{n_s} = \frac{110}{300}$$

$$n_s = \frac{150{,}000}{110}$$

n_s = 1363.6 turns on the secondary winding.

Copper Losses In a Transformer

Power transformers are very efficient, but they do have some loss in electrical energy. The wire used to wind the primary and secondary coils has resistance, and this resistance uses up some of the electricity. If excessive current flows through the coils, the wire can become hot, and additional energy may be lost in the form of heat. Because of this loss, called copper loss, transformers are rated according to the voltage and current carrying capacity of each of the windings. When heavy current is needed larger wire is used on the windings.

Eddy Current Losses In a Transformer

Another loss in the transformer occurs in the iron core. Since iron is a

◆ 26. A small step-down transformer is shown on the left. The iron laminations and the primary and secondary coils are shown on the right.

conductor of electricity, magnetic lines flowing through the core will cause current to be induced in the core. The current in the core is called *eddy current,* and is a waste of power because heat generated in the core serves no useful purpose in the transformer.

Eddy current losses are reduced by using thin sheets of soft iron, called laminations, for the core, as shown in Figure 26. These strips of iron laminations are painted with shellac or varnish so that they will be insulated from each other. Through the use of these laminations the path to carry the current in the core is reduced; thus the losses due to eddy currents is cut down.

Hysteresis Losses In a Transformer

Each time the alternating current changes direction of flow in a transformer, the magnetic polarity in the iron molecules of the core is changed. This is much the same as when stroking a piece of steel with a bar magnet. The magnet will align the poles of the molecules in one direction when stroked with one of the magnet poles and will reverse the alignment of the molecules if stroked with the opposite magnet pole. Friction produced between the molecules as they change magnetic polarity develops heat in the steel.

As the alternating current acts on the transformer core, a certain amount of energy is needed to continually change the magnetic polarity. This loss in energy is called hysteresis loss. To reduce the hysteresis loss in transformers a very soft iron is used in the core. Silicon steel is one of the materials used as it can change polarity easily and thus reduce the hysteresis loss in the core.

◆ **27.** In a transformer, the power input is found by multiplying the input current by the input voltage. The output power is found by multiplying the output current by the output voltage. These would be equal except for the losses that must be considered.

Power Ratio in Transformers

A transformer cannot generate power. By this we mean that if the power used in the secondary is 100 watts, the power in the primary must be at least 100 watts. In other words, we cannot get more power out of a transformer than we put into it. Transformers are not 100% efficient because some loss occurs due to the copper losses, hysteresis, and eddy currents. As a result of these losses, the power in the secondary will always be less than that in the primary. Well designed commercial power transformers are about 95% efficient.

All power transformers are designed for a definite primary voltage and a maximum primary current. This is known as the power rating of the transformer. By using the power formula, the power input of the transformer can be calculated. For example, a transformer that has a 117 volt primary with a maximum current rating of 2 amperes would have a power input that would be calculated as follows:

◆ **28.** A stepdown autotransformer uses a single winding for the primary and secondary.

$$\text{Power} = E\ I$$
$$P = 117 \times 2$$
$$P = 234 \text{ watts}$$

If this transformer was 100% efficient, the secondary power would equal the input power and thus the secondary output would also be 234 watts. Since transformers are not 100% efficient, the power ratio formula is:

$$P_{output} = Pn \text{ input}$$
$$n = \text{Efficiency factor}$$

This formula may also be stated as:

$$E_s\ I_s = n\ E_p\ I_p$$
$$E_s = \text{Secondary voltage}$$
$$I_s = \text{Secondary current}$$
$$n = \text{Efficiency factor}$$
$$E_p = \text{Primary voltage}$$
$$I_p = \text{Primary current}$$

The Autotransformer

A one winding transformer shown in Drawing 28 is called an autotransformer. Part of the single winding is used for the primary and the other part is used as the secondary. It may be designed for either a step-up or a stepdown transformer and the same principle as stated for regular transformers

◆ 29. This stepup autotransformer increases 117 volts to 150 volts.

◆ 30. A variable voltage autotransformer using a multi-point switch to select the desired voltage.

applies since the primary induces a voltage into the secondary.

A step-down autotransformer uses fewer turns of wire for the secondary than for the primary. The lower voltage secondary is tapped, or connected at the desired voltage as illustrated in Drawing 28. The voltage may be decreased by using fewer turns for the secondary winding or increased by using more turns for the secondary.

A step-up autotransformer uses only a portion of the single winding for the primary. The two outside leads of the entire coil are used for increasing the secondary voltage. (Figure 29). Autotransformers are only used when it is not necessary to have the primary and secondary windings insulated from each other.

Variable voltage autotransformers may be made by providing numerous taps to the transformer and using a movable contact to select the desired voltage. In Drawing 30 a combination step-up and step-down transformer is shown. A variety of voltages may be obtained from such an arrangement. Commercially manufactured transformers with trade names such as Powerstat and Variac are variable voltage autotransformers.

Other Uses of Transformers

Transformers have many uses. All types of transformers are in use in the home and in industry. It is possible to have more than one secondary winding on a transformer. For example, in many radio receivers a single transformer steps up the voltage to 300 volts with one set of windings and another winding steps the voltage down to 6 volts. The secondary can have as many different windings as necessary to step the voltage either up or down.

Train transformers used to run toy trains step down the 115 volts A.C. to from 5 to 25 volts. This lower voltage is connected to the train tracks and makes it safe to handle all parts of the circuit. Door chimes and door bells require a low voltage and transformers are used to step down the 115 volts to between 10 and 20 volts. Television sets use transformers in many ways. In one circuit of a television set the voltage is stepped up by a transformer to as high as 20,000 volts.

INTERESTING THINGS TO DO

1. Making a Transformer

Materials needed:

1 Wood base, ½" x 3" x 5"
1 Piece cardboard, fiber, or plastic tubing, 1" diameter, 1¾" long
2 Fiber or masonite washers, ⅛" thick, 1¾" outside diameter
85' Soft iron wire, 16, 18, or 20 gage (Cut approximately 200 pieces 5" long)

1 Spool magnet wire, No. 32, enamel-covered
1 Spool magnet wire, No. 24, enamel-covered
2' Stranded radio hook-up wire
1 Piece sheet steel, 20 gage, ½" x 3"
1 Piece sheet steel, 20 gage, 1¼" x 6"
2 Terminal screws

The transformer you are about to make has an output of 12 volts and will operate any of the projects described in this book that are intended to work on alternating current.

Make a winding form for the transformer by making holes in the center of the fiber or masonite washers large enough to make a snug fit on the ends of the 1" tubing. See Drawing 34. Glue the washers to the tubing and drill a ³⁄₃₂" hole through one of the washers close to the tubing. Cut a piece of radio hook-up wire 6" long and insert one end of it through the hole in the fiber or masonite washer. Solder one end of the hook-up wire to the end of the spool of No. 32 magnet wire. Wrap the soldered joint with a piece of Scotch electrical tape and proceed to wind 1,800 turns of wire between the

two washers. See Photograph 32. Wind the wire on the form as evenly as possible and when the winding is completed, carefully drill another ³⁄₃₂" hole through the washer, close to the winding. Cut another piece of radio hook-up wire 6" long and insert one end of it through the hole in the washer. Solder the hook-up wire to the end of the completed winding and insulate the joint with a piece of electrical tape. Wrap the winding with a layer of thin cardboard. This completes the pri-

◆ 32. Using a hand drill clamped in a vise to wind the transformer. A long bolt holds the coil form. One end of the bolt is tightened in the chuck of the hand drill. It is necessary to determine how many revolutions the chuck makes for each revolution of the handle. One hand of the operator feeds the wire on the form while the other hand turns the drill handle.

◆ 31. Step-down transformer.

mary winding.

Drill two $\frac{3}{32}''$ holes through the fiber or masonite washer, opposite to the ones drilled previously. One of the holes should be drilled close to the cardboard wrapping and the other near the outside edge of the washer. Cut a piece of radio hook-up wire 6" long and insert one end of it through the inner hole in the washer. Solder the hook-up wire to the end of a spool of No. 24 magnet wire, wrap the joint

◆ 33. The wire core is placed in the center of the coil form. Ends of the wires are bent so that they touch each other.

PRIMARY LEADS CONNECTED TO LINE CORD AND INSULATED WITH SPAGHETTI TUBING

INSULATED WITH SPAGHETTI TUBING

5"

3"

TOP VIEW

SECONDARY TERMINALS

1 1/2"

1"

1/8"

1 3/4"

COIL FORM

WIND 1800 TURNS OF NO. 32 ENAMELED MAGNET WIRE FOR PRIMARY

PRIMARY LEADS

WIND 200 TURNS OF NO. 24 ENAMELED MAGNET WIRE FOR SECONDARY OVER PRIMARY WINDING

METAL RING

1/2"

END VIEW

5/32" DRILL

3"

METAL STRAP FOR HOLDING COIL ON METAL STRAP

1/2"

6"

1 1/4"

20 GA SHEET STEEL BEND AND SOLDER TO MAKE RING FOR HOLDING SOFT IRON WIRE

◆ 34. Drawing of the step-down transformer.

with a piece of tape and proceed to wind 200 turns of wire over the cardboard wrapping. Insert another 6″ piece of radio hook-up wire through the outer hole in the washer and solder it to the end of the No. 24 magnet wire. Insulate the joint with a piece of tape. Wrap the winding with several layers of thin cardboard. This completes the secondary winding.

Fill the center of the winding form with pieces of the 5″ soft iron wire, allowing an equal amount of wire to extend from each end of the form, as shown in Photograph 33. Force extra pieces of wire through the center of the form, so that all of the iron wires will be held firmly in place. Bend each piece of iron around the coil form and cut the ends off so that they overlap about ½″ on the outside of the form. Slip short pieces of radio spaghetti tub-

ing over the coil leads when the iron wires are being bent around coil form to protect the insulated covering on the leads. Make a ring to fit snugly around the transformer with the 1¼″ x 6″ piece of sheet steel and force it over the steel wires surrounding the coils. Drill and shape the ½″ x 3″ piece of sheet steel as shown in the drawing and solder it to the metal ring This piece will serve to secure the transformer to the wood base. Place two terminal screws at one end of the wood base and secure the transformer to the base, so that the secondary leads are at the same ends as the terminal screws. Secure the leads to the terminal screws. Connect an attachment plug cap, or a piece of lamp cord and a plug cap, to the primary terminals. The transformer is now ready for its initial tryout.

REVIEW QUESTIONS

1. How is current induced in a coil by means of a bar magnet?

2. Explain what happens to the lines of force around a coil when the current is started and stopped.

3. What is necessary to induce a current in one coil by means of current in another coil?

4. Name the two windings of a transformer.

5. What type of current is always produced in the secondary coil of a transformer?

6. What type of current is necessary in the primary winding of a transformer to induce a current in the secondary winding?

7. What is the difference between a step-up transformer and a step-down transformer?

8. If a step-up transformer has 400 turns on the primary winding and 1,200 turns on the secondary winding how much will this transformer increase the voltage?

9. Name several uses for step-down transformers.

10. What is the purpose of the iron core in a transformer?

11. How does mutual induction operate in a transformer?

12. What is counter emf?

13. What is meant by inductive reactance?

14. What make up the impedance of a circuit?

15. A transformer connected to a 120 volt A.C. source of electricity has 400 turns on the primary winding. If we wish to obtain 10 volts from the secondary winding, how many turns of wire do we need for the secondary?

16. What are copper losses in a transformer?

17. How are eddy current losses reduced in transformer construction?

18. Why is a soft iron core used in transformers?

19. Explain why the power output of a transformer is not equal to the power input.

20. How does an autotransformer differ from a regular transformer?

UNIT 18
PROTECTING HOME ELECTRICAL CIRCUITS

Electrical Power Leads into the Home

At the local substation electricity is reduced to a fairly low voltage for distribution around the city. Voltages are usually 2,400 volts or higher on the power poles going to residential areas. Before the electricity is brought into the home the voltage must again be reduced. A transformer called a *pole transformer* usually mounted on top of a power pole is used for this purpose. The pole transformer in Figure 35 provides the electricity for several homes and reduces the voltage to either 115 volts or 230 volts.

When 115 volts is brought into the home it requires two wires and is called a *two-wire service.* The use of 230-volt service in the home is becoming more common and is called a *three-wire service.* In a three-wire service one wire is called the *neutral wire.* Figure 35 shows how it is possible to obtain 115 volts by connecting to the neutral wire and to either of the other wires. The 230 volts, used on water heaters and electric ranges, is available from the other two leads.

35. A pole transformer steps down the voltage before it reaches the home. By using the two outside wires, 230 volts is available. For 115 volts, one of the outside wires and the center neutral wire are used.

The top symbol can be used for any fusible element.

SECONDARY RACK

ENTRANCE CAP

SERVICE
DROP

DRIP LOOP

RIGID CONDUIT
STRAP

RIGID CONDUIT
CONTAINS SERVICE WIRES

OUTDOOR
METER

ENTRANCE ELL

SERVICE SWITCH
BOX

TO LIGHTING
CIRCUITS

CONNECTOR

GROUND WIRE BX

CONNECTOR
WATER METER

WATER PIPE

GROUND STRAP

WATER METER
SHUNT

◆ **36. The principal parts of a typical house wiring system are shown in the above illustration. Local electrical codes may require different locations for these service connections.**

The power service leads going into the home are connected to a kilowatt-hour meter that keeps a record of the quantity of electricity used by the home. This meter was discussed in Unit 14.

Distributing the Electricity

After going through the meter, the electricity is connected to a *distribution panel*. This panel is a box that contains the switches used to turn off the electricity in the house and it also encloses the safety devices used to protect the various circuits in the home. Either fuses or circuit breakers are used to safeguard the electrical circuits. They open the circuit and stop the flow of electricity whenever too much current starts to flow. If too much current is allowed to flow, the wires in the house could get hot and start a fire.

These safety devices protect the circuit against "short circuits" and from overloads. Short circuits often occur when the insulation covering the wires connected to an electrical appliance such as a floor lamp becomes worn. The broken insulation allows the wires to touch each other and the result is a short circuit if the lamp is plugged into the house outlet. To prevent a fire from starting the safety device immediately opens the circuit and stops the electricity from flowing. After the cord has been repaired the fuse can be replaced or the circuit breaker reset.

If too many electrical appliances are plugged into a single electrical circuit the quantity of current needed to operate the appliances could very easily cause heating in the house wiring. This is prevented through the use of protective devices that open the circuit.

In the home there are usually from three to six branch circuits. Each

◆ 37. Three of the fuses are cartridge-type fuses. The fuse on the right is a plug fuse.

branch circuit has a separate fuse or circuit breaker. When branch circuits are used, an overload or a short circuit stops the electricity from flowing in only one part of the house. The rest of the circuits may be used until the defect has been repaired.

Fuses as a Safety Device

Fuses are of two types, the *plug fuse* and the *cartridge fuse*. See Photograph 37. The plug fuse is the most common type of fuse found in the home where 115 volts is used. Cartridge fuses are used where heavy current is needed and on circuits using 230 volts or more.

The important part of the fuse is the thin strip of metal, usually zinc, that will melt when the current flow becomes too great (Illustration 38).

◆ 38. Construction of the plug fuse that is used in homes.

SOURCE OF
ELECTRICITY

FUSE

LAMP OR OTHER OUTLETS

◆ **39.** A fuse is connected in series or in one line of the circuit the same as a switch is connected in the circuit. The entire current from the circuit flows through the fuse. If the current flow is greater than the rating of the fuse it will "blow" and the circuit is opened.

◆ **42.** Cartridge-type fuses are used in this box, which has a switch that disconnects all circuits.

◆ **40.** A good fuse and a burned-out fuse. Fuses are enclosed in a case to make them safe to screw in and also to prevent the hot metal from scattering when the fuse "blows."

The size of the zinc strip is selected for the number of amperes of current that it will carry without melting. Each fuse is marked to indicate the amount of current it will handle before it "blows."

Most branch circuits in the home use a 15-ampere plug-type fuse. It is important to use only 15-ampere fuses in these circuits. If larger fuses are installed the wire of the circuit can be overloaded and a fire could result from the heat developed in the wire.

Using Circuit Breakers To Protect Circuits

The type of circuit protection that is commonly used in new homes is called a *circuit breaker* (Photograph 43). It automatically turns off the cur-

◆ **41.** Placing a fuse in the type of fuse box found in most homes.

RESET HANDLE

THERMAL TRIP

ARC BLOWOUT

CONTACTS

◆ **43.** Cutaway view of a circuit breaker unit.

rent when too many amperes flow in the circuit. The circuit breaker is a combination switch and safety device. When the switch is turned to the "on" position the circuit breaker contacts are closed. If a short or overload occurs the breaker opens the circuit. After the short has been repaired or the load cut down the breaker can be reset by turning the switch to the "off" position and then back to the "on" position.

The use of circuit breakers eliminates hunting for a fuse and also prevents a careless person from installing a large fuse that could overload the circuit. Circuit breakers are labeled, the same as fuses, with their current-carrying capacity.

There are two types of circuit break-

◆ 45. These drawings show the construction of a magnetic circuit breaker. The coil has all of the current from the circuit flowing through it. When the breaker is set the contact points are closed and the circuit is complete. If too much current flows through the circuit the coil pulls the iron armature down, opening the contact points. The catch holds the armature from moving upward to close the contact points again.

ers—the heat strip breaker and the magnetic breaker.

Heat Strip Breaker

The *heat strip breaker* uses a strip made of two different kinds of metal either welded or riveted together. When too much current flows through the strip the metals get hot. The heat makes the metals expand but, since they are two different kinds of metal, one expands more than the other. Since the lower metal strip expands

◆ 44. These drawings show the construction of a heat strip circuit breaker. When the heat strip is cool, the catch holds the contact points together. If too much current flows through the terminal connections, the heat strip expands and bends upward. The catch releases the arm and the spring opens the contact points. To use the breaker again it must be reset so that the contact points are closed.

more than the upper piece, the heat strip curves upward. This bending of the heater strip allows a spring in the switch to open the contact points. See Illustration 44. The amount of current necessary to open the contact depends upon the design of the heater strip.

The Magnetic Circuit Breaker

The *magnetic circuit breaker* uses an electromagnetic coil to open the circuit. See Illustration 45. A coil is connected in series with the circuit so that all of the current must pass through it. When the current becomes too great the magnetic pull of the coil moves the metal bar called the *armature* toward the coil. As the armature moves toward the coil it breaks the contact points and opens the circuit.

Both the heater strip breaker and the magnetic breaker must be reset by hand before the circuit is closed again.

Relays

A device that operates very much like the magnetic circuit breaker is a relay. The relay might be called an electrically operated switch that has many advantages over a manually operated switch. When opening and closing circuits with high voltages, the relay makes it possible to control these circuits without the danger of coming in contact with the high voltage. Also, circuits using high current can be much more readily controlled through the use of a relay.

The basic parts of a relay consist of a *coil*, a *magnetic core*, an *armature*, and a *set of contacts*.

◆ 46. A drawing of a normally open relay. When the coil is energized the armature is pulled toward the electromagnet, closing the contacts. The circuit from terminals A and B is completed and current flows through the colored parts of the relay.

Drawing 46 shows a normally open relay. When current flows through the coil the magnetic flux becomes strong enough to overcome the force of the spring and to attract the armature down. This movement of the armature causes the contacts to close. These contacts, which are wired to terminals A and B, of the relay, are used just like the terminals on a regular switch. If the contacts are closed, terminals A and B form a completed circuit.

Controlling High Voltage With Low Voltage

A comparatively low voltage can be used to close a relay and the contacts on the relay used to control a high voltage circuit. Relays make it possible to control circuits by remote control since the switch for operating the relay can

◆ 47. A low voltage relay circuit being used to control a 117 volt A.C. circuit is shown in the photograph. The schematic with the high voltage portion in color is on the right.

be some distance away from the relay.

An example of a low voltage circuit controlling a high voltage circuit is shown in Figure 47. The four dry cells producing six volts D.C. are used to close the relay contacts, which turns on the 117 volt lamp. The six volt D.C. relay coil is connected to the dry cells and when the manually operated switch is closed the relay contacts complete the circuit to the 117 volt A.C. lamp. When the low voltage circuit is not energized, the lamp remains off.

Just as found on different designed switches, it is possible to obtain a variety of contacts with relays. These contacts are either normally open or normally closed. Figure 48 illustrates the symbol drawing for several type relays.

When using relays it is necessary to know whether the relay is a D.C. or A.C. coil relay and also to know the voltage rating of the coil. Direct current relays will chatter (vibrate) when used on alternating current.

◆ 48. Symbols of three different types of contacts used with relays.

INTERESTING THINGS TO DO

1. Making a Circuit Breaker.
Materials needed:

1 Piece of soft steel rod, ⅜" diameter, ⅛" thick
2 Pieces wood, ¼" x 3" x 5"
2 Fiber or masonite washers, 1" diameter
1 Piece fiber or cardboard tubing, ¹⁄₁₆" wall, ⅜" inside diameter, 1⅜" long
5' Soft iron wire, No. 18
1 Spool enamel-covered wire, No. 22
1 Piece sheet steel, ⅜" x 2¼", 20 gage, for contact arm
1 Piece sheet copper, ⅜" x ⅜", 20 gage, for contact on contact arm
1 Piece sheet steel, ⅜" x ½", 20 gage
1 Piece sheet copper, ⅜" x 1¼", 20 gage, for stationary contact
1 Piece sheet fiber, 1" wide, 2½" long, ⅛" thick, for reset lever
1 Piece sheet steel or brass, 1¼" x 3½", 22 gage, for holding coil in place
2 Terminal screws
Miscellaneous screws, nuts, and washers (see text)

◆ **49. A magnetic circuit breaker**

This circuit breaker will take the place of a fuse by opening the circuit when the current exceeds the amount for which it is set. The breaker may be adjusted to operate on currents from 1 to 3 amperes and it is adjusted by moving the coil toward or away from the contact arm. As the coil is moved away from the contact arm, more current will be needed to operate the breaker. Less current will be required as the coil is moved closer to the contact arm.

Make a coil form by drilling the fiber washers so that they will fit over the fiber tubing and glue one of them at each end of the tubing. Drill two small holes in one of the washers for the coil leads. Cut the piece of iron wire into short sections 1¾" long and pack them into the center of the fiber tubing, as shown in the drawing. Wind the form with six layers of No. 22 magnet wire. Solder the piece of soft iron rod to the piece of sheet steel, 1" from one end. Shape the opposite end to fit snugly around a 6–32 machine screw for the contact arm, as shown in the drawing. Bend the short piece of sheet steel and solder it to the contact arm opposite to the round piece of steel. This piece fits into the slot in the fiber reset lever when the arm is in the "on" position. Bend the smaller piece of sheet copper and solder it to the end of the contact arm, as shown in the drawing. Drill and shape the larger

TERMINAL
SCREW

FIBER OR
CARDBOARD
TUBING

WIND 6 LAYERS
OF NO. 22 GA
MAGNET WIRE

SHEET METAL STRAP
TO HOLD COIL
IN PLACE

FILL TUBING WITH
PIECES OF SOFT IRON
WIRE 1 5/8" LONG

RESET LEVER

COIL FORM

WOOD BASE

SHEET
COPPER

5/32"
DRILL

STATIONARY CONTACT

SAW SLOT

5/32" DRILL

SHEET FIBER

20 GA
SHEET STEEL

SOFT STEEL

SHEET COPPER CONTACT

20 GA SHEET STEEL

CONTACT ARM

RESET LEVER

◆ **50. Drawing of circuit breaker**

piece of sheet copper to serve as the stationary contact. Drill and shape the piece of sheet fiber for the reset lever. Secure the parts to one of the pieces of wood, as shown in the assembly drawing. The movable contact arm is held in line with the center of the coil with a 6–32 machine screw, 1¼" long, hexagon nuts, and brass washers. Make certain that the arm swings freely on the machine screw, otherwise the breaker will not operate properly. The

strap for holding the coil should secure the coil firmly when the screws are tightened, but it should allow the coil to be adjusted when two of the screws are loosened. Wire the circuit breaker as shown by the broken lines on the drawing. Join the two pieces of wood together so that the breaker will stand in an upright position. When the circuit breaker is being used it should be connected so that it will be in series with the lamp or device it is to con-

◆ **51. Circuit breaker diagram**   ◆ **52. Relay wiring diagram**

trol, as shown in Figure 51.

While this circuit breaker was designed for low-voltage transformer or
battery circuits, it will function satisfactorily on higher voltages if it is
enclosed in a metal box to prevent
contact with current-carrying parts.

2. Making a Sensitive Relay

Materials needed:

1 Loudspeaker output transformer, or small
  choke coil. (see text)
1 Wood base
4 Fahnestock clips
4 Strips sheet steel, No. 22 ga., ½" wide, for
  armature, contact strips, and coil holding
  strip. (see text)
1 Piece copper wire, No. 14, bare, for contacts.

Relays that will operate on current
values as low as a few milliamperes are
generally referred to as "sensitive relays." The one described below will
close or make the contacts come together with about six milliamperes
flowing through its coil. Winding a coil
for such a relay would be an extremely
tedious job because of the small wire
used and the large number of turns
required, but an excellent substitute
is available in the primary winding of
the output transformer that is often
discarded with a defective radio or tele-

vision loudspeaker. Small choke coils
such as used in radio power supplies
may also be converted to sensitive relays.

Remove the top section of the transformer or choke coil core so that the
ends of the core will be about even
with the top of the coil. On some
transformers this section is in one unit,
while on others the metal laminations
are interleaved so that the core will
have to be taken apart and reassembled. Clean the bottom of the core and
solder a strip of metal to it so that the
core may be secured to the wood base.
Since transformers and choke coils of
different manufacture will vary in size,
no bending dimensions are given. Both
the armature strip and the contact
strips should be shaped so that the
armature contact touches the lower
contact when it clears the top of the
laminations by about $\frac{1}{32}$". The upper
contact should be made when the armature is about $\frac{1}{16}$" above the top of
the core. Make the contacts by riveting
short pieces of copper wire in holes in
the metal strips and then filing them
flat. Final adjustment of the contacts
can be made by bending the contact
strips upward or downward.

COIL

ARMATURE

COPPER OR
SILVER CONTACTS

LAMINATED
CORE

PRIMARY WINDING
LEADS

FAHNESTOCK
CLIP

WOOD BASE

METAL STRIP
TO HOLD CORE
TO WOOD BASE

DRILL FOR CONTACT RIVET   1/8" DRILL

1/2"

SEE TEXT FOR
BENDING INSTRUCTIONS
UPPER CONTACT STRIP

1/4"   DRILL FOR CONTACT RIVET   1/8" DRILL

1/2"   1/4"   ARMATURE STRIP

SEE TEXT FOR
BENDING INSTRUCTIONS

DRILL FOR CONTACT RIVET   1/8" DRILL

SEE TEXT FOR
BENDING INSTRUCTION
LOWER CONTACT STRIP

◆ 53. Drawing of sensitive relay

◆ 54. The completed sensitive relay

REVIEW QUESTIONS

1. What is the voltage of a three-wire service brought into a home?

2. What is the purpose of safety devices used in home wiring circuits?

3. Name two types of fuses.

4. Draw a diagram showing how fuses are connected in a lighting circuit.

5. What size fuse is used in most branch circuits in the home?

6. Name two types of circuit breakers.

7. How is a circuit breaker reset after it has opened the circuit?

8. Why is it important to locate the trouble in an electrical circuit before replacing a fuse or resetting a circuit breaker?

9. How is a heat strip constructed?

10. Explain how a magnetic circuit breaker operates.

11. What is the moving part of a magnetic circuit breaker called?

This is how the basic switch symbols are to be drawn.

This is the symbol for the common spring-return push button.

The buzzer may be identified by adding the abbreviation AC or DC within the square.

This symbol is used for the familiar call bell.

UNIT 19
ELECTRICAL WIRING IN THE HOME

Floor

Joist — Porcelain Tube

Porcelain Knob

Rubber Covered Wires

◆ **55. Concealed knob-and-tube wiring is one type of wiring system found in homes. Although formerly common, it is now prohibited in most localities.**

Wiring Systems

Electrical circuits in most homes are connected to wall outlets, lights, and power outlets such as stoves and hot water heaters. Special protective covering must be provided for the wires that are used inside the walls, in the ceiling, and under the floor. Several systems are used to safeguard the wiring in the home. The main types of wiring are (1) knob-and-tube wiring, Figure 55; (2) nonmetallic sheathed cable, Figures 56 and 57; (3) armored cable, known as AC (also BX,

Courtesy Crescent Insulated Wire & Cable Co.
◆ **57. Non-metallic sheathed cable.**

Courtesy General Cable Corp.
◆ **56. Method of fastening nonmetallic sheathed cable to floor joists and ceiling, and to switch and receptable outlet boxes.**

Courtesy Crescent Insulated Wire & Cable Co.
◆ **58. Armored cable is properly called "AC."**

JOIST

TOP PLATE

HEADERS

STUD

BRIDGING

DOOR OPENING

FOR SWITCH

OUTLET

ROUGH FLOOR

NAILING STRIP

SOLE PLATE

Courtesy Republic Steel Corp.

◆ 59. This illustration shows the installation of thin-wall steel tubing in a wood studding partition wall.

which is a trade name), Figure 58; and (4) electrical steel tube called conduit wiring. Each locality has regulations regarding the type of wiring system that may be used.

Convenience Outlets

Wall outlets called *convenience outlets* are mounted in metal boxes called *outlet boxes.* The outlet is usually of the duplex type as shown in Figure 60. Two wires carry the flow of electricity to the wall outlet. These wires start at the switch box where they are connected to a fuse or circuit breaker. Several outlets may be connected in parallel to the same pair of wires. Number

◆ 61. This is a wiring diagram using a single pole switch.

◆ 60. This is a duplex convenience outlet

Using Single-Pole Switches

In every lighting circuit it is necessary to be able to turn the lights on and off. Wall switches called *tumbler switches* are used for this purpose. The switch is always connected in one wire of the circuit as shown in Figure 61. This is called a *single-pole switch*. A single-pole switch is one that has a single contact that can be opened and closed by pushing the tumbler either up or down. See Figures 62 and 64.

14 or 12 wire is usually used for convenience outlets.

◆ 62. This illustration shows how the circuit in Figure 61 would be connected when used in the home. All splices and connections are made inside of the boxes. Solderless connec- tors are used to join the wires together. The dotted line represents the neutral wire. This wire is usually solid white in color.

◆ 63. Solderless connectors often used for splicing purposes are screwed on to the splice. The cone-shaped spiral spring inside of the molded body presses the wires together, making solder unnecessary.

◆ 64. Single-pole switch. To protect the switch it is placed inside of a metal box called a switch box. The front of the switch is covered with a switch plate, usually made of a plastic material.

◆ 65. Two single-pole switches are sometimes placed side by side in the wall so that each can control separate lights in the room. Switch No. 1 controls outlet box No. 1 and switch No. 2 controls outlet box No. 2.

◆ 66. Two three-way switches can be used to control a single light from two different locations.

Using Three-Way Switches

Many times it is desirable to turn lights on and off from two different locations. A good example of this is found in a large room having a doorway at each end. A switch is placed near each entrance so that it is possible to turn the light on or off from either door. See Figure 66. The controlling of lights from two separate locations is done through the use of two *three-way switches*. Three-way switches have three terminals for wire connections instead of two terminals as found on single-pole switches. Figures 67 and 68 show the principle of operation of the three-way circuit.

Mercury Switches

The most common type of switch makes or breaks the contacts through the mechanical movement of the tumbler. This switch makes a distinct "click" each time it is opened or closed as the moving blade goes in or out of the contact points. A switch that is

◆ 67. Two three-way switches controlling a single lamp. In this position the circuit is complete as switch *A* is in contact with terminal 2 the same as switch *B*.

◆ 68. Switch *A* has been turned so that it is in contact with terminal 3. This opens the circuit and the lamp is off. To turn the light on again switch *B* can be turned to terminal 3 or switch *A* must be turned back to terminal 2.

· F I R S T · F L O O R · P L A N ·

◆ 69. A blueprint of the first floor plan of a house showing the location of the various electrical outlets. Symbols are used for each of the outlets.

very desirable because of its silent operation is called a *mercury switch*. The mercury switch has a small quantity of liquid mercury that is moved against the contact points. Through the use of mercury it is possible to have a switch that does not "click" when it is turned on or off.

Reading Electrical Blueprints

When plans for homes are developed by an architect the placement of all of the electrical outlets, lights and other electrical connections are shown on the blueprints. Symbols are used to represent each of the electrical outlets.

The duplex outlet is the standard kind and the small numeral "2" is generally not used with the symbol.

The circle at the left is the latest standard. The letter "E" may be used to prevent confusion with other kinds of symbols.

The letter "S" is the symbol for any single-pole switch.

The small "3" tells that the symbol is for a three-way switch.

INTERESTING THINGS TO DO

1. Connecting a Single-Pole Switch to a Light Socket.

Materials needed:

1 Light socket or receptacle
1 Fuse block
2 10-ampere fuse plugs
1 Single-pole switch
  Connecting wire

Connect one terminal of the fuse block to one of the socket terminals. Connect a wire from the other socket terminal to a switch terminal. Connect the remaining switch terminal to the fuse block. The correct wiring is shown in Photograph 70. This is the type of circuit used to control a light when it is necessary to turn it on or off from only one location. Whenever a home or building has been wired properly, the wiring is so arranged that the neutral or grounded side of the lighting circuit is connected to the screw or shell terminal of the socket. This is done so that if one accidentally touches the base of a lamp while removing or replacing it and while standing on a damp floor, he will not receive a shock. With the help of your instructor trace the wiring in your school shop and wire the switch circuit so that it will follow the safety procedure outlined above.

◆ 70. Using a single-pole switch to control a light.

◆ 71. Using two three-way switches so that a light can be controlled from two locations.

2. Connecting a Three-Way Switch.
Materials needed:

1 Light socket or receptacle
1 Fuse block
2 10-ampere fuse plugs
2 Three-way switches
 Connecting wire

A three-way switch is used when it is desired to turn a light on or off from two locations, such as the ends of a hall or the bottom and top landings of a stairway. A three-way switch has a single terminal at one end of the switch and two terminals at the opposite end. The single terminal is connected within the switch so that it makes contact with one of the other terminals at all times, whether the switch lever is in the up or down position.

Connect one terminal of the fuse block to one of the socket terminals. Connect the other socket terminal to the single terminal on one of the switches. Connect a wire from the remaining fuse block terminal to the single terminal on the other three-way switch. Connect the remaining two terminals on one switch to similar ter-

minals on the other switch. These connections between the two switches are generally referred to as *travelers*. Connect the fuse block to a 115-volt circuit and if all connections have been made properly the lamp may be turned on or off from either switch. The correct-wiring is shown in Figure 71.

3. Connecting a Four-Way Switch.
Materials needed:

1 Light Socket or receptacle
1 Fuse block
2 10-ampere fuse plugs
2 Three-way switches
1 Four-way switch
 Connecting wire

Wherever it is desired to turn a light or group of lights on or off from more than two locations, two three-way switches, together with one four-way switch for each additional control point, must be used. By adding one additional four-way switch to the circuit for each control point, the number of control points are unlimited. This type of switching circuit is very convenient for long hallways or stairways with a number of landings and makes it possible for a switch at any point to work

◆ 72. Connecting a four-way switch circuit so that a light can be controlled from three locations.

independently of the other switches.

A four-way switch has two terminals at each end which are connected within the switch so that at either position of the switch arm, two terminals are connected directly across to the opposite terminals, or diagonally across to the opposite terminals. When you have finished wiring your circuit you may trace the path of current through the switch connections and see just how each switch can control the light independently of the other switches. In wiring the four-way circuit the procedure for wiring the three-way circuit is followed, with the exception that a four-way switch is connected between

◆ 73. The completed dimmer switch. The silicon rectifier is connected to two terminals of the dual switch.

the two wires that would normally connect the two three-way switches together. Connect the fuse block to a 115-volt circuit and if all connections have been made properly the lamp may be turned on or off with any of the switches. The correct wiring is shown in Figure 72.

3. Making a Home Lighting Dimmer

Materials needed:

1 Dual lighting switch, S. P. S. T.
1 Dual switch plate
1 Silicon rectifier, 6 amperes, 400 volts

Means for controlling brightness is becoming an attractive feature for home lighting. Subdued lighting is not only desirable for T.V. viewing, but it also creates a more pleasant atmosphere for the enjoyment of music or just meeting with friends.

The dimmer you are about to make is a simple arrangement of a silicon rectifier and a dual switch. Dual switches consist of two single pole switches combined in one unit and arranged to operate horizontally, so that they can replace a switch of the regular type.

Attach the rectifier to two of the switch terminals as shown in Figure 73. Some switches have two of the terminals connected together inside the switch body, so, if that type switch is used the rectifier should be connected across the two separate terminals. Wire the dual switch to the circuit as shown in the diagram, Figure 74. The current and voltage ratings for the rectifier were purposely specified at high values to permit it to operate at normal temperatures. Rectifiers of this type are subject to damage when overheated.

In operation the rectifier passes only one-half cycle of the alternating cur-

◆ 74. **Wiring diagram for light dimmer. Each switch may be operated independently.**

rent supply, which has an effect similar to reducing the current flowing through the lamp by approximately one half.

REVIEW QUESTIONS

1. Name four types of wiring systems.

2. Why are protective coverings necessary for house wiring?

3. Give the common name used for wall outlets.

4. What size wire is usually used for wall outlets?

5. Draw a wiring diagram showing how a switch is connected in a circuit to turn a light off and on.

6. Why are convenience outlets and wall switches placed in metal boxes?

7. Draw a wiring diagram showing how two three-way switches are used to turn lights on and off from two locations.

8. Why are mercury switches used in some homes?

9. Draw a diagram of a room in your home, using symbols to show the location of convenience outlets, lights, and switches.

UNIT 20
TYPES OF LIGHTING

Incandescent Lamps Used To Produce Light

The incandescent lamp was mentioned in Unit 12. An incandescent lamp is one in which light is produced by the heating of a filament inside a glass bulb. Thomas Edison introduced the first practical incandescent lamp in 1879. Edison's lamp bulb contained a carbon filament sealed inside of an evacuated glass bulb (Illustration 75). All of the air had to be removed from the bulb to keep the carbon from burning up.

The modern incandescent lamp contains a spiral tungsten filament that will withstand very high temperatures. To prevent the tungsten from burning up, the oxygen is pumped out of the glass bulb. A small amount of argon and nitrogen gas is then put inside the bulb. This gas increases the light-producing ability of the bulb. Most incandescent lamps are designed to burn from 750 to 1,000 hours.

Shapes and Sizes of Incandescent Lamps

Incandescent lamps come in many shapes and sizes. The general-service type lamps used in the home range from 25 to 300 watts. The larger the wattage the greater the amount of electricity needed for operation of the lamp and the greater the output of light. These bulbs use what is known as a *medium screw-type base*. The glass may be either clear or inside-frosted. Inside-frosted is widely used as it reduces glare. Small lamps used for night lights and Christmas tree lights have either an *intermediate screw-type base*

◆ 75. Edison's first electric lamp appeared in 1879.

INCANDESCENT LIGHT

This symbol is used for all incandescent-filament lights.

INTERMEDIATE SCREW

MOGUL SCREW

MEDIUM SCREW

CANDELABRA SCREW

◆ 76. Shown in this photograph are four sizes of screw-base type lamps commonly found in the home.

or a *candelabra base*. Lamps from 300 watts to 1,500 watts use a large base called a *mogul base*. See Photograph 76.

Three-Way Incandescent Lamps

Many table and floor lamps use a *three-way lamp*. This means that the lamp can produce three different amounts of light. They contain two filaments wired so that either may be used independently or the two filaments used in parallel so that both are on at the same time. See Illustration 77. These three-way lamps are usually 50-100-150–watt or 100-200-300–watt lamps. A three-way socket is used for these lamps and special three-way type switches are required to turn on each of the filaments. For example, in the 50-100-150 bulb the switch in the first position turns on the 50-watt filament, in the second position it turns on the 100-watt filament, and in the third position both filaments are in use.

Fluorescent Lamps Used To Produce Light

Fluorescent lamps have become very popular as a means of lighting. This popularity is due to their ability to produce more light with less electricity than incandescent lamps and also fluorescent lamps will last a lot longer without burning out.

50 WATT   100 WATT

◆ 77. A three-light lamp contains two filaments. The switch is used to select either filament or both can be used at the same time.

The fluorescent lamp gives off light from an "electric discharge," or arc. An electric discharge can give off light just as lightning produces light when it discharges between the sky and the ground. In the fluorescent lamp an electric discharge is made to occur between the two ends of the sealed glass tube.

flow of electrons produces enough heat to vaporize the mercury. When current flows through a mercury vapor it produces a light called *ultraviolet light*. This ultraviolet is called *violet radiation* and is not a very bright light.

The inside of the fluorescent glass tube is coated with a very thin layer of powdered chemicals called *phosphors*.

PHOSPHOR COAT INSIDE OF GAS–FILLED TUBE

FILAMENT

PLASTIC BASE

GLASS TUBE

◆ 78. Fluorescent lamps last longer than incandescent lamps and produce more light with less electricity.

Construction of the Fluorescent Lamp

A fluorescent lamp is made of a large glass tube that has had all of the air removed from it (Illustration 78). After the air has been removed a small amount of gas, such as argon gas, and a very small amount of mercury are placed inside of the tube. At each end of the glass tube is a small lamp filament that is called an *electrode*. These filaments are not intended to produce light but are made so that when they get hot they will throw off electrons. A special coating is placed on the filaments to give off the electrons. The electrons that are thrown off the filaments will flow through the argon gas from one electrode to the other. This

When the ultraviolet radiation from the mercury vapor hits the coating of phosphors it bursts into a brilliant glow of fluorescent light. The color of the light given off by the fluorescent coating depends upon the type of powder used.

The Starter Switch

The filaments at each end of the fluorescent tube are not needed once the flow of electrons has been started in the tube. After the arc between the two electrodes is started the current will continue to flow—as long as the circuit is completed. The filaments can be disconnected from the circuit as soon as the arc starts.

A switch called a *starter switch* is connected in series with the filaments

♦ 79. **The automatic starter is connected in series with the filaments of a fluorescent-tube circuit. As soon as the arc starts through the tube the starter automatically opens the filament circuit and the filaments are turned off.**

as shown in Illustration 79. As soon as the filaments become hot enough to give off electrons the starter switch is made to automatically open the filament circuit. These automatic starter switches are usually made of some type of bimetal strip that will open once the filaments become hot. The starter switch is mounted near one end of the tube so that it can easily be replaced if it becomes defective.

The Ballast

The arc in a fluorescent lamp will not start a flow of electrons unless there is a sudden high voltage produced between the two electrodes. It is necessary to get an electric arc to jump from the electrode at one end of the lamp to the electrode at the other end. To obtain this sudden high voltage a coil called a *ballast* is connected in series with the circuit, as shown in Illustration 80. The ballast is a coil of wire wound around an iron core.

When the fluorescent lamp is first

turned on the hot filaments give off electrons. At this time current is flowing through the ballast coil. Then the starting switch automatically opens. When this happens the magnetic field around the ballast coil suddenly collapses as the current momentarily stops. This sudden collapse of the magnetic field around the coil induces an instant high voltage in the ballast coil. This surge or "kick" of high voltage is strong enough to strike the arc across the lamp that starts the electron flow and lights the lamp.

The flow of electrons through the mercury vapor and the argon gas could easily become very great and burn out the lamp. Once the lamp starts it would draw more and more current. The ballast again goes into action since it is in series with the circuit. It performs like a resistor to keep the current from becoming too high. Here the ballast acts like a control valve and limits the amount of current flowing through the tube.

From this we can see that the ballast has two functions (1) to start the arc once the filament has started electrons

♦ 80. **When the starting switch is opened the ballast produces a high-voltage surge that strikes the arc in the fluorescent tube.**

◆ 81. The high voltage of the transformer is connected to each end of the neon tube. The arc between the two electrodes lights up the sign.

to flow and (2) to protect the tube from having too much current flowing through it.

Neon Lamps

Most outdoor signs and advertising displays are lighted with neon lamps. Neon lamps consist of a glass tube with a terminal at each end. The tube is filled with neon gas. When a voltage is connected between the two terminals an electrical arc occurs, giving off a colored light. Pure neon gas gives off an orange color. To obtain additional colors other gases are added to the neon gas. Colors such as blue, green, red, yellow, and white are very common.

Some small neon tubes can be ignited with 115 volts. When large signs require longer neon tubes a higher voltage is necessary to light the tube. A step-up transformer is used to increase the voltage for the tube. See Illustration 81.

The longer the tube the higher the voltage must be stepped up. Step-up transformers with secondary voltages anywhere from 1,500 to 15,000 volts are used on neon signs. Since the neon lamp uses very little current, small wire can be used on the primary and secondary windings of the transformers.

INTERESTING THINGS TO DO

Making a Table Lamp.
Materials needed:

1 Piece wood, 1" x 5" x 8"
1 Piece wood, 1½" x 3½" x 8"
1 Threaded nipple, brass or steel, ⅛" pipe size, 1" long
1 Socket, brass, pull-chain, threaded cap
6' Lamp cord, parallel, No. 18
1 Attachment plug cap

Make a ¼" bevel along the upper edge of the piece of wood that is to be used for the lamp base. Starting at the center of one end of the base, drill a ⁵⁄₁₆" hole lengthwise halfway through it. Drill another ⁵⁄₁₆" hole through the base at a right angle to the first hole at the center, so that the two holes will meet. Beginning at the center of one end of the piece of wood that is to be used for the upright section, drill a ¹¹⁄₃₂" hole lengthwise, half-way through it. Drill another ¹¹⁄₃₂" hole through the other end of the wood block, so that the two holes meet. Screw the pipe nipple into one end of the

◆ **82. Table lamp.**

block so that only ¼″ extends above the wood. Secure the upright piece to the base with glue or wood screws as shown in Illustration 83. Insert the cord through the wood base and stand. Screw the socket cap to the nipple and connect the socket to the cord. Attach a plug cap to the other end of the lamp cord.

The lamp may be finished natural with clear shellac or lacquer, or painted to match any color scheme.

◆ **83. Table lamp assembly.**

REVIEW QUESTIONS

1. Who introduced the first practical incandescent lamp?

2. What kind of filament is found in the modern incandescent lamp?

3. Why is it necessary to remove the oxygen from the glass bulb in an incandescent lamp?

4. Give the reason why some glass bulbs are frosted.

5. How many filaments are used in a three-way incandescent lamp?

6. What is the purpose of the filament in a fluorescent lamp?

7. What material is used to coat the inside of a fluorescent lamp.

8. What is the purpose of the starter switch in a fluorescent lamp circuit?

UNIT 21
HEATING WITH ELECTRICITY

Types of Heating Appliances for the Home

Many types of heating appliances are used around the home. Some of these are:

Toasters	Portable electric
Waffle irons	heaters
Electric flat iron	Electric blankets
Water heaters	Heating pads
Laundry dryers	Coffee makers
Electric wall heaters	Electric range
Electric ironer	

All of these heating appliances use a resistance wire to produce heat. *Nichrome wire,* which is an alloy of nickel and chromium, is usually used as the heater wire. The wire is often wound in the form of a coil so that a long length of wire can be placed in a small space, as shown in Figure 84.

Sometimes a flat wire called *ribbon nichrome wire* (Figure 85) is used for elements. All elements must be mounted in or on some type of insulating material. When the element is out in the open, such as in toasters and wall heaters, ceramic forms or mica sheets are used as the insulating material.

In addition to the open elements some elements called *calrod elements* are enclosed in a metal tube. See Figure 86. The heating element is placed in the center of the hollow metal tube and an insulating material is packed in around it.

The element extends out each end of the tube and the ends of the tube are sealed so that air or moisture cannot get to the element. After the tube

GENERAL ELECTRIC   OFF   LOW   MED   H   *automatic grill waffle baker*

◆ 84. A spiral type heating coil is used in this electric waffle iron.

◆ 85. Flat wire called *ribbon nichrome* wire is usually used as the elements in electric toasters.

is sealed it is formed to the needed shape such as the spiral found in some electric ranges. In flat irons the calrod

element is sometimes cast into the base of the iron (Figure 87).

A hotter element can be produced by the calrod method since the element

◆ 86. A heating element used in an electric stove. This unit has an element called a *calrod* inside of the spiral metal tube.

◆ 87. Automatic electric iron with temperature control. Heating element is cast in the base of the iron.

CALROD
HEATING
UNIT

THERMOSTAT

TO
HEATER
CORD

◆ 88. This is a wiring diagram of an electric iron.

is placed much closer to where the heat is needed. Also there is no problem with air and moisture damaging the elements.

Regulating the Heat

Appliances such as electric blankets, electric dryers, waffle irons, and flat irons use automatic heat regulators. These heat regulators, called *thermostats,* open and close the electrical circuit according to the selected temperature. Thermostats are usually made of bimetal strips that are placed inside of the heating unit. They operate like an automatic switch and are connected in series with the heater element.

As the element gets hot it gives off heat that warms the thermostat. Since the thermostat is made of a bimetal strip, the heat makes the strip expand and bend upward. When the temperature is great enough the strip opens the contact and opens the circuit. As the

heater cools the temperature becomes lower and the bimetal strip bends back, closing the circuit so that the element again gives off heat.

Testing Heating Appliances

A simply constructed series lamp tester called a *continuity tester* can be used to check heating appliances. This tester consists of a cord with an attachment plug connected so that a 115-volt light bulb is in series with a pair of test leads. See Figure 89.

The attachment plug is plugged into a convenience outlet and when the two test leads are touched together this completes the circuit and the lamp lights. To test a heater appliance, one lead of the tester is placed on one prong of the appliance attachment plug and the other lead is placed on the other prong, as shown in Figure 89.

It is important that the two test leads do not touch each other. If the lamp does not light this shows that there is an open circuit and either the element is burned out or that there is a break in the heater cord. If the lamp lights, this would indicate a complete circuit and that the heating unit is good.

Testing for Shorts to the Frame

When one of the electric wires comes in contact with the appliance frame this makes the appliance a dangerous piece of equipment to use. Anyone touching the appliance could easily get an electrical shock. The continuity tester can be used for testing for shorts to the frame. One lead of the tester is placed on the prongs of the appliance plug and the other lead is touched to

◆ 89. An electric iron can be tested with a continuity tester to determine whether the heating unit is good.

the frame of the appliance.

If the lamp lights this shows that there is a complete circuit from the electric wiring to the frame. A complete circuit from the element or from any part of the electric wiring to the frame is often called a *ground*. All grounds must be repaired before the appliance can be used safely.

Checking the Heater Cord

After testing the appliance with the continuity tester and finding either a short or an open circuit, it is then necessary to locate the trouble. Most failures in portable equipment such as flat irons, toasters, waffle irons, and portable heaters occur in the heater

◆ 90. A continuity tester can be used to test a waffle iron for dangerous shorts to the frame.

◆ 91. A continuity tester is used like this to test the cord of an electric appliance for failure.

cord. The constant bending of these cords breaks the wires. The heater cord should be disconnected from the appliance and the continuity tester used to find out if the cord is at fault. Both wires must be tested to find out if there is continuity or a break in the wires. Also a check must be made to see if the wires are shorted together. If either a short or a break in the cord is located it is probably best to replace the cord with a new one.

Checking the Heater Element

With the cord removed from the appliance, place the tester leads across the two terminals of the heater element as shown in Figure 92. If the light fails to come on this shows that the element is burned out. In most appliances the burned-out element cannot be rewound and the old unit, including the heater wire and the insulating material, must be removed and a new unit installed.

◆ 92. This is how to use a continuity tester to check a heater element for a short or open circuit.

INTERESTING THINGS TO DO

1. Making a Continuity Tester

Materials needed:

1 Small plastic box (see text)
1 Neon lamp, NE-2
1 Rubber grommet, 3/8"
1 Fixed capacitor, 0.1 Mfd., 200 volts
2 Insulated pin jacks
2 Insulated pin plugs
3' Test lead wire
6' Lamp cord, parallel, No. 18
1 Attachment plug cap
2 Insulated test prods

The continuity tester shown on the previous pages is similar to those used in commercial electrical repair shops for testing appliances; but since the terminals of the lamp socket are exposed it is not recommended for student use. A more compact, completely enclosed tester is described below. Besides its small size it has another advantage in that it can be used to test continuity in circuits and electronic components with resistance as high as 200,000 ohms.

The plastic box need be large enough only to hold the capacitor and pin jacks, as shown in Figure 93. The box shown in the photograph measured 5/8" × 1¼" × 2½". Drill a 3/8" hole in the top of the box for the rubber grommet. Drill ¼" holes at opposite ends of the box for the lamp cord and the pin jacks. Insert the grommet in the hole in the box and gently press the neon lamp through the center of the grommet so that its end extends about 1/8" above the box. Place the pin jacks and the lamp cord in proper holes and secure the lamp cord to the box with glue or cement. Make connections as shown in Figure 94. The test prods may be obtained from an electronic supply house, or made with fiber rods and nails. Secure the pin plugs to one end of the test leads and the test prods to the other end. Plug the tester into a 117 volt A. C. circuit and touch the ends of the test prods together. If the neon lamp lights up brilliantly, the tester is ready to test your circuits.

LAMP CORD

CEMENT LAMP CORD TO CASE

CAPACITOR

NEON BULB

RUBBER GROMMET

PLASTIC CASE

PIN JACK

◆ 93. Bottom view of continuity tester with cover removed.

◆ 94. The completed tester.

2. Constructing an Electric Coffee Warmer.

Materials needed:

1 Coffee can (1-pound size), with lid
1 Piece asbestos transite, circular, 3/16″ thick. (The diameter will be the same as the inside diameter of the particular coffee can that is used.)
40′ Resistance wire, nichrome, No. 29
2 Machine screws, steel or brass, 6–32, 3″ long
2 Pieces pipe, 1/8″ pipe size, 2¾″ long
6′ Heater cord, asbestos covered, No. 18
1 Rubber grommet, 3/8″ inside diameter
4 Pieces sheet steel, 20 gage, 3/8″ x 1¼″
1 Piece brass rod, round, 1/8″ diameter, 20¼″ long
4 Machine screws, roundhead (RH) steel, 6–32, 1/4″ long
6 Machine screw nuts, hexagon, steel, 6–32
2 Machine screws, flathead (FH) brass, 6–32, 1/2″ long
2 Machine screw nuts, hexagon, brass, 6–32
1 Attachment plug cap

Make a number of 5/16″ holes in the lid of the coffee can, as shown in Photographs 95 and 96. Drill and shape

◆ 95. Coffee warmer.

the four pieces of sheet steel to serve as legs for the warmer, as shown in the section view, Drawing 97. Drill four 5/32″ holes in the bottom of the can near the outside edge and secure the legs in place with the RH machine screws. Cut the circular piece of asbestos transite so that it will fit the inside of the coffee can. Drill holes and saw slots in the asbestos transite as shown in the drawing. Place two brass machine

◆ 96. Parts of the electric coffee warmer.

ASBESTOS TRANSITE

COILED RESISTANCE WIRE

PIPE SPACER

COFFEE CAN

HEATER CORD

METAL LEG

SECTION VIEW

ASBESTOS TRANSITE

5/32" DRILL AND COUNTERSINK

1/2"

1/4"

5/32" DRILL

1 1/2"

1/2"

1/2"

SLOT WITH HACKSAW

PLATE

FOR HEATING ELEMENT

18"

1 1/4"

1/8"

SAW SLOT

1"

CRANK

FOR WINDING HEATING ELEMENT

SHEET OR SPONGE RUBBER

UNCOIL RESISTANCE WIRE TO EXTEND BETWEEN SLOTS IN ASBESTOS PLATE

◆ 97. Drawing of the electric coffee warmer.

screws in the circular piece to serve as terminal screws.

Bend the piece of round brass rod to the shape as shown in Drawing 97 to serve for winding the heating element. Look at Photograph 98 to see how to wind the element. Remove the coiled wire from the crank carefully and stretch it until it is 32″ long. Secure one end of the coiled wire to one of the terminal screws and place the wire on the circular asbestos piece. When extending the resistance wire from one slot to another, uncoil just enough

wire to reach between the slots, as shown on the drawing. Connect the remaining end of the coiled resistance wire to the other terminal screw. Attach one end of the heater cord to the terminal screws. Drill two $5/32''$ holes through the bottom of the coffee can in line with the two holes in the heating unit. Also make a hole in the side of the can near the bottom for the rubber grommet. Place the grommet in the hole and pass the end of the heater cord through it. Secure the completed heating unit to the bottom of the can

◆ 98. Place the crank illustrated in Drawing 97 between two pieces of wood about 1″ wide and 6″ long, so that about ½″ of rod extends beyond the side of the pieces of wood. Secure the wood pieces in a vise, so that it will require a little effort to turn the crank. Place one end of the nichrome wire in the slot at the end of the brass rod and turn the crank slowly until the turns of resistance wire reach the pieces of wood. Winding the heating element is a job which requires the help of two persons, one to turn the crank and another to feed the resistance wire. Just enough tension should be kept on the wire to wind it tightly on the rod. Once the turns of wire reach the wood pieces, the rod will feed through them automatically until all of the wire is wound on the rod.

with pieces of pipe serving as spacers and the 3″ machine screws. Connect a plug cap to the end of the heater cord. Cement pieces of rubber to the bottom of the legs to prevent marring the table and the project is complete for use.

When plugged into a 115-volt outlet this appliance will produce just the right temperature to keep coffee warm right on the dining table.

REVIEW QUESTIONS

1. Name several types of home appliances that use a heating element.

2. What kind of wire is used in heating elements?

3. Why are calrod heating elements considered a good type of heating element?

4. What is the heat regulator on most electrical appliances called?

5. Explain how a heat regulator used on home appliances operates.

6. Draw a circuit for a continuity tester like the one you learned about.

7. How is a continuity tester used to find out if the heating element is burned out?

8. Explain how a continuity tester is used to determine whether or not there is a ground in a heater appliance.

9. Where do most failures occur in portable heater appliances?

10. Why is it usually necessary to replace most heater elements with new factory-built units?

UNIT 22
THE ELECTRIC MOTOR

Purpose of Electric Motors

The construction of electric motors is very similar to that of electric generators. Just as the generator has a field and an armature so does the electric motor. Generators are used to produce electricity and need to be rotated. The electric motor uses the electricity developed by a generator or a battery to produce motion. Electric motors are used in such devices as fans, refrigerators, sewing machines, vacuum cleaners, washing machines, lathes, circular saws, and motion picture projectors.

Fundamentals of a Simple DC Motor

Motors and generators look very much alike and in some cases generators may be used for motors and some motors can be used for generators. In Units 8 and 16 we learned that a generator produced electricity if a coil was rotated in a magnetic field. The simple generator can be made into a motor to produce motion by connecting a battery to the brushes as in Illustration 99. The armature has a current flowing through the coils and that makes it an electromagnet. All electro-

MOTOR

The letters show that the machine is a motor.

◆ 99. Armature will start to rotate as poles on the armature repel like poles in the field magnet.

◆ 100. The armature has rotated so that unlike poles now attract each other.

◆ 101. The armature polarity is now changed by the commutator so that again like poles repel each other.

magnets have a north and a south pole so the armature has a north and south pole. The permanent field magnet also has a north and a south pole.

The brush on the left-hand side is connected to the negative terminal of the battery and current flow is such that this side of the armature becomes a north pole. The brush on the right-hand side is connected to the positive terminal and that side of the armature becomes a south pole. Thus the armature has a north pole next to the north pole of the magnet and a south pole next to the south pole of the magnet. Like poles repel each other so both poles of the armature try to push away from the poles of the magnet.

This repelling of like poles makes the armature rotate. As the armature rotates, the north pole of the armature is attracted toward the south pole of the magnet. Just before the two poles come together by their attraction for each other the polarity of the armature is changed by the commutator. Again the two like poles repel each other and the armature continues to rotate. See Figures 100 and 101. The direction that a current carrying conductor will move in a magnetic field is shown by the *Right Hand Rule,* Figure 102.

Motors with Electromagnetic Field Coils

An electromagnet can be used to produce the magnetic field instead of a permanent magnet. The electromagnet called a *field coil* consists of insulated wire wound around a steel core. The battery is used to produce the magnetic field for the field coil as well

♦ 102. The right hand motor rule. In the drawing, the thumb indicates the direction a current carrying conductor will move in a magnetic field.

as to provide the current for the armature. Figures 103 and 104 show how field coils may be connected in series or in parallel with the armature.

Armatures with Several Coils

To improve the operating efficiency of commercial motors several sets of coils may be used in the armature. By using several sets of coils it is necessary to have a commutator with a number of different segments to connect each of the coils to. In this way the brushes are always in contact with a set of coils that are directly across from the field poles. Using a number of coils in the armature produces a much smoother running motor.

Using Alternating Current on Motors

Some motors may be used on either

◆ **103. Electric motor with field coil connected in series with the armature coil.**

◆ **104. Electric motor with field coil connected in parallel with armature coil.**

direct current or alternating current. Motors using an electromagnetic field with a commutator may be operated from A C or DC. When alternating current is connected to these motors, the magnetic field is continually changing in both the armature winding and in the field coil winding. Since the currents in both the armature and the field coil are changing together, the polarity of each is changed at the same time. When one pole of the field coil is the north pole the armature pole nearest it is also a north pole and they repel each other. When the direction of current flow changes and this same field pole becomes a south pole, the armature pole is also changed to a south pole and they continue to repel each other. The commutator is the

device that makes the rotation of the motor possible.

Universal Motor Repairs

Small motors designed to operate on either alternating or direct current

◆ **105. The armature of an electric motor showing the commutator segments. The segments are insulated from each other and are connected to different sets of coils in the armature.**

◆ 106. Removing the brushes from an electric motor used on a sewing machine.

are called *universal* motors. These motors have the field coil connected in series with the armature coil as in Figure 103. This type of small motor is found in vacuum cleaners, fans, sewing machines, electric mixers, and similar household appliances.

The carbon brushes on universal motors sometimes become worn and must be replaced. When replacing brushes it is important to disconnect the appliance from the electric circuit before starting to work.

The new brushes should be the same type and size as those used by the manufacturer. The old brushes can be removed by unscrewing the brush-holder screws found on each side of the motor, as shown in Figure 106. Screws in the end of the brush holders press against a small spring that keeps the brush in contact with the commutator.

The commutator on these motors

◆ 107. Electric motors are made in many sizes and are specially designed to meet particular requirements.

sometimes needs to be cleaned. Usually it is necessary to disassemble the motor to clean the commutator. When taking the motor apart it is advisable to take out the brushes so that they won't become damaged when removing the armature. Use a very fine sandpaper and sand the commutator lightly. When the copper segments on the commutator shine this should be a good indication that the commutator is clean.

Oil should only be used on the bearings of an electric motor. Some motors have cups where the oil is to be placed. Use oil very sparingly and be sure that it does not get on the brushes or the commutator.

Induction Motors

The most common type of electric motor used on alternating current is the *induction* motor. Induction motors are used on refrigerators, garbage disposals, blowers, washing machines, and on many types of machinery. It can only be used on alternating current and does not require a commutator or brushes.

The induction motor consists of two main parts—the *stator,* which is the stationary set of coils wound in the frame of the motor, and the *rotor,* which is the rotating part of the motor. See Figure 108. The rotor is made of laminated steel with slots cut in it to hold copper bars. The copper bars that are in the slots of the steel core are all connected together at the end by two rings of copper. This type of rotor is called a *squirrel cage* rotor (Figure 109). The stator acts like a primary of a transformer and induces a current in the rotor.

◆ 108. An induction motor operates on alternating current and has no commutator or brushes.

Courtesy General Electric Co.

◆ 109. A squirrel cage rotor as it would appear when removed from the slots of the laminated sheet steel rotor core and reassembled.

When the magnetic field of the stator induces a current in the copper bars, the rotor becomes an electromagnet. The field of the stator attracts or repels the rotor and pushes it around. This pushing of the rotor by the stator is what makes the motor run. The main advantage of the induction-type motor is that there are no moving parts, such as brushes and commutators, that must be connected in the electrical circuit. Elimination of any direct connection between the stator and the rotor produces a fairly trouble-free motor.

Starting the Induction Motor

Most induction motors require a start to get the rotor moving. The usual method of starting an induction motor is to use two stator windings. One winding is called the *running winding* and the other is called the *starting winding*. See Photograph 110. The starting winding helps to start the rotor moving and is disconnected after the motor has reached running speed. When the starting winding is cut out of the circuit the running winding

Courtesy General Electric Co.

◆ 110. This is an alternating current motor with one end removed, showing the arrangement of the starting switch.

keeps the motor going. An automatic cut-out switch is arranged so that as the speed of the motor picks up it will open and disconnect the starting winding from the circuit. When the motor stops, the switch automatically closes and the starting winding is again in the circuit.

INTERESTING THINGS TO DO

1. Tin Can Motor.
Materials needed:

2 Pieces tin, $\frac{1}{2}$" x $5\frac{1}{4}$" (cut from a tin can)
2 Pieces tin, $\frac{1}{2}$" x $1\frac{7}{8}$"
1 Piece steel rod, $\frac{1}{16}$" x $2\frac{1}{2}$"
2 Pieces sheet brass, $\frac{3}{8}$" x $1\frac{1}{4}$", 16 gage
2 Pieces spring brass, $\frac{1}{4}$" x $1\frac{1}{8}$", 26 gage
1 Piece brass tubing, $\frac{1}{4}$" inside diameter,
    $\frac{1}{2}$" long, 22 gage
1 Piece fiber rod, round, $\frac{1}{4}$" diameter,
    $\frac{1}{2}$" long
1 Piece wood, $\frac{1}{2}$" x $2\frac{1}{2}$" x 3"
1 Piece wood, $\frac{3}{8}$" x $\frac{1}{2}$" x $\frac{3}{4}$"
2 Terminal screws, 6–32, 1" long
1 Spool magnet wire, No. 24, cotton- or
    enamel-covered

◆ 111. A tin can motor.

Lay out and drill the two pieces of tin as shown in the drawing for the field coil frame. See Figure 112. Place the two pieces together and solder along the edges near the center. Bend the two pieces to the shape shown and solder the remaining edges together. Wrap the flat end of the completed field coil frame with tape or thin cardboard and wind four layers of magnet wire over the tape or cardboard. Drill a $\frac{5}{32}$" hole through the small wood block and through the wood base and secure the field frame to the wood base with a roundhead machine screw. Shape the smaller pieces of tin as shown in the drawing to serve as the armature frame and solder the two pieces together along the edges. Insert the piece of round steel rod through the center of the armature frame and solder it to the frame. Wrap the armature frame with tape or thin cardboard and, starting at the center near the shaft, wind four layers of magnet wire on each side of the armature. Both coils should be wound in the same direction and the winding should begin and end at the center of the frame, so that the ends of the coil may be connected directly to the commutator.

Drill a hole through the center of the fiber rod, so that it will fit tightly on the shaft. Cut the brass tubing lengthwise into two equal sections, place the sections on the fiber rod, and secure them by winding a number of turns of thread around one end of the brass tubing. Allow enough space between the thread and the end of the brass tubing, so that the thread will not be burned when the armature wires are soldered in place. This completes the commutator.

◆ 112. Tin can motor parts and assembly.

Place the commutator on the steel shaft, next to the armature, so that the slots in the commutator are on each side of the armature. Solder the ends of the armature windings to the section of the commutator that is on the same side of the shaft.

Drill and shape the two pieces of sheet brass to serve as bearing brackets, as shown in the drawing. Place the brackets on the armature shaft and secure the brackets to the wood base with 4–40 machine screws. Drill and shape the two pieces of spring brass to serve as brushes, as shown in the drawing.

Mount the brushes on the wood base, one on each side of the commutator, with 4–40 machine screws. The tension of the brushes should be adjusted so that they make good contact with the commutator, but they should not be so tight that they prevent the armature from turning properly.

When the proper position for the armature and commutator has been found, small machine screw nuts may be soldered to the shaft close to the outside of the bearing brackets, to keep the armature centered.

Make the connections for the motor by running a wire on the bottom of the wood base from a terminal screw to one of the brush screws. Connect one of the field coil wires to the remaining brush screw. Connect the other field coil lead to the remaining terminal. The motor should now be ready for its initial tryout. Although the motor was designed to run on the transformer that was described in another unit, it will run on other sources of power, such as dry cells or a storage battery. Depending upon the speed of rotation desired, any voltage between 4 and 10 volts may be used.

2. Alternating Current Motor.
Materials needed:

1 Piece steel rod, round, ⅜″ diameter,
    1″ long
1 Piece band steel, ⅛″ x ¾″ x 11″
2 Pieces steel rod, round, ½″ diameter,
    ⅝″ long
1 Piece steel rod, round, ⅛″ diameter,
    3¾″ long
1 Spool magnet wire, No. 24, enamel- or
    cotton-covered
4 Washers, fiber, 1/16″ thick, ⅞″ diameter
1 Piece wood, ½″ x 3″ x 6″
2 Machine screws, FH, steel, 10–24, 1″ long
2 Terminal screws

◆ 113. An alternating current motor.

This easily made motor will rotate at a speed of 3,600 revolutions a minute on 60-cycle alternating current, but unlike a motor that has a commutator and brushes it is not self-starting. It will run only on low-voltage alternating current and it was designed to work with the transformer that is described in Unit 17 of this book. The motor operates on the principle that the rotor will go around to keep in step with the change of direction of the current that flows through the field coils and, since the current is changing at the rate of 3,600 times a minute, the rotor will also rotate at a similar speed.

Shape the piece of band steel so that one end will form a circle 2½″ in diameter and drill holes in it as indicated on Drawing 114. Locate the holes exactly in the middle across the width of the band steel. Drill ¼″ holes through the center of the pieces of ½″ steel rod. Drill ½″ holes in the center of the fiber washers and place a washer over each end of the pieces of steel rod to make the field coil form. Countersink one of the washers on each form so that the head of the screw which holds it in place will be even with the fiber. See Photograph 113. Wind each

10-24 MACHINE SCREW

FIELD FRAME

SHAFT

ROTOR

TERMINAL SCREW

FIELD COIL

1/4" DRILL ——— 1/2"

STEEL ROD ——— 5/8"

WIND 6 LAYERS
NO. 24 MAGNET WIRE

FIBER
WASHER 7/8"

FIELD COIL
FORM

1/2"

6"

SIDE VIEW OF ASSEMBLED MOTOR

STEEL
ROD

BAND STEEL
1/8" × 3/4" × 11"

3/16" DRILL

1/8" DRILL

1 1/4"

1/8"
DRILL

1/8" DRILL

3/16"
DRILL

1"

3/8"

ROTOR

1/4"

1 1/2"

5/32" DRILL

FIELD FRAME

STEEL ROD

3 3/4"

ROTOR SHAFT

1/8"

◆ **114. Alternating current motor drawing.**

form with six layers of No. 24 magnet wire and secure the completed coil to the field frame with 10–24 machine screws and nuts. Make a temporary connection between one wire from each field coil and connect the remaining two wires to a dry cell. Place your magnetic compass near one of the field coils and note which end of the compass needle is attracted to the coil. Now place your compass near the other field coil and note which end of the compass is attracted to it. If each coil attracts a different pole of the compass they are connected correctly and the

connection between them can be made permanent. If both coils attract the same end of the compass, the coil connections will have to be reversed before the permanent connection is made. Secure the field frame to the wood base with wood screws and connect two wires from the field coils to the terminal screws by passing the wires through the base and connecting them to the heads of the screws.

Drill a hole through the middle of the 3/8″ steel rod to serve as the rotor, as shown on the drawing. Place the rotor in the field frame between the two field coils. Insert the rotor shaft through one of the ⅛" holes in the frame, the hole in the rotor, and the hole in the opposite side of the frame. Place the rotor at the exact center of the rotor shaft and solder it to the shaft. The motor is now ready to run.

Connect the motor to your transformer, grasp the rotor shaft between a thumb and forefinger and spin the shaft. The first few attempts at starting the motor may not be successful, but once you learn the knack of the proper amount to spin the shaft, starting the motor will be easy.

3. Demonstrating Motor Action and the Right Hand Rule

Materials needed:

    1 Horseshoe shape magnet
    1 Dry cell
    1 Switch, momentary contact
    18" Copper wire, No. 10 or 12.
    Wood and sheet metal for mounting magnet and wire loop.

A dramatic demonstration of motor action can be made with a magnet, dry cell, switch, and loop of wire, as shown in Figure 115. Any horseshoe shape magnet may be used, but the stronger it is the greater will be the effect.

Mount the magnet so that one pole

◆ 115. **Construction details for demonstrating motor action.**

or end is directly above the other. Bend the piece of wire into a U shape and mount it with metal brackets so that it will swing freely between the pole pieces of the magnet and be exactly at the center of the poles when it is at rest. Connect the free ends of the heavy wire in series with the switch and dry cell with flexible wire. When all connections have been made, close the switch momentarily. Which way did the wire swing? If the polarity of the magnet is not marked, try to determine the position of its north and south poles by means of the right hand rule shown at Figure 102.

◆ 116. The completed unit for showing motor action. With polarities of the magnet as shown, the wire loop will move to the right when the switch is pressed. Use the right hand rule and determine the direction the current must be flowing through the wire loop.

REVIEW QUESTIONS

1. Name several uses for electrical motors.

2. What is the purpose of the commutator on a simple motor?

3. Draw a diagram of a simple motor using an electromagnetic field.

4. Why do motor armatures sometimes have several sets of coils?

5. Why can some motors be used on both direct current and alternating current? What are the motors called?

6. How are commutators cleaned?

7. Name two important parts of an induction motor.

8. What is one of the main advantages of an induction motor?

9. Explain the construction of a squirrel cage rotor.

10. What are the two windings used in an induction motor called?

UNIT 23
THE AUTOMOBILE ELECTRICAL SYSTEM

The modern automobile uses electricity in many ways. Electricity is used to (1) crank the engine, (2) provide lights for night driving, (3) ignite the fuel that gives power to the engine, (4) operate instruments such as fuel gage, temperature gage, and oil pressure gage, (5) light signaling devices such as stop lights and turning lights, and (6) operate many accessories such as radios, horns, heaters, and windows. The complete wiring for the automobile requires many circuits as shown in Figure 118.

The Storage Battery

We learned about the storage battery in Unit 7. It is a very good source of electricity because it can deliver large amounts of current and can be recharged when run down. Each cell of a storage battery delivers 2 volts. To obtain 12 volts from a storage battery it is necessary to have six cells connected in series. A 6-volt storage battery has three cells connected in series. Automobiles use either 6-volt or 12-volt storage batteries.

To reduce the number of wires used for the electrical circuits in the automobile the steel frame of the chassis is used as one wire in the circuit. This is possible because the low voltage of the battery is not dangerous. Some automobile manufacturers design their engines to have the negative terminal of the battery connected to the frame and others connect the positive terminal to the frame. The battery terminal connected to the frame is said to be *grounded* to the frame. A heavy flexible cable called a *ground cable* is used for this purpose.

The Starting Motor

The automobile uses a direct current motor to crank the engine and get it started. Modern engines are difficult to turn over and the motor called the *starting motor* must be very powerful. The principle of the direct current motor was discussed in Unit 22. Photograph 119 shows the construction of a starting motor.

The battery provides the current necessary to rotate the engine. When the starter switch is pushed down this completes the circuit and the engine starts. The starting motor shaft is coupled to the engine flywheel and as it rotates it turns the engine over.

In cranking the engine the starting motor draws a large amount of current from the storage battery. The amount of current varies from 150 to 500 amperes, depending upon the design of the motor.

◆ 117. Drawing of the basic circuit used for the starting motor.

IGNITION SYSTEM

DISTRIBUTOR

IGNITION RESISTOR

SPARK PLUGS

IGNITION COIL

IGNITION-STARTER SWITCH

JUNCTION BLOCK

BATTERY

REGULATOR

AMMETER

GENERATOR

GENERATING SYSTEM

CAR FRAME

FRAME

STARTING MOTOR

STARTING SYSTEM

HORN SYSTEM

HORN RELAY

HORN BUTTON

HORNS

LAMP SWITCH

TAIL LIGHTS

FOOT DIMMER SWITCH

PARKING LIGHTS

HEADLAMPS

BEAM INDICATOR LAMP

LIGHTING SYSTEM

Delco-Remy Div.—General Motors Corp.

◆ **118. The typical electrical system of an automobile. As shown above, it consists of 5 subsystems, the charging system being necessary to the operation of the other four systems.**

Because of the very heavy current flow necessary to operate the starting motor, most engines use a solenoid switch. As shown in Figure 117 the solenoid is controlled by turning on the ignition and closing the starting switch. When the coil of the solenoid is energized, it pulls the plunger down and the contacts form a complete circuit from the battery to the starting motor. These contacts are made to carry the very large amounts of current necessary to run the starting motor which in turn cranks the engine. Once the engine is

Courtesy Delco-Remy Div.—General Motors Corp.

◆ 119. This illustration shows the construction of a direct current motor used to start an automobile.

Courtesy Delco-Remy Div.—General Motors Corp.

◆ 120. The construction of a two-brush automobile generator is shown in this illustration.

running, the starting switch is turned off so that the solenoid coil loses its magnetism and a spring forces the plunger to open the solenoid contacts.

The Generator

The storage battery can supply the electrical needs of the automobile for only a short time. A generator is needed to charge the battery and to help provide current for the rest of the electrical system. The generator is usually driven by a belt that is coupled to the engine.

The direct current generator was discussed in Unit 8. To generate electricity an armature coil is rotated in a magnetic field. The brushes collect the direct current from the commutator and this current is used throughout the automobile.

After the engine has been started by the starting motor, the generator is rotated by the engine and it begins generating direct current. As the generator builds up voltage it charges the battery. This is indicated on the

◆ 121. Generator regulators control the voltage supplied by an automobile generator.

ammeter found on the dashboard of the automobile. In some automobiles a warning red light on the dashboard indicates that the generator is not charging. When the generator is charging the light goes out.

A special device called a *generator regulator* (Photograph 121) is used to keep the voltage supplied by the gen-

From Automotive Fuel and Ignition Systems, *American Technical Society*

◆ 122. This basic wiring circuit for an automobile shows the generator and the regulator, which maintains constant voltage.

erator from going too high. The generator regulator, often called the *voltage regulator,* provides an automatic control on the voltage output of the generator. The voltage regulator usually prevents the voltage from the generator from going higher than 7.2 to 7.4 volts in a 6-volt system. On a 12-volt system the voltage is regulated from 14.0 to 14.2 volts. A voltage slightly higher than the battery voltage is needed for the generator to charge the battery. Through the use of this generator regulator the voltage of the entire electrical system remains fairly constant. See Figure 122.

The Alternator

The increased demands for electrical accessories on automobiles such as power windows, power seats, and two way radio systems, has made a very heavy load on the direct current generating systems. Many of the accessories are used when the automobile is going at low speed and this is when the direct-current generator develops very little voltage.

One method of overcoming some of the problems found in the direct-current generator is to use an alternating-current generator and rectifier system. This system provides good voltage output at low speeds and also has excellent efficiency at high speeds.

The alternating-current generator is called an alternator and consists primarily of a rotor and a stator. The rotor includes a field coil which is connected to slip rings. The field coil draws only about 2 amperes of current and is connected to the battery by brushes which are in contact with the slip rings, as illustrated in Figure 123. When the rotor is turning the magnetic lines of force in the rotor field coils cut across the coil windings located in the stator. An alternating-current is

◆ 123. Drawing of basic parts used in a rotating field alternator.

Courtesy Leece-Neville Co.

◆ 124. Section drawing of a 12 volt alternator. Colored areas show the windings, slip rings and rectifiers. The rectifiers convert the AC output to DC.

CAPACITOR
SCREW
SHIELD
INSULATOR
HEAT SINK
SCREW
SCREW
WASHER
TERMINAL
NUT
WASHER
NUT
WASHER
BUSHING
RETAINER
SHIELD
PULLEY
WASHER
NUT
BRUSH
TERMINAL
SPRING
HOLDER
INSERT
SPACER
STATOR
RECTIFIER
ROTOR
BEARING
WASHER
SCREW
WASHER BRUSH
TERMINAL
BEARING

Courtesy Plymouth Div.—Chrysler Corp.

◆ 125. An exploded view of the complete alternator.

generated in the stator windings.

In order to have a direct-current for charging the battery, the alternating-current produced by the alternator is passed through a rectifier. The rectifier, which is usually made of either silicon diodes or selinium diodes, changes the alternating current into direct-current, Figure 124 and Figure 125.

The Ignition System

Automotive engines operate through the explosion of a mixture of gasoline and air in the engine cylinders which produces power to drive the crankshaft. The purpose of the ignition system is to develop and deliver a high voltage arc of electricity to spark plugs in the cylinders to fire the mixture at the right time. The basic ignition circuit is shown in Figure 127.

A very high voltage is needed to jump the gap of the spark plug. Since the battery will deliver only 12 volts (6 volts in some cars), a step-up transformer must be used to obtain the high voltage required by the spark plugs. This is accomplished by the ignition coil, Figure 128. This coil has a primary winding with 200 to 300 turns of

GAP

Courtesy General Motors Corp.

◆ 126. Construction of a spark plug. The spark from the ignition coil jumps across the gap to ignite the fuel.

◆ 127. These are the basic parts of an automobile ignition system.

heavy wire wrapped around a steel core. The secondary coil consists of 16,-000 to 23,000 turns of fine magnet wire wrapped on the same steel core as the primary winding. This type of transformer is able to step up the voltage to over 20,000 volts.

Since both the battery and generator produce direct current it is necessary to start and stop the current in the primary winding in order to induce a current in the secondary winding. This is the function of the distributor, Figure 129. The distributor contains a breaker cam which is rotated by the engine to open and close the breaker points and make or break the primary circuit. Also, attached to the breaker cam is a rotor, which is connected to the high voltage secondary of the ignition coil. The rotor turns with the cam and makes contact with each of the spark plug wires one at a time. This connects the high voltage to each of the spark plugs so that the air-fuel mixture will be ignited at the proper time.

The system in operation is illustrated in Figure 130. When the points are closed, current flows through the primary circuit (indicated by solid arrows) building up a large magnetic field in the primary winding of the coil. When

Courtesy Echlin Manufacturing Co

◆ 128. The ignition coil steps up the battery voltage to provide the high voltage required by the spark plugs.

Courtesy Delco-Remy Div.—General Motors Corp.

◆ 129. The view on the left is a top view of the distributor with the cap removed to show the points and condenser. At right is a cross section showing the rotor which fits over the breaker cam.

Courtesy Echlin Manufacturing Co.

◆ 131. A cutaway view of the ignition condenser which is connected across the points. When the points are open the heavy current goes through the condenser to prevent arcing of the points.

the points open, the field collapses, inducing a large surge of high voltage in both the primary and secondary of the coil. This high voltage in the secondary is routed through the rotor to the spark plugs where it arcs across the gap to ignite the fuel, (dashed arrows). The collapse of the magnetic field in the coil also induces a large current in the primary. Since the points are open at this time, the current has no complete path and will jump across the points. This current is so high that the points would be burned up unless some means were used to reduce the arcing. This is done by the use of a *condenser* across the points. (In electronics work, the term *condenser* has been replaced by *capacitor*.) When the field of the coil collapses, most of the high current will be bypassed through the condenser.

◆ 130. These simplified drawings show the operation of the ignition system. In the drawing above, colored lines and arrows show the path of primary current when points are closed and the magnetic field is building up in the primary of the coil. The drawing above shows what happens when the points open; the primary field collapses, inducing a surge of high voltage in the secondary circuit to the plugs and through the condenser.

◆ 132. A schematic of a transistor ignition system. The "Transistor Unit" shown in the drawing also has a circuit containing resistors and diodes in addition to the transistor. It has been simplified for clarity. In this system only a small amount of current goes through the points to "switch" the transistor which then carries the heavy primary current. Because of the higher primary current that is handled by the transistor a special coil is required for this system.

Transistor Ignition

The conventional ignition system was invented more than fifty years ago by Charles Kettering, and is sometimes called the "Kettering system." While it has been modified and improved to some degree during the fifty years of it's existence, there has been no basic change to make it keep pace with the developments made in the automobile. The needs of the automobile of today have gone beyond the conventional systems ability to supply them. Transistor ignition is one of the developments which may replace it.

The larger horsepower engines require more voltage at high speeds for efficient ignition of the fuel. In the conventional system, the points make and break the primary circuit slower or faster depending on the speed of the engine. If the engine is going very fast, the points will open and close quickly and the primary of the coil will not have time to build up to a very high voltage. So, at higher speeds the voltage will decrease making the engine less efficient.

In order to get a higher voltage, more current could be used to build a stronger magnetic field in the coil, but the points can handle only so much current without burning. The limitations of the present systems are due mostly to the inability of the points to handle the large amounts of current that are needed to raise the voltage. Other defects found in the conventional system are limited life of the points, and condenser, along with the maintenance necessary to keep these units in working condition.

The transistorized ignition system, Figure 132, eliminates these defects and provides far more dependable service than could be obtained from the older system. The transistor is capable of handling large amounts of current and its function in the circuit is to "switch" the primary circuit on and off so that the points carry only a very small current. Since the points now carry such minute portion of the total current, arcing between them is eliminated and a capacitor such as used in the conventional system is not required. However, a special coil with a higher turns ratio and current rating must be used.

Courtesy Chevrolet Motor Div.
General Motors Corp.
◆ 133. A sealed beam headlamp.

Automobile Lights

Good lights are very important requirements for the safe use of an automobile. The laws of most states require that the headlights must provide enough light to enable one to see objects at least 350' ahead. In addition tail lights, stop lights, and license plate lights are all required by law.

Headlights are of the sealed-beam type (Photograph 133). Since the entire unit is sealed against dirt, moisture, and corrosion, there is little loss in the amount of light produced by the sealed beam throughout its life. These sealed units include the bulb, which consists of two filaments, the glass lens, and the reflector.

The bulbs are an incandescent type that will operate off the low voltage produced by the battery or the generator. The sealed-beam headlight has two filaments. One filament produces the light for the upper beam used in

country driving. The other filament produces the passing beam light, which is focused downward. A switch called a *dimmer switch* mounted on the left side of the floor board is used to select either the upper or lower beam. When the upper headlights beam is turned on, a beam indicator bulb on the dashboard lights up, producing a small spot of red light. On some automobiles this lowering and raising of the beam is done automatically by means of a photoelectric cell. This photoelectric cell is operated by the light from an approaching automobile.

Courtesy General Electric Co.
◆ 134. Illustrated here are types of bulbs used in automobile headlights.

Courtesy Littelfuse Inc.

◆ **135. These are typical fuses used in automotive vehicles.**

POINTS — BRASS BUTTON — SPRING — PLUNGER TIP — WINDING — FRAME — PLUNGER

From Automotive Fuel and Ignition Systems, *American Technical Society*

◆ **136. A circuit breaker used in automobiles. If too much current flows through the coil the plunger forces the armature upward and opens the contact points.**

Protecting Automobile Circuits

Fuses or circuit breakers (Illustrations 135 and 136) are used to protect the lighting and accessory circuits in the automobile. These protective devices are used to prevent the wires from becoming damaged if a short circuit occurs. If either a fuse "blows out" or the circuit breakers open the circuit, it is important to locate the trouble and repair it before turning the switch on again.

Directional Signal Lights

Directional signal lights that indicate whether the driver is going to turn right or left have become a very useful accessory on automobiles. The lights mounted on the front and rear of the automobile flash on and off at the rate of almost 90 times per minute. When the switch lever mounted on the steering column is turned on, an indicator bulb on the dashboard also flashes. This indicator bulb shows a small arrow of light to indicate to the driver the direction which the outside lights are flashing. See Illustrations 137 and 138.

RESISTOR — SIGNAL LIGHT POINTS — HOT WIRE — PILOT LIGHT POINTS — PILOT — TO LIGHTS

From Automotive Fuel and Ignition Systems, *American Technical Society*

◆ **137. The basic circuit of the flasher switch used on directional signal lights. When the switch is turned on, current flows through the "hot wire" and resistor. The resistor in the circuit prevents the bulb from lighting. The "hot wire" has current flowing through it, making it expand. As it expands, the signal light points come together and the bulb lights, because the resistor is shorted out of the circuit. The coil near the pilot light points has enough current flowing through it to pull the points closed and light the arrow on the dashboard. As soon as the current stops flowing through the hot wire it cools, contracts and opens the signal light points. The bulb is turned off but as the "hot wire" heats again the points are closed and again the bulb lights. This heating and cooling of the "hot wire" is what makes the bulb flash off and on.**

TURN SIGNALS

SWITCH

LEFT TURN

RIGHT TURN

FLASHER

6 AMP FUSE

PILOT LIGHT

BATTERY

◆ **138. The circuit of a directional turn indicator. Note that only one pilot light is shown. In a two pilot light system the switching would be much more complicated.**

INTERESTING THINGS TO DO

Ignition and Spark Plug Tester.

Materials needed:

1 Piece fiber tubing, ½″ outside diameter, ¹⁄₁₆″ wall, 7″ long
2 Pieces wood dowel, ⅜″ diameter, ½″ long
1 Radio resistor, 4.7 megohms, ½-watt
1 Neon lamp, ¹⁄₂₅-watt, type NE–2
3′ Stranded radio hook-up wire
1 Battery clip
1 Box nail, 6-penny

This handy tester will help locate trouble in your automobile ignition system. When the clip is attached to some metal part of the frame or engine and the pointed end of the tester is placed in contact with the top of the

◆ **139. Ignition and spark plug tester.**

spark plug, the neon lamp will light up brilliantly, if the spark plug and distributor are operating properly. If the neon lamp lights up dimly or fails

◆ 140. Drawing of ignition and spark plug tester.

to light at all, either the spark plug or distributor is at fault. With a defective distributor the neon lamp will show reduced light on all of the spark plugs. When little or no light shows at only one or two spark plugs, the trouble can usually be traced to defective plugs.

File a section of the fiber tubing at the center with a rat-tail file, so that the electrodes of the neon lamp will be visible. Drill a hole through one of the sections of wood dowel slightly smaller than the box nail and press the nail through the hole. Solder one end of the radio resistor to the head of the nail. Connect the other end of the resistor to one of the neon lamp leads. The resistor and neon lamp should be spaced and connected, so that the neon

lamp will be at the center hole in the fiber tubing when they are inserted into the tubing, as shown in the drawing. Connect the piece of radio hook-up wire to the remaining lead on the neon lamp and wrap the wire with a strip of friction tape close to where it will pass through the section of wood dowel. This will prevent any strain on the neon lamp leads. Insert the assembled neon lamp and resistor into the tubing and glue the wood dowel with the nail in place. Drill a 1/8" hole through the remaining piece of wood dowel, pass the hook-up wire through it, and glue it in the end of the fiber tubing. Attach a battery clip to the end of the hook-up wire and the tester is ready to use.

REVIEW QUESTIONS

1. Name several uses for electricity in the automobile.

2. How many cells are used in a 12-volt storage battery?

3. How is the chassis of the automobile used as part of the electrical circuit?

4. Why does the storage battery need to be in excellent condition to start an engine?

5. What is the purpose of a generator in an automobile?

6. Why is a voltage regulator necessary?

7. Explain the purpose of an ignition coil.

8. How is the distributor used in the automobile ignition circuit?

9. What is the purpose of the spark plugs?

10. Why are sealed-beam lights used?

11. What methods are used to protect automobile electrical circuits?

Using

Electronics

for Communication

~~~~~~

UNIT 24
THE TELEPHONE

The modern telephone is one of the most frequently used electrical devices. It can change sound into a flow of electric current that can be sent over long distances and then change the current back into sound. The telephone was invented by Alexander Graham Bell, who sent the first message over a telephone circuit on March 10, 1876.

Sound Waves

Sound is made by a movement of air. This movement of air is called *air vibrations*. When someone speaks, air is set into waves of vibrations. See Illustration 1. These vibrations hit a human eardrum and sound is heard. Each sound has a different number of

◆ 1. When someone speaks air is set into vibrations. These vibrations are called *sound waves*.

◆ 2. This is the kind of picture used to show a waveform.

211

The microphone symbol is simple to draw.

◆ 3. Construction of a telephone microphone.

vibrations per second. The number of vibrations per second is called the *frequency*.

Vibrating frequencies that can be heard by the human ear range from 20 cycles per second to about 20,000 cycles per second. They are called *audio frequencies* because they are audible to the human ear. A frequency of 15,000 cycles per second is a very high-pitched vibration that very few people can hear. Vibrating frequencies are often drawn in picture form as shown in Illustration 2.

The Telephone Transmitter

The part of the telephone into which you speak is the telephone transmitter, called a *microphone*. A simple microphone consists of a round, thin,

flexible diaphragm connected to a small cup that holds some grains of carbon. See Illustration 3. These grains of carbon are called *carbon granules;* they are made of roasted coal. The granules are held in the cup of a round disk that can move back and forth in the cup. This disk is connected to the diaphragm by a small rod. When voice waves hit the diaphragm it moves with the sound vibrations. The vibration of the diaphragm makes the small disk move inside of the cup of carbon. As the diaphragm is moved back and forth the carbon grains are packed more closely and then less closely.

◆ 4. Carbon granules of a microphone are loosely packed and provide a resistance to the current flow. The milliammeter shows that some current is flowing in the circuit.

◆ 5. Sound wave pushes diaphragm back and packs carbon granules together; when granules are closer together the resistance of the cup of granules is lowered. Current flow, as shown by the milliammeter, is increased as resistance is reduced.

THIN FLEXIBLE IRON DIAPHRAGM

PERMANENT MAGNET

COIL OF WIRE

◆ 6. A telephone receiver construction is shown here.

If a battery is connected across the cup as shown in Illustration 4, a current would flow through the carbon, since it is a conductor of electricity. The carbon acts like a resistor connected across the battery. When the diaphragm moves as in Illustration 5, the carbon is packed closer together and more current will flow through the circuit. The current increases because as the carbon granules move closer together the resistance of the circuit is reduced. We know that more resistance reduces the flow of electricity and less resistance increases the flow of electricity. When the diaphragm moves

back the carbon grains become loosely packed and the current is reduced because the resistance in the circuit is increased.

The current flowing through the circuit will vary with the vibrations of the air waves that hit the diaphragm. The microphone produces a changing electric current that is varied with the sound waves.

The Telephone Receiver

The part of the telephone that is held to the ear is called a *receiver*. The telephone receiver must be able to change the electric current produced by the microphone back into sound waves. A simple receiver consists of a permanent magnet with a coil of wire wound around it and a thin flexible iron diaphragm mounted in front of the magnet and coil. See Illustration 6. The permanent magnet attracts the iron diaphragm and pulls it in slightly. When a current flows through the coil it becomes an electromagnet. The diaphragm has two magnets working on it —the permanent magnet and the electromagnet. If the current through the coil is changing, it will either increase

◆ 7. The illustration shows how interior parts of a modern dial telephone are arranged.

◆ 8. A simple telephone circuit using a step-up transformer to couple the transmitter to the receiver.

the pull on the diaphragm or reduce the pull on the diaphragm. The current in the electromagnet moves the diaphragm back and forth. This movement of the diaphragm pushes the air back and forth in front of it. The movement of air in front of the diaphragm produces sound that can be heard by the human ear.

A Simple Telephone Circuit

To connect a telephone transmitter to a telephone receiver it is usually necessary to use a step-up transformer.

The step-up transformer is used to step up the small voltage produced by the microphone so that a much greater voltage is available for the receiver. See Illustration 8. The primary of the transformer is connected to the microphone and the secondary is connected to the receiver. The varying direct current produced by the movement of the carbon granules in the microphone induces an alternating current in the secondary of the transformer. The stepped-up secondary voltage is used to move the diaphragm of the receiver.

Courtesy Bell Systems

◆ 9. The mobile radiotelephone service in cities makes it possible to place and receive telephone calls in an automobile.

◆ 10. This is how the connections for a two-way telephone circuit are made.

A Two-Way Telephone Circuit

To have a two-way telephone circuit it is necessary to have a receiver and a transmitter at each end of the line, as shown in Illustration 10. A step-up transformer is also used at each location. The two lines connecting the telephones together may be some distance apart. When the phones must be located several miles apart the resistance of the wire lines reduces the strength of the current so that the receiver diaphragm will not move. To increase the strength of such telephone circuits an amplifier is needed. If the telephones are many miles apart a number of different amplifiers located along the route must be used.

INTERESTING THINGS TO DO

Making a Carbon Microphone.
Materials required:

1 Piece wood, ½" x 2" x 3"
1 Piece sheet steel or brass, ½" x 9½", 24 gage
1 Metal bottle cap, approximately 1¼" diameter
1 Felt washer, outside diameter to fit inside of bottle cap
1 Piece sheet brass, circular, diameter ⅛" less than inside of bottle cap
1 Piece thin cardboard, circular, 3⅛" diameter
2 Machine screws, FH, brass, 6–32, ¾" long
5 Machine screw nuts, hexagon, brass, 6–32
1 Machine screw, RH, brass, 4–40, ¼" long
2 Machine screw nuts, hexagon, brass, 4–40
1 Machine screw, RH, steel, 6–32, ½" long
1 Piece carbon rod (removed from an old dry cell)

Drill the strip of sheet metal as shown in Drawing 12 and bend it to form a ring 3" in diameter. Solder the

◆ 11. The Carbon Microphone.

two ends together where they overlap. Drill ⅛" holes through the center of the brass disk and the circular piece of cardboard. Secure the brass disk to

SECTION VIEW

— METAL RING
— CARDBOARD DISK
— FELT WASHER
— METAL BOTTLE CAP
— SHEET BRASS DISK
— CARBON GRANULES
— TERMINAL SCREW
— WOOD BASE

BACK VIEW

CONNECT TO SCREW IN CARDBOARD DISK
BOTTLE CAP
SOLDER

9 1/2"
1/4"   1/4"
5/32" DRILL   5/32" DRILL   1/2"

SHEET STEEL OR BRASS STRIP FOR FORMING METAL RING

MICROPHONE
SECONDARY COIL
PRIMARY COIL
DRY CELLS
HEADPHONES

A STEPDOWN TRANSFORMER IN A MICROPHONE CIRCUIT

1/8" DRILL

SHEET BRASS DISK
(SEE TEXT FOR SIZE)

7/8"

FELT WASHER
(SEE TEXT FOR SIZE)

◆ 12. Drawing of the Carbon Microphone

the cardboard with the 4–40 machine screw and hexagon nut. Glue the felt washer to the brass disk so that the head of the brass machine screw is exactly in the center of the washer.

Crush the carbon rod into small pieces about $1/16''$ in diameter. For best results the broken pieces of carbon should be screened through a piece of window screen. Fill the bottle cap about three-fourths full with the carbon granules. Cement the cardboard circle to the bottle cap, making cer-

tain that the felt washer fits snugly inside the bottle cap. Cement the cardboard circle containing the bottle cap to the metal ring. Trim the cardboard to the same size as the metal ring after the cement has set.

Drill a $5/32''$ hole through the center of the wood base and secure the metal ring to it with a 6–32 machine screw. Drill two $5/32''$ holes in the wood base and place flathead machine screws in them to serve as terminals. Solder a piece of No. 30 magnet wire to the

13. The microphone connected to a transformer and a pair of earphones.

back of the bottle cap and connect the opposite end to one of the terminal screws. Connect another piece of No. 30 wire to the screw in the center of the cardboard and connect the opposite end to the remaining terminal screw. The microphone is now ready to operate.

A simple circuit for a microphone may be made by connecting the microphone in series with two dry cells and a pair of headphones. A much improved circuit, shown in Photograph 13, may be made by using the transformer which is described in Unit 17. This circuit makes the transformer step up the varying voltages caused by the microphone, so the sound in the headphones is increased many times. With two microphones and two sets of headphones a complete telephone system may be connected together.

REVIEW QUESTIONS

1. Who invented the telephone?
2. How is sound transmitted?
3. What are audio frequencies?
4. Name the principal parts of a telephone transmitter.
5. Explain how the carbon granules in a microphone produce a varying electric current.
6. Name the principal parts of a modern handset telephone receiver.
7. Explain how the diaphragm of a telephone receiver produces sound.
8. Draw a simple telephone circuit showing the receiver and transmitter.
9. Why is the transformer used?
10. When two telephones are a long distance apart, what must be used to increase the signal strength?

UNIT 25
RECEIVING RADIO WAVES

Radio Frequencies

A radio receiver is a standard article in almost every home. In addition to its use in the home, it is also used to provide communication between ships at sea, to control airplanes, to guide air missiles, and for many other purposes. Radio signals cannot be seen but are being sent out in every direction by many types of radio stations. These radio signals are called *radio waves.*

Radio waves are produced by alternating current that is changing directions of flow very rapidly. We learned that audio frequencies range from 20 cycles per second to 20,000 cycles per second. These are the frequencies that are used to produce sound. Radio waves are made up of alternating current that has a frequency that is greater than 20,000 cycles per second. There are a great many radio waves; some have a frequency as high as 300 million cycles per second or more. Radio broadcasting stations that are received by a standard broadcast receiver have frequencies from 535,000 cycles per second to 1,605,000 cycles per second.

Because radio frequencies have such a large number of cycles per second it is usual to express the frequency in *kilocycles* per second. *Kilo* means one thousand. A broadcast station that states that it is operating on a frequency of 600 kilocycles means that its frequency is 600,000 cycles per second.

Courtesy National Broadcasting Co.

◆ 14. These are the transmitting towers of the NBC 50,000-watt station WRCA, Port Washington, Long Island.

ANTENNA

This symbol may be used for any antenna.

◆ 15. Radio waves leave the transmitting antenna going out in every direction.

Sending Out Radio Waves

When very rapid alternating currents, called *radio frequencies,* flow through a wire they tend to leave the wire and to start traveling through space. They go out in every direction.

At a broadcast station a large transmitter is used to generate radio-frequency waves. The transmitter is connected to a tower called an *antenna.* The radio waves flow up the antenna and leave it to go out into the air. See Illustration 15.

Some waves follow the ground and are called *ground waves.* The ground waves do not go very far and soon become too weak to be received. Some radio waves go up into the sky; they are called *sky waves.* The sky waves may go straight out into space and

become lost. Other waves hit a layer of electrified particles called the *Heaviside layer.* The Heaviside layer acts like a mirror reflecting the waves back to the earth. See Illustration 16. It is because of the Heaviside layer that radio signals can be received many thousands of miles away from the transmitter. The Heaviside layer varies in height above the earth from 50 to 200 miles.

Radio waves travel at the speed of light, 186,000 miles per second. At this speed, signals are received almost instantly after being sent out.

Putting the Sound with the Radio Waves

When we tune a radio receiver to a broadcast station we hear the sound of the announcer or music. The sound could not be heard very far if the radio waves were not used to carry it through the air.

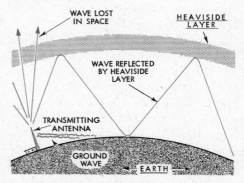

◆ 16. Radio waves go out from the transmitter in all directions. Ground waves follow the ground. Some sky waves are lost in space. Other sky waves hit the Heaviside layer and are reflected back to earth. Waves may be reflected back and forth between the Heaviside layer and the earth so that they sometimes travel very long distances.

◆ 17. This block diagram of a transmitter shows how the audio frequencies are combined with the radio-frequency carrier wave.

A microphone similar to the telephone microphone is used in the broadcast station to pick up the sound of the announcer's voice or the music. This voice or music is the audio frequency that we hear when we turn on a radio receiver.

The microphone changes the sound vibrations into a varying electric current. An amplifier is then used to increase the strength of the sound frequencies. After the amplifier makes the audio waves stronger they are combined with the radio waves by the transmitter. The radio-frequency wave being produced by the transmitter is called a *carrier wave* because it carries the audio frequencies with it. Diagram 17 shows what happens when the sound waves are combined with the radio waves. When the audio-fre-

quency waves combine with the radio-frequency wave, at the transmitter, the radio-frequency wave is said to be *modulated*. The purpose of a radio receiver is to tune in on the radio waves and then separate the sound so that it can be heard through the loudspeaker.

Amplitude Modulation

If the voltage or current of the radio frequency waves are varied when modulated by the sound wave, we say that the amplitude of the radio waves are changed. This varying of the amplitude of the radio frequency is called *amplitude modulation* as illustrated by the modulated radio frequency wave in Drawing 18. Amplitude modulation is often abbreviated as *AM* and it is the type of modulation used for standard broadcasting stations.

UNMODULATED RADIO FREQUENCY CARRIER

AUDIO-FREQUENCY MODULATED VOLTAGE

AMPLITUDE MODULATED CARRIER

UNMODULATED RADIO FREQUENCY CARRIER

AUDIO-FREQUENCY MODULATED VOLTAGE

FREQUENCY MODULATED CARRIER

◆ 18. Graphic representation of Amplitude Modulation. At top is the carrier wave of the transmitter. The audio wave from a microphone is imposed on the carrier and the two combine to produce the modulated carrier wave shown at the bottom.

◆ 19. Graphic representation of Frequency Modulation. When the audio frequency modulating signal is imposed on the carrier, the frequency of the carrier signal increases or decreases according to the amplitude and polarity of the audio wave.

Frequency Modulation

One other method of modulation called frequency modulation (FM) is used for broadcasting the audio portion of a television signal and also on FM broadcast stations. In frequency modulation the audio or sound is superimposed on the carrier by varying the frequency of the carrier. When the modulated signal is applied to the carrier wave, the frequency of the carrier is increased during one half cycle of the modulated signal and decreased during the other half cycle of the opposite polarity, Drawing 19. The amplitude of the carrier remains the same during modulation and the sound or audio is represented by the change in frequency of the carrier. One advantage of FM broadcasting is that static or noises do not affect the carrier and thus do not interfere with the signal.

Receiving Radio Waves

To receive radio waves it is necessary to have a radio receiver that will tune in the desired stations. Radio receivers use either an outside antenna wire or a wire inside of the cabinet for the antenna. If the receiver is a long distance from the transmitter, an outside wire antenna that has been raised above the housetops will help bring in the waves.

When the radio waves hit the receiver antenna a very weak current will begin to flow in the antenna wire. Since there are a great many stations all sending out radio signals, a number of different radio-frequency currents can be coming in contact with the receiving antenna at the same time. It then becomes necessary to be able to select only one station at a time. A *tuner* is used in the receiver to tune in

◆ 20. A coil with a slider may be used to tune a radio receiver.

each of the different stations. When we turn the dial of a radio receiver, we are adjusting the tuner to the station that we wish to hear.

The Ground System

The tuner of a radio receiver is connected to the antenna and also to the ground. The ground may be a wire connected to a water pipe or sometimes to the metal frame of the radio receiver. Every electrical circuit requires two paths for the current to flow through. In a radio signal the air is one path, and the ground is the other path.

Tuning with a Coil

The purpose of the tuner is to select the station that is sending out radio waves on a fixed frequency. The tuner must select one frequency and not permit any of the other signals to be heard in the receiver.

One method of making a tuner is to use a coil of wire with a slider that comes in contact with each of the turns on the coil, as shown in Illustration 20. One end of the coil is connected to the antenna, and the ground is connected to the slider. By moving the slider, the length of the coil of wire between the antenna and ground can be changed. When the radio waves strike the antenna a current starts to flow down the antenna and through the coil to ground. The alternating current of the radio waves will flow first in one direction and then in the other direction, as shown in Illustrations 21 and 22. This current is a flow of electrons in the coil, and the more turns of wire used on the coil the longer it will take the electrons to flow through the coil.

When the slider is moved so that only a few turns of wire are connected between the antenna and ground, the electrons can flow through the coil in one direction and then back in the other direction in a very short time.

After the electrons flow through the coil and back again another radio wave strikes the antenna. If this radio wave is in step with the current flowing in the coil, the second wave will start more electrons flowing at the same time that the electrons in the coil are ready to start back again. The coil of wires is then in tune with the radio wave.

The other radio waves that strike the antenna will not be in step with the electron flow in the coil, and they will not be able to flow in the coil. These unwanted radio signals are not accepted by the tuner.

A large number of turns of wire will tune to a low frequency because it takes longer for the electrons to flow through the coil. A small number of

◆ 21. Radio waves hit the antenna and start electrons flowing through coil to ground.

◆ 22. When the alternating current of the radio waves changes direction the electrons flow from ground to antenna.

turns of wire tune to a high frequency. See Illustrations 23 and 24. When the coil is tuned to a particular frequency it is said to be in *resonance* with that frequency.

Tuning with a Variable Capacitor

Another method of tuning a radio receiver is to use a coil of wire with a *variable capacitor* connected across each end of the coil. (*Capacitors* were formerly called *condensers* and the term is still sometimes used.) A variable capacitor consists of a group of

metal plates all joined together, called the *stator* plates, and another group of plates all joined together by a shaft so that they can be rotated, called the *rotor* plates. See Illustration 25. The rotor plates slide inside the stator plates without touching each other. Air separates the rotor plates from the stator plates. The variable capacitor has the same effect in tuning the circuit as changing the number of turns on a coil. See Illustrations 26, 27, and 28.

◆ 23. The tuner receives low-frequency stations when there are many turns of wire in the coil between the antenna and ground.

◆ 24. The tuner receives higher frequency stations when there are very few turns between the antenna and ground.

◆ 25. Three kinds of variable capacitors are shown here. They were formerly called condensers.

The capacitor acts like a storage place for electrons. It can store either a few electrons or many electrons. When the rotor is turned so that all of the plates are inside of the stator plates the capacitor is able to store more electrons than when it is opened.

When the capacitor is closed and stores lots of electrons, the circuit acts like a coil with many turns of wire. It then tunes to a low frequency. See Illustration 27. If the capacitor is opened and the plates are separated, very few electrons are stored. The tuner will now receive higher frequency signals because there will not be as many electrons to flow through the circuit. Each movement of the capacitor tunes the coil to a new frequency.

CLOSED CAPACITOR HAS LARGE PLATE AREA. TUNES TO LOW FREQUENCY

◆ 27. When the variable capacitor is almost closed it stores lots of electrons and tunes to a low frequency. The frequency is determined by the time it takes for all of the electrons to flow from one side of the capacitor through the coil to the other side of the capacitor and then back again.

STATOR PLATES
ROTOR PLATES
SYMBOLS
COIL   SHAFT

◆ 26. Coil and variable capacitor that are used as a radio tuner.

OPEN CAPACITOR HAS SMALL PLATE AREA. TUNES TO HIGH FREQUENCY

◆ 28. When the capacitor is opened it stores few electrons. This circuit tunes to a higher frequency.

Construction of a Capacitor

We have briefly discussed the use of variable capacitors in tuning circuits, but since capacitors are so very important in all phases of electronics, a more complete discussion is given. A capacitor consists of two or more metal plates which have been placed close to each other as shown in Figure 29. The plates do not touch each other, and they are separated by air or some other insulating material called the "dielectric". If a battery is connected across the plates as in Figure 30 electrons will flow onto plate "A" which is connected to the negative terminal of the battery. The electrons on plate "B" will be repelled by the electrons on plate "A". Thus the electrons on plate "B" will flow toward the positive terminal of the battery. This electrons movement will stop when the charge or electromotive force between the plates is equal to the electromotive force of the battery.

Now if the battery is disconnected plate "A" has a negative charge and plate "B" with a shortage of electrons will have a positive charge. If the wires from the two plates are touched together the electrons on plate "A" will flow to plate "B" until both plates

have an equal number of electrons. The plates are said to be neutral and the capacitor is then discharged.

◆ 29. An uncharged capacitor has an equal amount of positive and negative charges on each plate. The plates are separated by an air dielectric.

◆ 30. When the capacitor is charged, plate A has a surplus of electrons. Plate B is positive since it has a deficiency of electrons.

◆ 31. If the plates are connected by a wire, electrons will flow from plate A to plate B until the charge is equal.

VARIABLE CAPACITOR

The curved line represents the moving element of a variable capacitor.

GANG-TUNING CAPACITOR

A dash line is used to indicate that there is a mechanical connection.

◆ 32. Paper capacitors are made of alternate layers of paper and foil.

Determining the Capacitance of a Capacitor

We have learned that a capacitor can store electricity. Its storing capacity depends upon (1) the area of the plates, (2) the dielectric of the insulating material, and (3) the distance that the plates are apart.

In capacitors using paper as a dielectric, two sheets of metal foil are rolled together with the paper placed between the metal plates as in Figure 32. The longer and the wider the metal foil the greater the area of the two plates. By having a large area for the plates they will be able to store more electrons and thus produce a ca-

pacitor with ability to hold more electrons. See Figure 33.

The insulating material such as the paper has what is known as a dielectric constant. Air is said to have a dielectric constant of 1 and other materials are compared with air. For example, paper has a dielectric constant of about 3 depending upon the type and the thickness of the paper. A capacitor with paper as a dielectric will then have 3 times more capacitance than a capacitor with air as the dielectric. Of course, this is assuming that the distance between the plates of the paper capacitor and the air capacitor were exactly the same.

The closer the plates are to each other, the more effect the charge on one plate will have on the other plate, Figure 34. This means that the closer the plates are together the greater the capacitance of the capacitor.

The Unit of Capacitance

The fundamental unit of capacitance is the *farad*. For most practical purposes the farad is too large a unit, so that, usually capacitors are measured in *micro-farads* or *micro-micro-farads*. Microfarad means one millionth of a farad and it is abbreviated μf. Micro microfarad means one millionth of a microfarad and it is abbreviated $\mu\mu$f.

SMALL CAPACITANCE   LARGE CAPACITANCE

◆ 33. If the area of the plates of a capacitor is increased, the capacitance is increased, providing the dielectric and distance between the plates remain the same.

Ⓐ LARGE CAPACITANCE   Ⓑ SMALL CAPACITANCE

◆ 34. The closer the surface of the plates are in a capacitor, the greater the capacitance, if the plate area and the dielectric are the same.

◆ 35. Fixed capacitors come in various sizes and voltage ratings. The two capacitors on the left are of the plastic type. The upper right is a mica capacitor. The capacitor on the lower right is a ceramic type.

Types of Capacitors

Capacitors are called either fixed or variable capacitors. A variable capacitor used to tune broadcast receivers is usually a .00035 microfarad. This same capacitor in micro microfarads would be a 350 micromicrofarad capacitor. This means when the rotor plates are completely inside of a stator plate it has a capacitance of 350 micromicrofarads. When the rotor plates are turned so that they are all out of the stator plates, the capacitance should be about zero.

Fixed ceramic capacitors using titanium dioxide for the dielectric are fast becoming one of the most popular type capacitors because they are small and are not easily affected by temperature changes. Mica also is a very useful dielectric and mica capacitors are usually molded in a plastic case.

Electrolytic Capacitors

A very common capacitor used in electronic circuits is the electrolytic capacitor. Electrolytic capacitors provide a very large capacitance in a small container. It is possible to have a 500 microfarad electrolytic capacitor in a can only one inch in diameter and two inches long. These capacitors may be either of the wet or dry type.

It is extremely important to observe the polarity markings of electrolytic capacitors when wiring them in circuits. If the capacitor is connected backwards so that the polarity is reversed the capacitor will be ruined and the circuit will be shorted.

Breakdown Voltage

Capacitors are made to withstand certain voltages. To exceed this voltage rating ruins the capacitor. This voltage rating, called the *working voltage,* is marked on the capacitor or is shown in the color coding.

FIXED
CAPACITOR

The curved line indicates the outside electrode in fixed paper or ceramic capacitors and the negative electrode of an electrolytic capacitor.

◆ 36. Ceramic capacitors are usually color coded with bands like resistors but smaller ones may use dots. Temperature is very important in a ceramic capacitor and is given first.

◆ 37. The color code on mica capacitors shows the information indicated.

Color Coding Capacitors

Paper and electrolytic capacitors are usually labeled to indicate their capacitance. Mica and ceramic capacitors use either a labeled marking or a color coding. The color code gives the capacitance in micro-micro-farads. Ceramic capacitors use a band marking system as in Figure 36. Mica capacitors use a six dot system as in Figure 37.

Connecting Capacitors in Parallel

To increase the capacitance in a circuit, it is possible to connect capacitors in parallel. Placing capacitors in parallel is the same as increasing the area of the plates in a capacitor as illustrated in Figure 38.

If a circuit needs additional capacitance, several capacitors may be connected in parallel. For example, when two capacitors of 10 microfarads and 12 microfarads are connected in parallel, the total capacitance is 22 microfarads.

The formula for capacitances connected in parallel is:

$$C_{\text{TOTAL}} = C_1 + C_2 + C_3 + \text{etc.}$$

Connecting Capacitors in Series

When capacitors are connected in series, the total capacitance in the circuit is decreased. Capacitors connected

Color Code for Ceramic Capacitors

Color	Significant Figure	Decimal Multiplier	Capacitance Tolerance More than 10μμfd (in %)	Capacitance Tolerance Less than 10μμfd (in μμfd.)	Temp. Coeff. deg. C.
Black	0	1	± 20	2.0	0
Brown	1	10	± 1		−30
Red	2	100	± 2		−80
Orange	3	1000			−150
Yellow	4				−220
Green	5		± 5	0.5	−330
Blue	6				−470
Violet	7				−750
Gray	8	0.01		0.25	30
White	9	0.1	± 10	1.0	500

Capacitor Color Code

Color	Significant Figure	Decimal Multiplier	Tolerance (%)	Voltage Rating
Black	0	1	—	—
Brown	1	10	1	100
Red	2	100	2	200
Orange	3	1000	3	300
Yellow	4	10,000	4	400
Green	5	100,000	5	500
Blue	6	1,000,000	6	600
Violet	7	10,000,000	7	700
Gray	8	100,000,000	8	800
White	9	1,000,000,000	9	900
Gold	—	0.1	5	1000
Silver	—	0.01	10	2000
No color	—	—	20	500

◆ 38. When capacitors are connected in parallel it has the effect of increasing the plate area and the total capacitance is increased.

in series provide the same effect increasing the spacing between the plates of the capacitor as shown in Figure 39.

The formula for capacitances in series is:

$$\frac{1}{C_{TOTAL}} = \frac{1}{C_1} + \frac{1}{C_2} + \frac{1}{C_3} + \text{etc.}$$

$$C_{TOTAL} = \frac{1}{\dfrac{1}{C_1} + \dfrac{1}{C_2} + \dfrac{1}{C_3} + \text{etc.}}$$

If two capacitors of the same capacitance are connected in series, the total capacitance in the circuit is cut in half. When two 10 microfarad capacitors are in series, the total capacitance is then

equal to 5 microfarads.

Many times in high voltage circuits the voltage ratings of the capacitors are not great enough for the circuit. In such instances it is possible to place capacitors in series to obtain the necessary voltage rating. For example, if the output voltage of a circuit is 700 volts and if a 10 microfarad capacitor having a voltage rating of 450 volts is available, it could not be used in the circuit. Two such capacitors could, however, be connected in series so that the voltage rating would be increased to 900 volts. The total capacitance in the circuit with the two 10 microfarad capacitors in series would then be 5 microfarads, Figure 40.

The Effect of Alternating Current on a Capacitor

When a direct current is applied to a capacitor, current stops flowing when the plates of the capacitor become fully charged. Since the dielectric material is an insulator it prevents further current from flowing through the circuit. If instead of D.C. we apply an alternating current to the plates of a capacitor, current will flow in the circuit. With A.C. the electrons flow first in one di-

◆ 39. Capacitors connected in series have the same effect as increasing the distance between the plates and capacitance is decreased.

◆ 40. When capacitors are connected in series the voltage rating is equal to the sum of the working voltages of the capacitors.

◆ 41. When alternating current is applied to a capacitor, the capacitor will charge during the first half cycle as shown in the top drawing. When the current reverses and the next half cycle flows, the capacitor discharges and is recharged to the opposite polarity as shown in the bottom drawing. This charging and discharging continues as long as A.C. is applied.

rection and then reverse and flow in the opposite direction. Figure 41 shows that electrons flow toward one plate of the capacitor during one half of the alternating current cycle and then when the current reverses they flow toward the other plate of the capacitor. Thus, electrons go back and forth in the circuit even though they do not flow directly through the capacitor. As a result of this current flow, it is customary, when using alternating current, to say that current flows through the capacitor.

Capacitive Reactance

When a capacitor is placed in an A.C. circuit it offers opposition to the current flow much like a resistor. The capacitor creates a counter-electromotive force that opposes the flow of cur-

rent in the circuit. A small capacitance will have much more opposition to current flow than a large capacitance. Also, when a low frequency is applied to a capacitor it will have a greater opposition than when a high frequency is used. Thus, both the value of the capacitor and the frequency determine the amount of current that flows in the circuit.

This opposition to current flow is called capacitive reactance and it is stated in ohms. The amount of capacitive reactance depends upon the value of the capacitor and the frequency of the circuit. The formula for capacitive reactance is:

$$X_c = \frac{1}{2\pi f C}$$

X_c = Capacitive reactance in ohms
f = Frequency in cycles per second
C = Capacitance in farads

Inductance

In the tuner circuit we have learned that by changing the capacitance we can tune the circuit to a different frequency. Another method of selecting the desired frequency would be to change the number of turns on the coil. By changing the turns on the coil we can change its inductance. This is often done with switches or sliders which make contact with turns on the coil. Many of the coils used in tuning electronic circuits are called *"air core coils"* because they have no magnetic material in their centers. Another coil called a *"slug tuned"* type has a metal core which is moved in and out to vary its inductance. The term *inductance* may be defined as the property of a circuit which opposes a change of current through it. The inductance of coils used for tuning radio circuits is usually expressed in terms of *millihenrys,* or *microhenrys. Milli* means one thousandth and *micro* means one millionth. The inductance of the larger coils called "choke coils" that are usually used in power supplies is generally expressed in henrys. The inductance of a coil is determined by:

(1) the diameter of the coil.
(2) the length of the coil
(3) the number of turns of wire
(4) the core

Inductive Reactance

The opposition to current flow through a coil is called inductive reactance and is measured in ohms. The amount of reactance is directly proportional to the frequency and the size of the coil. That is, the higher the frequency, or the larger the coil, the more reactance there will be in the circuit. The formula for inductive reactance is:

$$X_L = 2\pi fL$$

X_L = Inductive reactance in ohms
f = Frequency in cycles per second
L = Inductance in henries

Impedance

When we speak of the *impedance* of a circuit we mean its total resistance to the flow of alternating current. This can consist of the resistance of the coil and its inductive reactance, or a circuit containing capacitive reactance supplied by a capacitor.

◆ **42. An alternating current cycle showing the current lagging behind the voltage.**

◆ **43. Alternating current cycle showing the current leading the voltage.**

When a coil is connected to a source of alternating current, the counter-electromotive force developed within the coil prevents the current from reaching its maximum value instantly. The current is said to "lag" behind the voltage, as shown in Figure 42. When a capacitor is connected to an alternating current supply, an opposite effect occurs. Here the counter-electromotive force developed in the capacitor by the charging current prevents the source voltage from reaching its maximum value until the capacitor is fully charged. The current is then said to "lead" the voltage, as shown in Figure 43. Since the effects of lagging and leading currents tend to neutralize each other when they are equal, they must be considered when determining the total impedance of a circuit. For example, in the circuit shown in Figure 44, a coil and capacitor are connected in series. The coil has a resistance of three ohms and an inductive reactance of eight ohms. The capacitor has a capacitive reactance of four ohms, which

R = 3 OHMS X_L = 8 OHMS

10 V
AC

X_C = 4 OHMS

◆ **44. A coil and capacitor connected to form an impedance circuit. The resistance of the coil, R, is always shown as a separate unit in series with the coil.**

PARALLEL RESONANT
CIRCUIT

SERIES RESONANT
CIRCUIT

◆ **45. Resonant circuits may be either series or parallel. The frequency at which they are resonant is determined by the amount of inductance of the coil and the capacitance. Large inductances and capacitances make the circuit resonant at low frequencies. Small inductances and capacitances tune to high frequencies.**

will cancel four ohms of the inductive reactance and leave a total of four ohms as the effective reactance of the circuit. Substituting the above values in the impedance formula, we find that the total impedance of the circuit is:

$$Z = \sqrt{R^2 + X^2_L}$$
$$= 3^2 + 4^3 = \sqrt{25} = 5 \text{ ohms}$$

Resonance

When an inductance and a capacitor are adjusted so that their reactances are equal, they are said to be in resonance to the frequency of the voltage source to which they are connected. The process of tuning a radio signal from a broadcasting station means that we have adjusted either a capacitance or an inductance so that their reactances are the same. When they are so adjusted the circuit will respond to one frequency and reject all others.

Calculating Resonant Frequency

The frequency of the supply line to which a coil and capacitor will become resonant is governed by the inductance of the coil and the capacitance of the capacitor. This frequency may be calculated by the following formula:

$$F = \frac{1}{6.28 \times \sqrt{LC}}$$

$F =$ Frequency in cycles
$L =$ Inductance in henrys
$C =$ Capacity in farads

Resonant circuits present one of the most interesting phases of our study of electronics, because many of the principles under which they function appear to run contrary to what we have learned about current flow in series and parallel circuits. For example, in Figure 44 the combination of inducance, capacitance, and resistance was calculated to have an impedance of five ohms. Assuming a supply of 10 volts, AC, and substituting Z for R in the Ohm's law formula, $I = \dfrac{E}{Z}$, we find that two amperes would flow in the circuit. Now let us assume that we have replaced the capacitor with one having a reactance of eight ohms. On first thought we might conclude that adding the additional reactance to the circuit would reduce the current flow through it, but if we measured the current flow with an ammeter we would find that rather than decreasing the current flow has increased to 3.3 amperes. When we increased the capacitive reactance to eight ohms we made it equal to the reactance of the coil. Since both units had the same reactance their effects were cancelled, leaving only the three ohm resistance of the coil to determine the current flow.

Resonance experiments at the high frequencies used in radio are often difficult to perform, owing to the lack of adequate measuring equipment. Since the principles of resonance are the same regardless of the frequencies used, we can perform experiments with 60 cycle alternating current which will provide a thorough understanding of what takes place in resonant circuits. To conduct these experiments we will need the following.

- 1 24 volt door chime transformer
- 1 S.P.S.T. toggle switch
- 1 Rheostat, wire wound, 25 to 50 ohms
- 1 Capacitor, non-electrolytic, 10 mfd, 250 volts or higher
- 3 Miniature lamp receptacles
- 3 Pilot lamps, 6-8 volts
- 2 Lbs. magnet wire, 24 ga., enameled covered
- 20 Pieces iron wire, 16 or 18 ga., five inches long
- 1 Coil form (see Figure 46)

The center of the coil form may be made from a piece of one inch wood dowel, drilled out to ¾", or a piece of micarta or brass tubing. If brass tubing is used it should be slotted its full length on one side to prevent eddy currents from being set up in the tube when magnetic lines pass through it.

◆ 46. Details for making coil form.

Series Resonance

Connect the parts as shown in Figure 47. Adjust the rheostat to about its center position, connect the transformer to a 117 volt AC supply and turn on the switch. Place pieces of iron wire in the core center, one by one, until the lamp reaches maximum brilliancy. When further addition of pieces of iron wire to the coil center causes the lamp to get dimmer, the point of resonance will have been reached. The purpose of the rheostat is to prevent excessive voltage from burning out the lamps. It should be adjusted as needed to keep the lamp voltage within safe limits. By moving the iron wires in a group toward and away from the point of resonance we will be duplicating the action of tuning a high frequency ra-

◆ 47. Series resonant circuit.

◆ 48. In a series-resonant circuit, resonance is indicated by high voltage across the terminals of the capacitor and the inductance. As shown above these voltages rise to 132 volts with a line voltage of only 24 volts.

dio signal with a slug-tuned coil, just as it is done in tuning a typical broadcast receiver.

If we connect a 150 volt AC voltmeter across the terminals of the capacitor it will indicate about 132 volts. The voltmeter placed across the terminals of the coil will show the same reading. At this point we may wonder how it is possible to get such high voltage readings when the input voltage is only 24 volts. The explanation lies in the fact that the high voltage readings do not represent the line voltage, but are due to counter electromotive force developed in the coil and capacitor by the current flowing through them. If we calculate the reactance of the 10 μf capacitor with the reactance formula shown in the section on capacitors, we will find that it has a reactance of approximately 265 ohms at 60 cycles. By measuring the resistance of the coil

with an ohmmeter, or calculating it from the amount of wire used, we will get a value of about 52 ohms. We learned that when a circuit is resonant the capacitive reactance and the inductive reactance cancel their effects and leave only the resistance of the circuit to control the amount of current flow. Since we know that the resistance of the coil is 52 ohms and the applied voltage is 24, we can quickly determine by the use of Ohm's law that the current flowing in the circuit will be approximately one-half ampere.

Now, here is where we can account for the high voltage. The reactance of the capacitor has been calculated to be 265 ohms and since at resonance capacitive reactance and inductive reactance are equal, the coil will also have a reactance of 265 ohms. Using Ohm's law again and solving for E, ($E = 265 \times .5 = 132.5$ volts) we find that a current of 0.5 ampere flowing through a reactance of 265 ohms will produce a counter-electromotive force of 132.5 volts. This corresponds very closely to the voltmeter measurement of 132 volts.

If we place separate voltmeters across the coil and capacitor both would indicate the maximum voltage simultaneously. Actually, if the meter pointer could respond to the rise and fall of the voltage and our eyes could follow the meter pointer, we would see each meter register maximum voltage alternately while the other meter showed zero voltage. Although the separate coil and capacitor units show high voltage, their combined effect on the voltage of the circuit is zero. This can be shown by connecting a voltmeter across coil and capacitor and noting the reading. The meter will indicate not the combined voltage of the two units, 264 volts, but only the supply line voltage of 24 volts.

Series resonant circuits should be handled with caution, not only for personal safety, but for the safety of equipment as well. Even moderate voltages such as 117 can rise to the dangerously high levels of 600 to 700 volts under certain conditions of series resonance.

Parallel Resonance

Connect the parts as shown in Figure 49. Adjust the rheostat so that all of the resistance will be in the circuit. This can be adjusted later to provide a safe operating voltage for the light bulbs. Connect the transformer to a 117 volt AC supply and turn on the switch. The light bulb, L_1, and either

◆ **49. Parallel resonant circuit.**

L_2 or L_3 should now light fairly brightly. Place pieces of iron wire in the coil center until L_1 goes out and L_2 and L_3 reach maximum brilliancy. At this point it may be necessary to re-adjust the rheostat. When further addition of pieces of iron wire to the coil center causes L_1 and either L_2 or L_3 to get brighter the point of resonance will have been reached. By moving the iron wires in a group toward and away from the point of resonance, we can duplicate the action of tuning a radio signal as we did in the series resonance experiment.

Unlike a series resonant circuit, the voltage across the coil and capacitor remains constant in a parallel resonant circuit. As we observed when adjusting the parallel circuit, the current from the supply line as indicated by L_1 decreased materially when resonance was reached, yet the current flowing within the circuit increased by a similar ratio. Like the series resonant voltage that is many times greater than the supply line voltage, the large current that flows in a parallel resonant circuit with little assistance from the supply line, may be easily accounted for.

With the circuit in a resonant condition, we will assume that current

◆ 50. In a parallel-resonant circuit, resonance is indicated by a high current flow within the circuit and a small current flow in the supply line. The lamps within the circuit above light up to nearly full brilliancy, yet no visible glow appears in the lamp connected in the supply line.

from the charged capacitor is beginning to flow around the parallel circuit and through the coil, as shown in Figure 51. As the current from the capacitor continues to flow in the coil, its magnetic field continues to expand until the capacitor is completely discharged. At that point the coil's magnetic field begins to collapse. This induces a current in the coil which flows in an opposite direction to charge the capacitor again, as shown in Figure 52. As the capacitor becomes fully charged the action begins all over again. An interesting feature of parallel circuits is that they require little current from the line to keep them functioning. In fact, if it were possible to make a coil

◆ 51. Capacitor discharge in a resonant circuit.   ◆ 52. Capacitor charging in a resonant circuit.

without resistance and a capacitor with a perfect dielectric, current would oscillate back and forth in the circuit indefinitely, once it was given an initial start. As it is, the only current taken from the supply line is just enough to overcome the resistance and capacitance losses in the circuit.

Most radio receivers and transmitters use parallel resonant, circuits for tuning purposes. When used in radio transmitters they are usually called "tank circuits" and are generally connected with heavy copper or silver conductors to keep resistance losses to a minimum.

REVIEW QUESTIONS

1. What are radio frequencies?
2. If a broadcast station states that it is operating on a frequency of 900 kilocycles, what is its frequency in cycles per second?
3. Explain what happens to radio waves when they hit the Heaviside layer.
4. What is the speed of radio waves?
5. Why is a radio-frequency wave sent out by a transmitter called a carrier wave?
6. What is the purpose of a tuner in a radio receiver?
7. Why will a coil with many turns of wire tune to a lower frequency than a coil with a few turns of wire?
8. What separates the rotor plates and the stator plates in a variable capacitor?
9. Why does a variable capacitor that has been closed, so that all of the rotor plates are inside of the stator plates, tune to a lower frequency?
10. What is the unit of measure that is used to indicate the capacitance of capacitors?
11. Why are radio-frequency transformers sometimes used in the tuner circuit?
12. Using radio symbols, draw a diagram showing a radio tuner. The radio tuner should be connected to an antenna and a ground. A variable capacitor should be used to tune the circuit.
13. What is the difference between AM modulations and FM modulations?
14. What is the dielectric in a capacitor?
15. List the factors that determine the capacitance of a capacitor.
16. What is the unit of capacitance?
17. Change .0001 microfarads into micro-microfarads.
18. List several different types of capacitors.
19. What is meant by "working voltage" of a capacitor?
20. If capacitors of .1 microfarads, .5 microfarads and .25 microfarads are connected in parallel, what would the total capacitance be?
21. If two capacitors of 4 microfarads are connected in series, what is the total capacitance?
22. What determines the inductance of a coil?
23. How can you increase the resonant frequency in a circuit with an inductance and a capacitance?

UNIT 26
HEARING THE RADIO SIGNALS

The Purpose of a Radio Receiver

The radio wave sent out by a broadcast station is a high-frequency wave called a carrier wave because it is carrying the voice frequencies with it. These radio-frequency waves are being changed in strength, or modulated, by the audio waves. If we were to connect a pair of earphones across a radio tuner and try to listen to a broadcast station, we could not hear anything. The alternating current of the radio waves is so rapid that they could not be heard. The diaphragm of the earphone could not vibrate at all because the current would be changing directions so rapidly. Some method must be used to change the radio waves into sound waves.

The purpose of a radio receiver is (1) to tune in a radio station, (2) to separate the audio frequencies from the radio frequencies, and (3) to change the electrical audio vibrations into sound vibrations. See Diagram 53.

Using a Semiconductor As a Detector

In listening to standard broadcast signals it is necessary to select the desired radio frequency signal and to change the amplitude modulated radio waves back into sound waves. A device that removes the modulation or audio from the radio frequency signal is called a *detector*. One of the simplest detectors is a semiconductor made of germanium or silicon called a crystal diode. An explanation of the theory of semiconductors is included in the unit on semiconductors. Figure 54 shows the construction of a germanium-

◆ 54. **Construction of a germanium point-contact diode. The diode will permit alternating current to flow through it in one direction, but not in the opposite direction.**

◆ 53. **In this block diagram are illustrated the basic principles of radio receiver functioning.**

RADIO FREQUENCY WAVE IN TUNER

CRYSTAL DIODE

AUDIO FREQUENCY WAVE. THE EARPHONES RESPOND TO THE SHAPE OF THE WAVE "ENVELOPE" SHOWN BY THE COLOR LINE

◆ 55. A simple radio receiver using a diode as a detector. The detector permits the audio signal to be separated from the radio frequency signal.

COIL WINDING

PERMANENT MAGNET

IRON DIAPHRAGM

◆ 56. This cross-section view shows the construction of an earphone.

point-contact diode. Such a diode acts like a one way valve that will permit current to flow freely through it in one direction, but will allow very little current to flow in the opposite direction.

In Figure 55 a tuner consisting of an antenna coil and a variable capacitor are used to select the desired signal. Connected across the tuner is a crystal diode and a pair of earphones. When the modulated radio frequency signal in the tuner circuit is applied to the diode, the diode will permit the alternating current to flow in one direction but not in the other direction. Since the current flow is only in one direction we now have a varying direct current flowing through the earphones. In an amplitude modulated signal the variation in amplitude appears in both the positive and negative portion of the alternating current radio frequency signal. With the diode in the circuit, half of the radio frequency cycle is permitted to flow and as shown in Figure 55 the audio is still with the signal. It

is this audio signal that we wish to hear.

Using the Earphones with the Diode

The earphones are constructed very much like the telephone receiver. See Illustration 56. A permanent magnet is used to provide a pull on the thin metal diaphragm. Two sets of electromagnetic coils are connected so that when a varying current flows through them they can make the diaphragm vibrate.

Without the diode the earphone diaphragm would not be able to react to the very rapid high frequency radio

HEADPHONES

This symbol is the one to use for a double headset.

currents. Now that the diode is in the circuit a varying direct current flows through the earphone coils and this current is always flowing in the same direction even though it is pulsating.

The earphone diaphragm can not vibrate at the speed of the radio frequency portion of the signal but it can react to the variations in amplitude of the signal. As the amplitude of the signal varies the current in the earphone coils vary causing the diaphragm to vibrate. The vibrations produced by the earphones are the same as the audio signal which was made by the sound waves hitting the microphone in the radio broadcasting station.

The Electron Tube Diode

The electron tube, often called a vacuum tube, may also be used as a detector. The simplest electron tube is called a diode which means that it has two basic elements. The two elements, one called the filament and the other called the plate, are sealed in a glass bulb or metal container. The air and

ELECTRON TUBE.

These elements are combined to form the symbol for any electron tube.

DIODE TUBE SYMBOL

◆ 57. A diode electron tube consists of a cathode and a plate. The cathode is often referred to as the filament.

gas is removed from the tube to form a vacuum within the tube. The vacuum is necessary to prevent the filament from burning out, when heated, and also to remove all gases so that the electron flow is not affected.

Thermionic Emission

The filament is made of a thin wire of such material as oxide coated nickel, tungsten, or thoriated tungsten. If a source of electricity is connected to the filament terminals, Figure 57, the filament will become hot and will turn red in color. The red-hot filament releases free electrons which boil off its surface. This releasing of free electrons from the hot surface of the filament is called *thermionic emission*. These electrons leave the filament to form a cloud of electrons around the filament. This is called a "space charge."

The voltage used to heat the filament may be AC or DC. The AC voltage is usually obtained by using a transformer which steps down the AC line voltage to the smaller amount needed by the filament. Direct current for the filament may be supplied from batteries or a power supply. If bat-

◆ 58. Illustration showing the construction of a heater-type filament and cathode.

◆ 59. Schematic drawing of a diode electron tube detector.

teries are used, they are called "A" batteries. Common voltages for the filament are 1.5, 6.3 and 12.6 volts.

Electron Tubes with a Cathode

When using direct current on the filament of a tube the filament will produce a constant emission of electrons, but if alternating current is connected to the filament the electron emission would change with the alternating current. In tubes that are to be used with alternating current on the filaments, an oxide coated sleeve is placed over the filament. See Illustration 58. This covering over the filament is called the cathode.

In tubes with a cathode the filament is called a heater because it heats the cathode. When the cathode gets hot, it starts throwing off electrons and since it is quite massive, the temperature of the cathode does not change with the alternating current. Thus the heater heats the cathode and the cathode emits a steady flow of electrons. The cathode is not considered an additional element in the tube as it does the work of the filament. A lead from the cathode must also be made to one of the prongs in the tube base.

The Diode Electron Tube Detector

The diode electron tube operates much the same as the semiconductor diode in that it rectifies or changes the radio frequency signal into pulsating direct current. Figure 59 illustrates a schematic diagram of a basic circuit using the electron tube as a diode detector. The filament is connected to a low voltage alternating current which heats the cathode and the cathode emits a constant flow of electrons. When the signal in the tuning circuit produces a positive charge on the plate it pulls the negatively charged electrons from the cathode to the plate. These electrons flow through the tuning circuit and return to the cathode through the earphones. When the radio frequency signal in the tuner produces a negative charge on the plate, the plate repels the electrons emitted by the cathode, and no current flows through the earphones. Each time the plate is positive current flows through the earphones and each time the plate is negative no current flows through the earphones.

From this explanation we can see

◆ 60. When the plate is positive, electrons flow from the cathode to the plate.

Plate Current Flow

If we can give the plate a positive charge by connecting it to the positive side of a battery as in Figure 60 the electrons boiling off the cathode will be attracted to the plate. Since the electrons have a negative charge and the plate has a positive charge, a current will flow through the vacuum tube.

Should the battery polarity connected to the plate be reversed so that the plate has a negative charge no current will flow in the tube. When the plate has a negative charge, it will repel the electrons from the cathode. Thus, the vacuum tube will conduct current only when the plate is positive with respect to the cathode. The vacuum tube can conduct current only in one direction and only when the plate has a positive charge. If the plate voltage is increased the plate current will also be increased until the cathode can give up no electrons. When the plate current will not increase, even though the plate voltage is increased the tube has reached its saturation point. See Figure 61.

that the diode tube operates much the same as the semiconductor diode by allowing the current to flow in but one direction through the earphones. The earphones react to the amplitude variations of the pulsating direct current flowing through them. This amplitude change includes the modulation produced at the broadcasting station and thus sound is heard in the earphones.

One disadvantage of the electron tube diode and the semiconductor detectors, is that they cannot increase the strength of the signal. If the signal is not very strong they cannot produce sound through the earphones. The electron tube can be used as a detector, and it also can be used to increase or amplify the strength of the signal. It is often referred to as a valve or control device that enables a very small voltage change to be amplified many times. To provide the power needed for an electron tube to operate as an amplifier, it is necessary to use an outside source of voltage such as a battery, or a power supply that will provide direct current. Voltage applied to the plate is called the "B" supply or the "B" battery.

◆ 61. A curve showing how the plate current increases as the voltage on the plate is increased. When the plate current will not increase, even though the voltage is increased, the tube has reached its saturation point.

It should be noted that the negative side of the battery is connected to the cathode and the positive side is connected to the plate. By having the negative terminal of the battery connected to the cathode the circuit is complete. Electrons flow from the cathode through the tube to the plate and return to the cathode. Should any of these connections be disconnected, the current will stop flowing. In tubes which do not have a cathode the electron return is to the filament.

Construction of a Triode

A simple three-element electron tube is called a *triode*. The triode consists of a filament, a grid, and a plate. See Illustration 62. The filament, located in the center of the tube is made of a thin wire of tungsten that contains a small amount of thorium. Next to the filament is a fine wire in the shape of a coil called the *grid*. The grid is supported by wires, held in the glass stem, so that it does not touch the filament or the plate. The grid is surrounded by a sheet metal rectangle called the *plate*. Some triodes have a cathode between the filament and the grid, Figure 62 and 63.

The Effect of the Grid

When a positive voltage is applied to the plate of an electron tube the plate pulls electrons from the cathode and a current flows through the tube. In a triode tube, the grid is placed between the cathode and the plate so that the electrons must pass through the grid to get to the plate. The spaces between the turns of wire on the grid

◆ 62. A triode tube has a filament, grid, and plate.

◆ 63. This is a cutaway section of a triode electron tube. The grid surrounds the cathode and the plate encloses both the cathode and the grid.

◆ 64. The control-grid controls the plate current flow. The greater the negative charge on the grid, the smaller the plate current flow through the tube.

are so wide that there is practically a free passage of electrons from the cathode to the plate.

If a small negative voltage is placed on the grid, it will repel some of the electrons going to the plate so that the plate current is reduced as illustrated in Figure 64. Since the plate has a fairly large positive charge most of the electrons will be pulled through the spiral grid, but some of them will be repelled by the negative charge on the grid. Should a larger negative charge be placed on the grid it will repel more of the electrons flowing toward the plate, and the plate current will be further reduced. It is usually necessary to keep a negative voltage on the grid. When batteries are used to place a voltage on the grid they are called "C" batteries, and the voltage is called *grid bias.*

The Electron Tube Amplifies a Signal

When an alternating current is applied to the grid of the tube, the grid voltage will vary, and produce a changing plate current in the plate circuit. The plate current wave form is identical to the alternating current wave form applied to the grid, and is also amplified because the plate current is many times larger than the grid current. See Figure 65.

To use the electron tube as an amplifier it is necessary to connect the plate circuit, or the output circuit to a load. This load may be a pair of earphones, a resistor, or a transformer, Figure 65.

A Grid Bias Detector

If the grid were connected directly to the tuner circuit, the alternating current in the tuner would flow onto the grid. The plate current would change very rapidly with alternating current on the grid and this change in

◆ 65. A radio tube amplifies the signal. A very small signal on the grid will produce a large change in plate current.

◆ 66. The "C" battery in this grid bias detector prevents the current from flowing during the negative cycle of the signal.

◆ 67. This is a grid leak and capacitor detector.

the plate current would be so fast that the earphones would not operate. It is necessary to have the tube work like a detector, so that the earphone diaphragm can be made to vibrate with the audio waves.

One method of using a triode tube as a detector is called grid bias detection. In such a detector a "C" battery is connected in the grid circuit as shown in Figure 66. The battery is connected so that the grid has a negative charge and this grid voltage is called "C" bias. Just enough negative voltage is placed on the grid so that when no signal is coming through, very little plate current will flow. As a signal is applied to the tuning circuit, the charge applied to the grid will also vary. During the positive portion of the signal the grid will become less negative and current will flow in the plate circuit. The adding of the positive voltage of the signal to the negative voltage of the "C" battery produces a less negative voltage on the grid.

As the signal changes to the negative

portion of the cycle, the grid gets an increased negative charge and no current flows in the plate circuit. Thus the signal is detected in the plate circuit the same as with the diode detector. This method of detection uses the electron tube as an amplifier.

The Grid Leak Detector

The diode detector and the grid bias detector work very well for strong signals or when an amplifier is used ahead of the detector. A more sensitive detector that gives better results for weak signals is called a grid leak detector. Such a detector uses a capacitor and a resistor connected in parallel, in the grid circuit, as shown in Figure 67. The plate or B voltage for the grid leak detector is from 45 volts to 150 volts, depending upon the type of tube used.

The Purpose of the Grid Capacitor

The capacitor, in the grid circuit has a very small capacitance. Its capacitance is 250 micromicrofarads or .00025

◆ 68. These three drawings illustrate how the grid capacitor affects the electron charge on the grid. During the signal's negative cycle, the electrons on side B are forced onto the grid. When the positive cycle is on side A, the grid collects a few electrons from the cathode.

microfarads. When the negative half cycle of the signal, in the tuning circuit, reaches side *A* of the capacitor in Figure 68, the electrons that were on side *B* are repelled. These electrons leave side *B* and flow on to the grid giving the grid a negative charge. Since the grid is cold there is no way that the electrons can leave the grid.

During the next half cycle of the signal, side *A* of the capacitor receives a positive charge causing the electrons on the grid to flow back toward side *B*. With the electrons leaving the grid, the grid does not have a negative charge; the electrons emitted by the cathode are free to flow toward the positively charged plate. Some of the electrons that flow toward the plate strike the grid and remain on the grid since it has a small positive charge.

As this process continues, the grid gets a greater and greater negative charge, and could become large enough to stop the entire flow of current from the cathode to the plate.

The Purpose of the Grid Resistor

The grid resistor, called the grid leak, has a quite high resistance. Usually a resistor of about two million ohms is used. This is a 2 megohm resistor since *meg* means million. The purpose of the grid leak resistor is to allow some of the electrons that are accumulated on the grid to leak off. By doing this the current flow from the cathode to the plate will continue, but only when permitted by the control grid.

As was stated before, if only the capacitor remains in the circuit the electrons trapped on the grid would soon

◆ 69. The high resistance grid leak permits some of the electrons on the grid to leak off.

stop the current flow in the tube. With the large resistance placed across the capacitor a path is provided so that the electrons can "leak" off and flow away from the grid. When side *A*, of the capacitor has a positive charge, the resistance permits a few electrons from side *B* to flow through.

With the combination of the capacitor and resistor in the circuit we now have a detector in operation. When the grid has a negative charge no current flows in the plate circuit; when the grid has a positive charge, current flows to the plate and through the earphones. The grid leak and capacitor has provided a detector action that makes it possible for the earphones to react to the amplitude of the pulsating direct current. This amplitude variation of the signal contains the audio portion of this signal which we want to hear.

The Regenerative Receiver

The grid leak detector may be made even more sensitive through the use of a plate coil, called a tickler coil. A receiver using a plate coil is said to be a regenerative receiver and this regeneration helps in amplifying the signal.

Figure 70 is a schematic drawing of a basic regenerative detector circuit. To make such a receiver we must wind a third coil for the tuner circuit. This third coil is placed close to the secondary coil and it is connected so that current flowing from the plate must also flow through the coil.

When a radio frequency signal flows in the primary coil, a current is induced into the secondary coil. The sec-

◆ 70. A schematic drawing of a regenerative receiver. The plate, or tickler coil, feeds energy back into the secondary coil. Regeneration is controlled with the potentiometer.

ondary coil applies the signal to the grid circuit, and, due to the detector action of the grid leak, a pulsating direct current flows in the plate circuit. The plate coil is coupled to the secondary coil so that the magnetic field of the plate coil induces a current into the secondary coil. We now have the energy of the plate circuit fed back into the tuning circuit. Since the variations in the plate circuit are the same as those in the secondary coil, the two currents are in step with one another. Thus, the energy fed back into the secondary coil is increased, and the signal is made stronger.

Controlling the Regeneration

When the energy of the plate circuit is coupled back into the grid circuit, the electron flow may be built up to such an extent that the receiver becomes a transmitter. We call this regenerative circuit an oscillator, as it is oscillating or generating, a radio wave. The signal may be picked up and heard on other receivers. These signals sound like a whistle or howl in the receiver.

In the regenerative receiver such oscillations can be heard in the earphones. These whistles and howls interfere with the ability to hear the desired audio signal and, therefore, must be controlled.

One method of controlling the regeneration, or feed back, is to connect a potentiometer across the plate coil as in Figure 70. Now the current flow has two paths to follow. Part of the current flows through the plate coil; and part of the current flows through the resistor. By adjusting the potentiometer so that just the correct amount flows through the coil, regeneration is controlled.

For best results with a regenerative receiver, the potentiometer should be turned until the signal is loudest and just before a whistle is heard in the phones. When the set starts to oscillate and the whistle is heard, turn the potentiometer back until only the signal can be heard.

INTERESTING THINGS TO DO

1. Making a Crystal Diode Radio Receiver.

Materials required:

1 Piece wood, ½″ x 4½″ x 4½″
1 Piece wood, ½″ x 1″ x 3½″
1 Spool wire, enamel-covered, No. 24
1 Piece spring brass, ⅜″ x 4⅜″, 26 gage
1 Piece tubing, brass, ¼″ outside diameter (OD), ¾″ long
3 Spring clips, Fahnestock, ¾″ long
3 Wood screws, RH, steel, ⅜″–6
1 Wood screw, RH, steel, 1¼″–6
1 Washer, brass, No. 6
1 Crystal diode, germanium

Drill a small hole partly through the small wood block ¼″ from one end and insert one end of the spool of wire in the hole to hold it in place. Wind 100 turns of wire on the block and secure the other end of the wire by drilling a small hole through the edge of the wood block and passing the wire through it. Shellac or lacquer three sides of the completed coil, but do not lacquer the side on which the slider is to bear. Glue the coil to the wood base.

◆ 71. Crystal Diode Radio Receiver.

Lay out and drill the piece of spring brass as shown on Drawing 71 and bend it to the shape shown to serve as the contact lever. Secure the contact lever to the wood base with the piece of brass tubing, washer, and long wood screw so that the pointed end will make an arc across the flat side of the

◆ **72. Drawing of crystal diode radio receiver.**

coil. Bear down slightly on the pointed end of the contact lever and move it back and forth across the coil several times to remove the enamel covering from the wire and to permit the lever to make contact with the wire. Secure the Fahnestock clips to the wood base with wood screws and make the connections shown on the drawing. Connect the crystal diode between the antenna clip and one of the phone clips, as shown on the drawing.

Connect a pair of headphones and antenna and ground leads to the proper clips and you should be able to tune in a nearby broadcasting station by moving the contact lever across the coil. A ground connection is usually made by attaching a piece of copper wire to a water pipe and connecting the other end to the "ground" connection on the receiver. The best length of antenna can be determined by trial

A long antenna will permit the receiver to pick up more stations, but they will be difficult to separate. Choose a length for the antenna that will permit you to receive the largest number of radio stations with little or no interference between them.

2. Capacitor-Tuned Crystal Receiver.

Materials required:

1 Piece wood, 3″ x 5″
1 Variable capacitor, .000365 μf
1 Spool magnet wire, enamel-covered, No. 28
1 Cardboard form, 1″ diameter, 3″ long
1 Crystal detector, cat whisker type
1 Crystal
4 Fahnestock clips

Drill four $\frac{1}{16}$″ holes about $\frac{1}{4}$″ apart and $\frac{1}{4}$″ from one end of the tubing, as shown on Drawing 74. Drill another $\frac{1}{16}$″ hole $\frac{1}{2}$″ from the same end of the tubing and insert one end of the magnet wire through the hole and out

♦ 73. Capacitor-tuned crystal receiver

through one of the lower holes to hold the wire firmly in place. Wind 100 turns of wire on the cardboard tubing. Drill a $\frac{1}{16}''$ hole close to the winding, pass the end of the winding through the hole, and secure it to one of the holes at the end of the tubing. Drill another $\frac{1}{16}''$ hole $\frac{1}{8}''$ above the first winding and wind 30 turns of wire on the form to serve as the primary winding.

Wind the primary winding in the same direction as the larger coil was wound. Secure the end of the coil in the same manner as the end of the first coil was secured. Cut a circle of wood so that it will fit into the terminal end of the coil and glue it in place. Secure the coil to the wood base with a wood screw. Secure the detector stand and Fahnestock clips to the wood base and connect the parts together as shown in the schematic diagram, Drawing 74. Instructions on the proper antenna and ground to use with a crystal receiver are given in the section describing the crystal diode receiving set. After a radio station has been tuned in on the receiver the most sensitive spot on the crystal may be found by moving the adjustable arm with the "cat whisker" across the crystal.

SECONDARY COIL
CRYSTAL DETECTOR
HEADPHONES
VARIABLE CAPACITOR
PRIMARY COIL

WIRING DIAGRAM

POTENTIOMETER

The potentiometer symbol shows three terminals.

CARDBOARD TUBING

PRIMARY COIL
WIND 30 TURNS OF
NO. 28 ENAMEL-COVERED
WIRE

SECONDARY COIL
WIND 100 TURNS OF
NO. 28 ENAMEL-COVERED
WIRE

1"

3"
1/8"
1/2"

SECONDARY COIL LEADS
PRIMARY COIL LEADS

◆ 74. Drawing for capacitor-tuned crystal set.

◆ 75. One-tube regenerative receiver

3. One-Tube Regenerative Receiver.
Materials required:

1 Antenna coil (see construction details in tuned crystal receiver, Drawing 74
1 Variable capacitor, .000365 μf (C_1)
6 Fahnestock clips
1 Fixed capacitor, mica, .00025 μf (C_2)
1 Resistor, 2,000,000 ohms, ½-watt (R_1)
1 Potentiometer, 10,000 ohms (R_2)
1 6J5 tube
1 Octal tube socket
1 Piece sheet steel, 4" x 7", 20 gage
1 Piece masonite, ⅛" x 1" x 4"
1 Rubber grommet, ¼"
1 Rubber grommet, ⅜"
2 Pointer knobs

Lay out the piece of sheet steel and drill holes where shown on Drawing

76. Bend the two ends of the sheet metal to a 90° angle to form the ends of the chassis. Secure the capacitor and coil to the top of the chassis in the approximate positions shown. Starting at the bottom end of the coil, count 30 turns of wire upward and solder a connection for the antenna. Secure the potentiometer in the ⅜" hole in the front end of the chassis. Make a terminal strip with a piece of masonite and Fahnestock clips and secure it to the back of the chassis. Wire the receiver as shown in the schematic diagram.

POTENTIOMETER

REGENERATION COIL

GRID RESISTOR

R_1

6J5

GRID CAPACITOR

C_2

VARIABLE CAPACITOR

C_1

TUNING COIL

CONNECT AT 30 TURNS FROM BOTTOM OF COIL

6.3 V   90 V

WIRING DIAGRAM

◆ 77. Wiring underneath the chassis of the one-tube receiver.

4"

3/8" DRILL   COIL

VARIABLE CAPACITOR

1/4" DRILL   1 1/8"

5/32" DRILL

7"

1"

1"

1 1/8"   3/8" DRILL

3/4"

1 1/2"

CHASSIS LAYOUT

◆ 76. Drawing of one-tube regenerative receiver.

When operating the receiver the potentiometer control knob is turned so the receiver is at the most sensitive point without distorting the signals. If the knob is turned too far the music or speech will become unintelligible and a high-pitched squeal will be heard in the headphones. The best operating point is where the receiver is the most sensitive, yet the music or speech is understood clearly. If the receiver fails to produce a high-pitched squeal at any position of the potentiometer knob, the connections between the primary coil and the potentiometer should be reversed.

This receiver will work satisfactorily with batteries or with either of the power supplies described in Unit 29 of this book.

REVIEW QUESTIONS

1. Name the three main purposes of a radio receiver.
2. What is a detector?
3. What is the function of a diode in a detector circuit?
4. What kind of current flows through the earphones of a detector circuit?

5. List the two elements in a diode electron tube.

6. Why is a vacuum necessary in an electron tube.

7. What is the purpose of the getter?

8. Explain how a cathode functions in an electron tube.

9. Name the three elements in a triode tube.

10. How does the grid control the plate current?

11. How does an electron tube amplify the signal?

12. How does the diode detector differ from the grid bias detector?

13. Name the purpose of the following batteries—"A" battery, "B" battery, "C" battery.

UNIT 27
ELECTRON TUBE AMPLIFIERS

Importance of the Electron Tube as an Amplifier

The most important advantage of an electron tube is its ability to make radio signals stronger. Semiconductors such as germanium and silicon may be used as detectors, but they will not amplify the signal.

In the electron tube, a very weak signal coming into the control grid can produce a much larger variation of the plate current.

Resistance-Coupled Audio Amplifiers

The signals produced by a detector are not very strong. Usually we like to use a loudspeaker, instead of earphones, so that several people can listen to the receiver at the same time. The audio-frequency signal can be made stronger through the use of another electron tube called an *audio-frequency amplifier*.

One method of coupling the detector to an audio amplifier is to use a resistance and capacitor combination

◆ 78. **Resistance coupling used to connect detector to an audio amplifier.**

known as a *resistance-coupling*. Another method of coupling uses a transformer between the detector and the amplifying tube, but it has been almost entirely replaced by resistance coupling. While resistance coupling does not provide an increase in signal strength as transformer coupling does, it has the advantage of providing very good quality audio signals and being much cheaper to use. A typical amplifier resistance-coupled to a detector and using a pentode tube is shown in

◆ **79. This block diagram and schematic diagram show the arrangement of a tuner, detector, and amplifier.**

Figure 79. A pentode tube has five elements consisting of *control grid, screen grid, suppressor grid, plate,* and *cathode,* as shown in Figure 80.

One of the undesirable characteristics of a triode tube is that the grid and the plate can act as a capacitor and interfere with the normal operation of the tube. By inserting another grid, called a *screen grid,* the effect of the capacitance is almost completely eliminated. This beneficial action, however, is offset somewhat by the action of *secondary emission* on the screen grid.

The stream of electrons which flow from the cathode to the plate is known as *primary emission.* Sometimes these electrons strike the plate with such

◆ **80. There are five elements in a pentode tube.**

CATHODE

CONTROL GRID

SCREEN GRID

PLATE

CONTROL GRID

CATHODE

PLATE

SCREEN GRID

HEATER

◆ 81. The tetrode tube has four elements.

ELECTRON FLOW

COUPLING CAPACITOR

AUDIO-FREQUENCY AMPLIFIER

DETECTOR

B+

B+

◆ 82. In resistance coupling, a fixed capacitor is used to couple the detector to the audio-frequency amplifier. Changes in electron-flow from the detector plate provide a variation in electron-flow to the coupling capacitor. The grid of the amplifier tube receives its signal through the coupling capacitor.

force that they dislodge other electrons from it. These electrons moving away from the plate are known as "secondary emission." Since a screen grid has a positive charge it tends to attract some of the secondary-emission electrons. This reduces the normal flow of electrons in the plate circuit. By inserting another grid known as a *suppressor grid,* the undesirable effects of secondary emission are overcome. Since the suppressor grid is connected to the cathode, which gives it a negative charge, it opposes the flow of electrons from the plate to the screen grid. This additional grid provides a tube that is very stable in operation and capable of amplifying a signal many times.

We have learned how a varying voltage on the grid of an electron tube can

cause a varying current to flow in its plate circuit. In a resistance coupled amplifier the varying current flows through a resistor called a *plate-resistor.* This produces a voltage drop across the resistor. The reactance of the coupling capacitor is so low that a large portion of the voltage drop will appear across the grid-resistor. Since the grid and the grid resistor are in series, the varying voltage across the grid resistor will cause the voltage on the grid to vary, which in turn will

INSULATED END BOND

INSULATED TUBE

CARBON   COPPER PIN HEAD

◆ 83. This is a cross-section of a carbon fixed resistor.

OUTPUT TRANSFORMER

AUDIO
AMPLIFIER

◆ 84. Using a cathode resistor and capacitor to place a small negative voltage on the amplifier grid; this prevents distortion of the signal.

cause similar changes in the output circuit of the tube.

Preventing Distortion of the Signal

The signal from the detector can provide a very strong alternating current to the grid of the amplifier tube. With such large variations of grid signal the plate current can be so high that it does not vary exactly like the grid signal. A true signal would not be produced in the loudspeaker. This is called *distortion* of the signal. To prevent this distortion, it is necessary to limit the amount of current that can flow through the tube. A resistor called a *cathode resistor* and a capacitor called a *bypass capacitor* are used for this purpose. They are connected as shown in Figure 84. This makes the grid have a small negative voltage and it is called placing "grid bias" on the tube.

Although most portable receivers use batteries to supply grid bias, practically all receivers that operate from alternating current use a method

known as *self-bias*. If we refer to the diagram in Figure 84, we can see that all of the current that flows in the plate circuit also flows through the cathode resistor. This produces a voltage drop across the resistor, and because the grid is connected to the cathode through the coupling resistor, the same voltage will be present at the grid. This is the grid bias, or bias voltage. The method used to supply this voltage is known as "self-bias" because it is produced by the current flowing through the plate circuit of the tube. It should be noted that where a cathode resistor is used, the cathode has a positive polarity only in relation to the polarity of the grid, which is negative. In the cathode-plate circuit the cathode is negative. The capacitor across the cathode resistor acts as a filter to bypass any AC current that might be present so that only DC current will go through the resistor, giving a uniform current flow to the cathode.

Loudspeakers

Loudspeakers are used so that the sound may be heard some distance away from the radio receiver. A cone is used in the loudspeaker to produce sound waves. As the cone moves back

SPEAKER

Letter symbols may be added to identify the kind of speaker.

◆ 85. This is how a permanent-magnet (PM) loudspeaker is constructed.

◆ 86. Connecting an output transformer to a permanent-magnet speaker. The secondary of the transformer connects to the voice coil, audio-frequency current flowing through the voice coil makes the cone move in and out, producing sound vibrations.

and forth, it moves the air in front and in back of it. This movement of air is what makes the sound waves that we hear.

One of the common types of loudspeakers, called a *permanent magnet speaker,* is shown in Figure 85. A small coil of wire wound on a hollow tube is glued to the bottom of the cone. This is called the *voice coil.* The coil is placed so that it can move freely over the pole of a very strong alnico magnet.

A transformer, called an *output transformer,* is used to couple the tube to the speaker (Figure 86). Audio frequency signals flowing from the plate of the amplifier tube induce a voltage in the secondary of the transformer. These current variations flow through the voice coil. The magnetic field created by the voice coil pulls the cone in out of the permanent field of the magnet. As the voice coil moves it also causes the cone to move.

◆ 87. A step-up transformer makes the audio signal stronger.

Uses for Audio Amplifiers

Audio amplifiers have many uses other than in radio receivers. They are used for such purposes as intercommunicating systems, telephone amplifiers, public address systems, and for reproducing high quality music from tape and transcription recorders in the home. For these uses a number of electron tubes may be coupled together to produce the required volume of sound.

High Fidelity Amplifiers

The audible range of sound extends from 20 to 20,000 cycles per second. True high fidelity would require amplifying equipment capable of reproducing faithfully any sound between the lower and upper limits of the audible range. At present the term *high fidelity,* commonly known as *hi-fi,* is accepted to mean the output from any

◆ 89. This is a complete audio amplifier. This type of amplifier can be used as a public address system.

high quality sound equipment. As shown in the block diagram, Figure 90, a hi-fi system is made up of a number of units. Since the output of the whole system can be no better than that of the individual components, each part is usually selected for the greatest possible frequency response.

The radio receiver in a hi-fi system generally includes an F.M. and an A.M. tuner. Tape recordings are often made from the tuners, either directly

◆ 88. Several kinds of electron tubes are shown here; they are designed to serve a variety of special purposes.

◆ 90. Block diagram of a high fidelity sound system.

or through a microphone. The microphone is usually a *crystal, ceramic,* or *dynamic* type. We learned how a crystal microphone works in an earlier chapter. The principle of a ceramic microphone is somewhat similar to that of a crystal microphone in that stresses produced by sound waves on a ceramic material cause a voltage to be generated between its contact strips. A cross sectional view of a dynamic microphone is shown in Figure 91. The moving coil is attached to the micro-

PROTECTIVE SCREEN HOLES DIAPHRAGM
HOLLOW MAGNET
RING MAGNET
MAGNETIC FIELD
COIL

◆ 91. Cross-section of dynamic microphone.

phone diaphragm. Sound waves striking the diaphragm cause the coil to move in a magnetic field. This induces a current in the coil which then flows to the input of an amplifier through a suitable coupling device.

A basic diagram of a tape recorder is shown in Figure 92. The tape used in a recorder consists of a thin plastic strip with a coating of small magnetic particles. The tape passes in front of the poles of an electromagnet known as a *recording head,* which is connected to an amplifier. In an unmagnetized state the magnetic particles on the tape point in random directions. When a signal from an amplifier energizes the recording head the magnetic particles are aligned in the direction of the tape travel and magnetized to varying degrees by the audio signal from the amplifier. The bias signal from the oscillator that is in series with the recording head helps to reduce distortion

◆ 92. Basic diagram of a tape recorder.

and tape noise.

Tape recorders for hi-fi reproduction generally use a head for playback that is similar in construction to the record-

ing head but operates in a different manner. When recording, the recording head magnetizes the tape by induction with an audio signal from an

◆ 93. Tape recorders come in many sizes. The one shown in the photograph is a small battery operated type, used mainly for interviews or taking notes in the field. Since it is generally used for recording voice, its frequency range is limited. The six-inch scale in the foreground shows its small size.

◆ **94. A typical hi-fi turntable.**

amplifier. When the tape is played back, a reverse action takes place. The magnetized tape now induces a signal in the reproducing head as it passes in front of it. This signal is in turn amplified in the same manner as the original recorded signal. Hi-fi tape recorders use separate recording and reproducing heads, but in hand-held tape recorders that are used mainly for voice, one head usually serves both purposes. Tape recorders are equipped with an erasing head energized by a high frequency oscillator, which serves to remove unwanted recordings by demagnetizing the tape.

Turn tables for playing hi-fi records and transcriptions are usually capable of running at speeds of $16\frac{2}{3}$, $33\frac{1}{3}$, 45, and 78 rpm and are available with variations in speed as little as 0.2 percent. A phonograph pick-up or cartridge for reproducing sound from a record is generally of a ceramic, crystal, or magnetic type and operate similarly to microphones using the same elements. Unlike microphones, which operate from pressure of sound on a diaphragm, the force which actuates a pick-up is supplied by a needle which travels in a groove on a record. The output of a pick-up cartridge is frequently very low, so an amplifier called a *pre-amplifier* is often connected between it and the main amplifier to bring the signal up to a higher level.

The range of audio frequencies to which a loudspeaker will respond efficiently is determined to a large extent by the size and construction of its cone. Since a single speaker will not deliver a satisfactory output from a full range of audio frequencies, three speakers with overlapping ranges are usually used with hi-fi equipment. The speaker which handles the high frequencies is

Photo courtesy Electro-Voice, Inc.

◆ 95. An exploded view of a high-fidelity speaker system showing placement of high, middle, and low range speakers. The cross-over networks are shown at the bottom of the cabinet.

Courtesy University Loudspeakers Inc.

◆ 96. A triaxial speaker.

called a *tweeter*. A speaker called a *woofer* reproduces the low frequencies, and a *mid-range* speaker takes care of the frequencies in between. Filters made up of capacitors, choke coils, and resistors, called *cross-over networks*, separate the frequencies and send them to the proper speaker. Three speaker units are often combined in one frame, with two smaller speakers nesting inside the larger cone. This arrangement is known as a *tri-axial* speaker. Although a tri-axial speaker has the advantage of economy, the method of mounting each speaker separately, as shown in Figure 95, is considered to be better for quality reproduction.

The box surrounding a loudspeaker,

known as a *baffle*, plays an important part in its proper operation. You can prove this to yourself by holding an uncovered speaker in your hands while it is playing and noting the harsh, tinny sound it delivers. Next place a temporary baffle with an opening in front of the speaker and you will sense immediately the change to pleasant listening. The purpose of a baffle is to prevent the sound waves from the front of the speaker from canceling those projected from the back of the speaker. This is accomplished by extending the distance of the sound path between the front and back of the speaker by means of a panel or enclosure.

Courtesy Allied Radio Corp.

◆ 97. Stereophonic pickup cartridge.

Stereophonic Reproduction

A phase of hi-fi that recently has come into popular use is known as *stereophonic reproduction,* usually abbreviated *stereo*. Stereo reproduces sound with such realism that the listener has the feeling of being right in the studio or concert hall with the performers. Since it creates the feeling of listening with two ears it is often referred to as *binaural* reproduction. The sounds reaching the ears from two separate speakers are timed slightly different to produce this effect.

Tape recorders for a stereo system have dual recording and reproducing heads to handle double track tape. The pick-up cartridge of a stereo record player usually has a needle which rides in a *V* shaped groove on the record. The sides of the groove have smaller grooves that were cut by a stylus needle at the time the record was made. Each side of the *V* shape groove represents

◆ 98. Diagram showing basic principles of a stereo record pickup. Signals are recorded on opposite sides of groove with slight time lag between the two signals.

← 6 TO 8 FT. →

◆ 99. A stereo speaker system. For the full stereo effect speakers should be placed from 6 to 8 feet apart with the listener in the darker area.

a separate channel. Although stereo pick-ups vary in size and shape, most of them use the basic principle shown in Figure 98. In operation the needle of a stereo pick-up follows the cuttings on the side. The action of the needle is the same as in regular pick-ups. Its movement sets up a small voltage in the crystal, ceramic, or magnetic unit that is being used, from which it goes to a pre-amplifier. Separate input channels are required on stereo amplifiers

to handle the output from dual tape recorders and phonograph pick-ups. Separate loudspeakers are also required, which for best results are usually placed 6 to 8 feet apart.

Radio-Frequency Amplifiers

To increase the radio signals before they reach the detector, an amplifier called a *radio-frequency amplifier* is used. It operates very much like the audio-frequency amplifier except that it amplifies the high-frequency radio signals instead of the low-frequency audio signals. See Diagram 100.

Transformer coupling is usually used to couple the radio-frequency amplifiers together. These transformers are coils like the coils used for the tuner of the detector.

OR

A-F TRANSFORMER (IRON CORE)

A transformer with a magnetic core is represented like this.

RADIO-FREQUENCY SIGNAL

RADIO-FREQUENCY SIGNAL AMPLIFIED

AUDIO-FREQUENCY

AUDIO-FREQUENCY SIGNAL AMPLIFIED

RADIO-FREQUENCY AMPLIFIER

DETECTOR

AUDIO-FREQUENCY AMPLIFIER

◆ 100. This block diagram shows where a radio-frequency amplifier is used in a receiver circuit.

One of the important uses for radio-frequency amplifiers is to improve the tuning of the set. Each radio-frequency amplifier can have its own tuner. A variable capacitor is used to tune the circuit. By tuning the amplifier, the receiver can be made to separate the broadcast stations better. Improving the set so that it can easily separate the stations is called making the set more *selective*.

Usually the variable capacitors are connected together so that the radio-frequency amplifiers and the detector are all tuned at the same time. Variable capacitors that are connected together are called *ganged capacitors*.

INTERESTING THINGS TO DO

1. Two-Tube Radio Receiver.
Materials required:

1 Antenna coil
1 Variable capacitor, .000365 µf (C_1)
1 Fixed capacitor, mica, .00025 µf (C_2)
1 Fixed capacitor, .01 µf (C_3)
1 Fixed capacitor, .001 µf (C_4)
1 Electrolytic capacitor, 25 µf, 50 volt (C_5)
1 Fixed resistor, 2,000,000 ohms, ½-watt (R_1)
1 Fixed resistor, 250,000 ohms, ½-watt (R_2)
1 Fixed resistor, 500,000 ohms, ½-watt (R_3)
1 Fixed resistor, 3,300 ohms, 1-watt (R_4)
1 Potentiometer, 10,000 ohms (R_5)
2 6J5 electron tubes
2 Octal sockets
2 Pointer knobs
1 Piece sheet steel, 6½" x 6½", 20 gage
1 Rubber grommet, ¼"
1 Rubber grommet, ⅜"
1 Piece masonite, ⅛" x 1" x 6"
9 Fahnestock clips

Lay out and drill the piece of sheet steel as shown on Drawing 102. Bend the ends along the broken line to an angle of 90° and mount the tube sockets where shown. Secure the variable capacitor and the antenna coil to the chassis in the approximate positions indicated on the drawing. Place the rubber grommets in the holes in the top of the chassis. Secure the potentiometer in the ⅜" hole in the front end of the chassis.

Mount the Fahnestock clips to the piece of masonite and secure the com-

◆ 101. A two-tube radio receiver using a regenerative detector and a resistance-coupled audio amplifier.

pleted terminal strip to the back end of the chassis. Mark the terminal strip to show two clips for the antenna and ground, two clips for the loudspeaker, two clips for the 6.3 volt filament supply, and three clips for the two + and − connections. Wire the receiver as shown in the schematic diagram. The same type coil is used with this set as was used in the one-tube receiver described in Unit 26 of this book. If you have not previously built that set, refer to its instructions for the correct coil connections and operating procedure. This receiver will operate with the power supply that is described on pages 289 and 290.

SCHEMATIC DIAGRAM

CHASSIS LAYOUT

◆ **102. Drawing of two-tube radio receiver**

REVIEW QUESTIONS

1. Why are audio-frequency amplifiers used?

2. What kind of a transformer is used in a transformer-coupled audio amplifier?

3. Explain why it is important that an electron tube produce a radio signal without distortion.

4. What are the advantages of a resistance-coupled amplifier over the transformer-coupled amplifier?

5. Explain the purpose of the voice coil in a loudspeaker.

6. What is the purpose of the cone in a loudspeaker?

7. What is used to connect the loudspeaker to an electron tube?

8. Name several uses for audio amplifiers.

9. What are electron tubes with more than three elements called?

10. What are the two main purposes of a radio-frequency amplifier?

UNIT 28
TRANSISTOR FUNDAMENTALS

The Transistor

One of the newest additions to the field of electronics has been the development of the *transistor*. Transistors can be used as amplifiers just like electron tubes. They are now being used in radio receivers, television sets, hearing aids, Geiger counters, transmitters, and in many other places.

The transistor has several advantages over the electron tube. (1) It is very small and takes little space. (2) It does not require a large power supply like the electron tube. Small flashlight cells will last a long time with transistor circuits. (3) It does not have a heater like the electron tube, so practically no heat is produced. (4) The transistor can take rough handling and not become noisy as some tubes do.

◆ 103. Comparing the size of a transistor and a small metal receiving tube.

The elements of a transistor are shown this way in a symbol.

N-Type Semi-Conductors

Transistors are made from materials called semi-conductors. A semi-conductor is a substance that is not as good a conductor of electricity as metal, but is a better conductor than an insulator. There are a number of semi-conductor materials, but the two most often used in the manufacture of transistors are germanium and silicon. Transistors require semi-conductors with special electrical properties.

Germanium, in its very purest form, is very much like an insulator as it has few electrons which are free to move about. By adding very small quantities of impurities to the germanium, it can be made to conduct electricity. The addition of such impurities as antimony or arsenic to the germanium will increase the number of electrons which are free to move about in the germanium crystal. See Illustration 104. When a germanium crystal has an excess of "free" electrons, it is called an N-type semi-conductor.

P-Type Semi-Conductors

A second method of making a semi-conductor is by the addition of aluminum or gallium to germanium. When the aluminum or gallium is added to the germanium, a shortage of electrons

◆ 105. A P-type semi-conductor has a number of free holes.

is produced in the crystal. Such a semi-conductor is called a P-type semi-conductor; and its usage brings into being a new concept in electricity. This new concept states that a shortage of electrons produces a hole in the semi-conductor. This hole is free to move about much the same as free electrons are in the N-type material. See Figure 105.

If a battery is placed across the ends of a P-type semi-conductor, a current will flow as shown in Figure 106. The side of the semi-conductor connected to the positive terminal of the battery will repel the holes in the semi-conductor. The holes which have a positive charge will move toward the negative side of the semi-conductor. The electrons from the negative terminal of the battery flow to the semi-con-

◆ 106. When a battery is connected across a P-type semi-conductor, current will flow through the material. The holes move toward point A and the electrons move in the opposite direction.

◆ 104. An N-type semi-conductor has a number of free electrons.

ductor and combine with the positive holes at point *A* of the semi-conductor. When a hole and an electron come together, they combine and neutralize each other. New holes are then formed in the P-type material and these 'new holes move toward point *A*. As these holes are formed, they release electrons in the semi-conductor and these electrons flow toward the positive terminal of the battery. Thus, a current flows through the semi-conductor.

Forming an N-P Junction

When an N-type and a P-type material are joined together, as in Figure 107, an area formed between the two semi-conductors is called a junction. If a voltage is applied across the two materials so that the negative terminal of a battery is connected to the N-type semi-conductor and the positive terminal of the battery is connected to the P-type semi-conductor, a current will flow through the circuit.

The holes which are positive in the P-type material will be repelled by the positive terminal of the battery and

will move toward the junction. Likewise, the electrons in the N-type material will be repelled by the negative terminal of the battery and they also will move toward the junction. In the area of the junction, the holes and electrons meet and combine with each other. More electrons from the battery flow into the N-type semi-conductor to replace those electrons that combined with the holes. Also, in the P-type semi-conductor, new holes are created to replace those that were cancelled at the junction. These newly formed holes release electrons which flow toward the positive terminal of the battery.

In the circuit with the negative terminal of the battery connected to the N-type material and the positive terminal connected to the P-type material, current flows through the circuit. Such a circuit produces a current flow that is called *forward bias.*

Reverse Bias on the N-P Junction

Should the battery polarity be reversed as in Figure 108, no current will flow through the circuit. The electrons

♦ 107. When a negative charge is applied to the N-type material and a positive charge to the P-type material, a current will flow through the N-P junction.

♦ 108. When a positive charge is applied to the N-type semi-conductor and a negative charge to the P-type semi-conductor, practically no current flows through the N-P junction.

in the N-type material will be attracted to the positive terminal of the battery, and the holes in the P-type material will be attracted to the negative battery terminal. Since both electrons and holes move away from the junction, there is very little opportunity for the holes and electrons to combine. Practically no current will flow in the circuit. When the polarity placed on an N-P junction is such that the N-type material is connected to a positive charge and the P-type material is connected to a negative charge, current will not flow. and this is called *reverse bias*.

The N-P Junction is a Detector

The N-P junction semi-conductor will permit current to flow in one direction, but when the polarity across the junction is reversed, current will not flow. If an alternating current is applied to a semi-conductor junction, the output from the semi-conductor will change the AC into pulsating direct current.

When discussing radio receiver detectors, we learned that both the ga-

◆ 109. This illustration shows the construction of a transistor with the diagram of a transistor symbol.

lena crystal and the diode vacuum tube were used to change the alternating radio frequency waves into pulsating direct current. This pulsating direct current made the earphones function to form the sound waves. A semi-conductor junction crystal can be used as a radio receiver detector the same as the diode tube or the galena crystal. Many modern transistor radio receivers use germanium crystals called junction diodes as detectors.

The Tunnel Diode

The *tunnel* diode is a recent development which because of its small size and unusual characteristics, is expected to play a large part in the development of devices for new electronic applications. In a regular junction diode the junction, or barrier, between the N and P elements prevents current from flowing in the reverse direction, but by making the barrier only one-millionth of an inch thick electrons are able to tunnel through it at a pressure of only a fraction of one volt. One of a tunnel diode's unusual characteristics is that it can be made to oscillate, switch, or amplify like a transistor or multi-element electronic tube. Some of the advantages claimed for tunnel diodes are:

1. Withstanding operating temperatures up to 650°F.
2. Electrical charges move through it at the speed of light, making it ideal for use at frequencies above 2,000 megacycles.
3. Its small size makes possible the

◆ 110. An N-P-N transistor consists of an N-type emitter, an N-type collector, and a P-type base.

◆ 111. When the proper voltage is applied to the emitter, base, and collector of an N-P-N transistor, current flows through the entire transistor.

construction of miniaturized electronic equipment such as a complete radio transmitter in a space no larger than a fifty-cent piece.

Forming a Junction Transistor

Junction transistors are formed by using three layers of semi-conductor materials placed together like a sandwich as shown in Figure 110. This is called an N-P-N junction. The two outside semi-conductors are of N-type material, and the center semi-conductor is of P-type material. The center P-type material is called the base. The base is extremely thin and is usually less than .001 inch wide. The N-type material on one side of the base is called the emitter, and the N-type material on the opposite side is called the collector. Leads coming from the transistor are identified as the emitter, the collector, and the base.

A second type transistor called the P-N-P transistor is similar to the N-P-N except that the base semi-conductor is of the N-type and the emitter and collector is of the P-type.

N-P-N Transistor Action

To understand the fundamental op-

eration of a transistor, we can assume that external batteries are connected to the transistor leads so that current will flow through the transistor. The battery marked X in Figure 111 is connected between the emitter and the base. Since the polarity across the junction is such that N-type material has a negative charge and the P-type material has a positive charge, this is forward bias and current flows through the junction.

If Battery Y in Figure 111 is connected across the collector and the base so that the negative terminal goes to the collector and the positive terminal goes to the base, no current flows.

◆ 112. A symbol for an N-P-N transistor. The arrow for the emitter points away from the base.

◆ **113. A weak signal applied to the emitter circuit through the microphone is amplified by the transistor.**

If the collector is connected to the positive terminal of Battery *Y*, Figure 111, electrons come through the base and are attracted toward this positive charge and will flow right on through the collector. Because the base is so thin, the electrons which flow from the emitter toward the base actually tend to flow right through it toward the collector. Thus, current flows through the entire transistor.

Applying a Signal to the Emitter

To learn how a transistor functions, we need to apply a signal to the emitter circuit. In Figure 113 a microphone transformer has been placed in the circuit of the emitter and the base. When someone speaks into the microphone, an alternating current appears in the secondary of the transformer. The pure direct current produced by the battery in the emitter circuit is now varied by the AC signal. Since the AC signal is first positive and then negative, the voltage in the circuit is either increased or decreased.

When the signal is positive, it subtracts from the voltage of battery *X*, and the electron flow through the emitter is reduced. The current flow through the output transformer connected in the collector circuit will also be reduced because electrons from the emitter flow into the base and through the collecter. When the input signal becomes negative, the emitter will have an increased voltage, as the negative signal will add to the voltage of battery *X*. Increasing the current flow in the emitter will also increase the current flow through the output transformer of the collector circuit.

From this we can see that a signal applied to the emitter circuit produces a similar signal in the collector circuit. Thus, the emitter controls the collector current. This action is similar to that found in the vacuum tube where the grid controls the plate current.

The P-N-P Transistor

A P-N-P transistor can be used for an amplifier the same as the N-P-N.

◆ 114. In a P-N-P transistor the positive holes in the emitter are repelled by the positive charge placed on the emitter by battery X. The holes flow through the thin base and into the collector. In the collector they combine with the electrons produced by the negative terminal of battery Y. Electrons in the emitter are attracted toward the positive terminal of battery X and new holes are then formed in the emitter.

When using the P-N-P transistor, the voltage polarities are opposite to those used on the N-P-N transistor. Figure 114 illustrates how the polarities are connected for the P-N-P transistor.

When wiring transistors in circuits, it is extremely important to know whether P-N-P or an N-P-N is to be used. By using the wrong battery polarities on transistors, they can easily be damaged.

Amplification in a Transistor

Because the battery polarity produces forward bias in the emitter circuit, current flows very readily. Since current flows easily, there is very little resistance in the circuit. In the collector and base circuit reverse bias is applied so that very little current flows in this part of the circuit. The collector-base has a fairly high resistance.

When a signal is applied to the emitter, current will flow through the output circuit of the collector. This cur-rent will flow even though a very large resistance is placed in the collector circuit. A very small change in emitter voltage will produce a current change in the collector circuit. This changing current is flowing through a large output load resistor. A small current of only a very few milliamperes, when flowing through a large load resistor, can produce a large voltage drop. Using Ohm's law, we know that Voltage = Current times Resistance ($E = I \times R$). A transistor amplifies because a small voltage change applied to the

◆ 115. A symbol for a P-N-P transistor. The arrow for the emitter points toward the base.

◆ 116. Circuit for demonstrating how a transistor amplifies.

emitter circuit will cause a large voltage change in the collector output circuit.

The ability of a transistor to amplify can be shown with a microammeter, milliammeter, transistor, potentiometer, and dry cells, connected as shown in Figure 116. Adjust the potentiometer so that readings of both meters will be on the low side and within the range of the meters, as shown in Figure 117. Re-adjust the potentiometer, so that both meters will show increased readings. Make this adjustment carefully so that you do not exceed the current rating of the transistor collector circuit. In the example shown in Figure 118, the new meter readings are 26 microamperes and 1 milliampere. Referring back to Figure 117, we can see that a current change of 11 microamperes in the *base-emitter* circuit has caused a change of nearly 500 microamperes, or 0.5 milliamperes, in the *collector-base* circuit. Since the *base-emitter* circuit represents the input circuit and the *collector-base* circuit the output circuit, we can see how the transistor amplifies. The output of

◆ 117. The base-emitter circuit on the left and the collector-emitter circuit on the right have been adjusted to show a low current reading.

◆ 118. By increasing the base-emitter current by a few micro-amperes an increase of nearly one hundred percent is produced in the collector current.

the transistor may be shown in terms of voltage change rather than current by replacing the milliammeter with a 1,000 ohm resistor and connecting a low range voltmeter across it.

Transistors may be coupled together to raise a signal to any desired level,

◆ 119. A transistor audio amplifier using a common collector for stage one and three and a common emitter for the second stage.

and like electronic tubes they may be connected in several different ways. A diagram of a typical resistance coupled amplifier using three transistors is shown in Figure 119. Multi-unit transistor amplifiers for hi-fi and stereo with frequency response and output equal to tube amplifiers are now available, with the added advantage of requiring much less space. Figure 120 shows a transistor amplifier and an electronic tube amplifier.

Transistor Circuits

Transistors may be connected in any one of three ways. These hook-ups, called configurations, are named common-base, common-emitter, and common-collector. In each circuit one of the electrodes is common to both the input and output circuit.

Courtesy Allied Radio Corp.

◆ **120. An electronic tube stereo amplifier and a transistor amplifier (top) compared for size.** Both have similar frequency response and output of 50 watts.

The basic hook-ups for transistor amplifier circuits are shown above. You can determine the type of a transistor amplifier circuit by noting which electrode provides a common connection for one of the input and one of the output terminals. For example, in the common base drawings in Figure 121, the base provides that connection. If you apply the same reasoning to the other diagrams you will see how they are so-named.

◆ **121. The basic circuits for transistor amplifiers.**

◆ 122. Several types of transistors used in electronic circuits.

INTERESTING THINGS TO DO

1. Transistor Radio Receiver.
Materials Required:

1 Antenna coil (see text)
1 Variable capacitor, .000365 μf (see text) (C_1)
1 Crystal diode, general purpose, G.E. or Sylvania 1N64
1 Fixed capacitor, .02 μf (C_2)
1 Resistor, 220,000 ohms, ½-watt (R)
1 Transistor, Raytheon 722 or G.E. 2N107
2 Pen light cells

This radio receiver may be built by placing the parts on a wood base and using the standard-size parts described with the crystal set in Unit 26 of this book. If you want to build a very small set that you can carry in your pocket, miniature parts to work with transistors may be obtained from radio mail order companies and wholesale radio houses. Using miniature parts makes it possible to build the complete receiver shown in Schematic Drawing 125 in a plastic box only 1″ deep, 2″ wide, and 3″ long.

To build the receiver in a small space use a Transistor Loop Antenna instead of a standard-size antenna coil. For the standard variable capacitor use a 365 μμf Super-Midget variable capacitor. The only other substitution will be a miniature-type fixed capacitor for

◆ 123. A transistor radio receiver built in a small plastic case. A match folder is next to the receiver.

◆ **124. A soap dish was used to hold this transistor radio receiver. A shaft has been soldered to the padder-type capacitor that is used to tune the receiver.**

SCHEMATIC DIAGRAM

◆ **125. Schematic diagram of transistor radio receiver.**

the capacitor, C_2. Wire set according to the schematic diagram. Phone tip jacks may be provided for the headphones if it is not desired to have them permanently attached to the set.

2. A Brushless Direct Current Motor

Materials required:

1 Spool magnet wire, enamel covered, 26 to 30 ga. (see text)
1 Piece brass rod, round, $\frac{1}{16}''$ diameter, $3\frac{1}{2}''$ long
2 Small magnets (see text)
1 Ball, styrofoam or balsa wood, 2" diameter
1 Wood base, $\frac{1}{2}'' \times 6'' \times 8''$
1 Piece spring brass, 24 ga., $\frac{5}{16}'' \times 1\frac{3}{4}''$
1 Piece spring brass, $\frac{5}{16}'' \times \frac{5}{8}''$
1 Piece sheet brass, 20 ga., $\frac{1}{2}'' \times \frac{3}{4}''$
1 Transistor (see text)
1 Transistor socket (optional)
2 Flashlight cells, 1.5 volt
1 Potentiometer, 5,000 ohms
2 Fahnestock clips

This motor operates on a new principle. It has no brushes or commutator. The current changing action of those items is supplied by a transistor.

The placement of parts as shown in the photograph may be followed, or they may be arranged to suit the builder's fancy.

Begin the motor by making a winding form for the coil, Fig. 126. The slots should extend into the center wood block so that pieces of wire may be passed under and around the completed coil to hold it together temporarily. Wind a few turns of thin cardboard around the center wood block, then wind 900 turns of magnet wire on the form. Any size wire from 26 to 30 may be used, and since the amount of wire required may vary, it is better to wind the form directly from a spool, rather than try to estimate the exact amount. After 900 turns have been wound, make a loop of wire about eight inches long, twist it together, then wind another 900 turns on the form in the same direction. The wire may be wound by placing the form in a hand-drill or lathe. Place tie wires around the coil and remove it from the form. Wrap the completed coil with tape, removing the tie wires as you proceed with the wrapping. Drill holes through the wood base for the coil leads and secure the coil to the base with glue or cement.

WOOD BASE

COIL WITH BEARINGS
AND SHAFT RETAINER

1/16" BRASS ROD

STYROFOAM
BALL

N S   N S

2"

3 1/2"

HOLES SHOULD BE
COVERED WITH PLASTIC WOOD
AFTER MAGNETS ARE
IN PLACE

VIEW OF ROTOR

WOOD
CENTER   CARDBOARD

THREADED
ROD

SLOT FOR
TIE WIRE

CENTER
PUNCH

DRILL FOR
WOOD SCREWS

1/2"

3/4"

LOWER
BEARING

2 1/4"

3"

3/4"

3"

WINDING FORM

1/8"

5/16"

1 3/4"

1"

UPPER
BEARING

5/16"

SHAFT
RETAINER

NPN
TRANSISTOR

B   C

E

L₁
900
TURNS

POT.

L₂
900
TURNS

+

3V

−

ROTOR

N
S
O
N
S

WIRING
DIAGRAM

◆ 126. Details of brushless direct-current motor.

◆ **127. Completed brushless direct-current motor.**

Sharpen one end of the round brass rod to a point. Drill a $\frac{1}{16}''$ hole through the center of the rotor ball. Drill another hole through the ball that is perpendicular to the first hole and large enough to hold the small magnets. The magnets are the small type usually obtainable from hardware and novelty stores. Drill and center punch the piece of brass for the lower bearing. Shape the upper bearing and shaft retainer as shown in the drawing. Clamp the bearing to the top of the coil, place the rotor ball on the shaft and locate the bottom bearing so that the rotor will revolve in the center of the coil. After the rotor has been properly aligned it should be cemented to the brass rod. The upper bearing may also be cemented to the coil. The sliding retainer holds the rotor shaft in

place, yet permits the rotor assembly to be removed easily.

Mount the potentiometer, transistor, and Fahnestock clips on the wood base and connect the parts together as shown in the wiring diagram. Although connections may be made directly to the transistor leads, a transistor socket is recommended if you wish to experiment with different types of transistors. The wiring diagram shows an NPN transistor, but a PNP will work equally well if the flashlight cell connections are reversed so that the transistor collector connection, "C", goes to the negative terminal of the cell. This change is important, otherwise the transistor may be damaged.

When all connections are complete the motor is ready for its initial tryout. First, make certain that the rotor spins freely. Then turn the potentiometer shaft to about its center position and connect the flashlight cells. Start the rotor and it should quickly reach a high speed on its own power. Further adjustment of the potentiometer will determine its best operating position.

The transistor circuit used in the motor is a common-emitter type. We learned that a bias voltage is necessary for the proper operation of that type of circuit and it is the varying of that voltage that makes the rotor spin around. When the rotor magnets are at a right angle to the coil the bias voltage is obtained from the three volt supply through the coil L_1.

In order to understand the operation of the motor, let us assume that the north pole of one of the rotor magnets is near coil L_2, and that the current flowing through the collector-base circuit and through the coil is in a direction to create a magnetic field that will attract the magnet. As the magnet approaches the coil it induces a voltage in coil L_1 which re-enforces the bias voltage between the emitter and the base. The increased bias causes a corresponding increase in the collector current, which increases the pull on the magnet until the momentum of the rotor carries the magnet away from the coil. As the rotor continues to revolve the south pole of the magnet approaches coil L_2. Due to the changed polarity a voltage is induced in coil L_1 which opposes the bias voltage. This reduces the collector current and makes the transistor inactive until a north pole of the magnet again approaches coil L_2, where the action begins all over again. The function of the potentiometer is to adjust the bias voltage for maximum speed of the rotor.

REVIEW QUESTIONS

1. What is meant by the term semiconductor?

2. Explain the difference between an N-type and a P-type semi-conductor.

3. How does a free hole differ from a free electron?

4. If current is to flow through an N-P junction, how must the battery polarity be connected to the junction?

5. What is an important use made of the junction diode?

6. Name the three principal parts of a junction transistor.

7. In a complete transistor circuit, what happens in the collector circuit when an AC signal is applied to the emitter?

8. What is the basic difference between an N-P-N and a P-N-P transistor?

9. Why is it extremely important to observe the battery polarities when connecting transistor circuits?

10. Name the most common configuration circuit used with transistors.

UNIT 29
POWER SUPPLIES

Direct Current for Radio Receivers

Radio receivers always need a source of direct current for the electron tube plate. B batteries can be used for this purpose, but they must be replaced when worn out. Most radio receivers are made so that they can be plugged into a convenience outlet that has 115-volt alternating current. The alternating current is then changed to direct current by the power supply. Power supplies use a *rectifier* to change the alternating current into direct current.

Selenium Rectifiers

Selenium is a chemical material that will permit current to flow through it in one direction. When alternating current starts to flow in the other direction it will stop the electrons from flowing.

A selenium rectifier (Photograph 128) is made of a group of iron washers that have been covered on one side with selenium. The selenium-coated washers are then placed together so that all of the coated sides are facing in the same direction.

Illustration 129 shows how the selenium rectifier is connected in an alternating current circuit. Since it will permit the current to flow in one direction and not in the other direction, a pulsating direct current will flow through the resistor. This type of rec-

◆ 128. A small and a large selenium rectifier are shown here. Rectifiers change alternating current into direct current.

◆ 129. Circuit using a selenium rectifier as a half-wave rectifier. Alternating current is rectified so that current through the resistor is a pulsating direct current. Current flows half of each cycle.

tifier is a *half-wave* rectifier as it produces a direct current during half of the alternating current cycle. No current flows during the other half of the cycle.

Filtering the Pulsating Direct Current

The pulsating direct current coming out of the rectifier would not work on the plate of an electron tube. The plate current would change with each of the pulses. Constant DC without any variations is necessary for the electron tube power supply.

It is necessary to smooth out the pulsating direct current and make it a pure direct current. This is done through the use of a *filter*.

The filter consists of two fixed capacitors and a resistor connected as in Illustration 130. These capacitors are

◆ 130. Half-wave selenium rectifier and filter circuit. Capacitors and resistor filter pulsating direct current so that a pure direct current is available at the output.

◆ 131. The small silicon rectifier on the left will handle as much current as the vacuum tube rectifier on the right.

very large ones having a capacitance of 20 microfarads or more. When the current flows through the filter, the capacitors become charged and store large quantities of electrons. As soon as the current stops flowing from the rectifier the capacitors furnish electrons to the circuit. Thus the capacitors tend to provide a constant flow of electrons to the radio receiver.

Each time the current flows through the rectifier a surge of electrons flows through the filter. The resistor is used to try to stop these sudden surges of electrons. Through the use of the resistor and the capacitors, a constant direct current is made available for the radio receiver.

Silicon Rectifiers

One of the most recent developments in the field of semi-conductors has been the use of silicon diodes as power supply rectifiers. A silicon diode consists of a P-N junction much like that used in a transistor. The P-type material has small amounts of aluminum added to the silicon and the N-type material has phosphorous added to the silicon. When an alternating current is applied to the diode, current will flow in one direction through the diode but will not flow in the opposite direction.

The silicon rectifiers have many advantages over other type rectifiers, and because of these advantages they are being used to replace old type rectifiers. These advantages include having a very high operating efficiency with little voltage loss, and being so small that they are often used in places where space is an important factor. In addition, their ability to handle high currents makes silicon diodes very popular as rectifiers.

◆ 132. A diode is a two-element electron tube.

Diode Electron Tube Rectifiers

Two-element electron tubes called *diodes* (Illustration 132) are used as half-wave rectifiers. The diode consists of a filament and a plate. A transformer is used to step up the voltage for the high-voltage supply, to provide filament voltage for the rectifier tube, and, also, to supply the heater voltage for the radio receiver tubes. See Diagram 133.

Alternating current flows through the secondary windings. When the plate of the diode tube is positive, it attracts the electrons being thrown off by the filament. Electrons flow through the tube from the filament to the plate and through the transformer. These electrons return to the filament through the load resistor. The filament is then the positive terminal for the power supply, and the high-voltage transformer lead is the negative terminal.

As the alternating current changes the direction of electron flow, the plate becomes negative and no current flows through the tube. Since current flows through the tube during only half of the alternating current cycle, the diode produces a pulsating direct current. Pulsating direct current from the half-wave rectifier cannot be used to operate a receiver until it has been filtered.

Full-Wave Electron-Tube Rectifiers

Half-wave rectified current is hard to smooth out because one-half of the time no current is flowing. The filter must be able to provide current during the time when the rectifier is not in operation. Rectifiers that rectify both of the alternating current cycles so that a more constant flow of current is available are often used. These rectifiers are *full-wave* rectifiers.

An electron tube for full-wave rectifiers uses two diodes in one glass envelope. Usually 250 volts or more are needed for a radio receiver power supply. The high-voltage secondary of

◆ 133. Half-wave rectifier using a diode electron tube. When plate is positive it pulls electrons from the filament and current flows through the tube. No current flows when plate is negative.

♦ 134. When plate *1* is positive, plate *2* is negative. Electrons flow from filament to plate *1* and out through the center tap of the transformer.

♦ 135. When plate *2* is positive electrons are pulled to it. Electrons flow out through the center tap of the transformer. Both cycles of alternating current are rectified.

the transformer is tapped in the center. Each side of the center connection produces 250 volts.

The double-diode tube has two plates and two filaments. One plate goes to one side of the high-voltage winding, and the other plate goes to the other side of the winding. See Diagrams 134 and 135.

When plate 1 is positive it pulls the electrons from the filament and current flows through that part of the tube. As the alternating current starts to flow in the other direction, plate 1 becomes negative and plate 2 becomes positive. Now current flows through plate 2 out through the center tap. The electron flow through the center tap is always in the same direction. The direct current pulses flowing through the load resistor look like Illustration 136. Current is flowing almost all of the time, but it is still necessary to have a filter system.

Filters with a Choke Coil

A much improved filter system can be made using a *choke coil* instead of a resistor. Most power supplies use a choke. The choke is very much like one winding of a transformer since it is made of many turns of wire wrapped around a laminated iron core. The choke is better than the resistor because it provides better filtering and does not cut down the voltage as much as the resistor does. See Diagram 137.

The choke coil tries to keep a steady current flowing. It can be compared to a flywheel in an engine that keeps the engine turning over at a constant

ALTERNATING CURRENT
ON PRIMARY OF
TRANSFORMER

PULSATING
DIRECT CURRENT
THROUGH FULL-WAVE
RECTIFIER

♦ 136. Illustration showing full-wave rectifier current flow.

♦ 137. Full-wave rectifier with a filter. The filter uses a choke coil and two capacitors to change pulsating direct current to pure direct current.

speed. The choke helps in smoothing out the pulsating direct current. A choke coil, like any coil, is called an *inductance*. The unit of inductance is the *henry*. Chokes with from 4 to 30 henries are used in power supplies.

A full-wave rectifier does not require as much filter as a half-wave rectifier. Smaller filter capacitors can be used. Capacitors with a capacitance of about 10 microfarads are most common.

The symbol shows how a power transformer may supply different voltages.

INTERESTING THINGS TO DO

1. Half-Wave Selenium Power Supply.

Materials required:

1 Piece sheet steel, 5″ x 3″, 20 gage
1 Power transformer (T), primary 117 volts, secondary 125 volts, center tap (CT), 6.3 volts. (Stancor PA–8421 or Thordarson T26R32)
1 Selenium rectifier, 50 milliampere (MA)
1 Electrolytic capacitor, dual, 20–20 μf, 150 volts (C_1, C_2)
1 Resistor, 1-watt, 33 to 100 ohms (R_1)
1 Resistor, 5-watt, 10,000 ohms (R_2)
1 Resistor, 5-watt, 20,000 ohms (R_3)
1 Toggle switch (optional)
1 Four-point terminal strip
1 Rubber grommet, ⅜″
1 Line cord and plug cap

Hook-up wire

This power supply is easy to build and requires fewer parts than a regular full-wave supply. Its power output is sufficient to operate either of the radio receivers which are described in the preceding units of this book.

Lay out and drill the piece of sheet steel as shown on Drawing 139 Bend each end of the sheet along the broken lines to form a 90° angle. Secure a rubber grommet in the hole on top of the chassis. Mount the selenium rectifier and the power transformer about

◆ 138. A half-wave selenium power supply. This power supply can be used on the one- and two-tube radio receivers.

where shown on the drawing. Since the mounting holes will vary with different makes of transformers and rectifiers, no holes are shown. Mount the dual capacitor, C_1 and C_2, and the resistors, R_1, R_2, and R_3, beneath the chassis and bring the leads up through the rubber grommet. Resistor, R_1, is merely to protect the selenium rectifier from sudden voltage surges from the capacitor and may have any resistance of from 33 to 100 ohms.

Secure the terminal strip to the top of the chassis and connect the power leads to it as shown on the schematic diagram. Mark the terminal strip so that it will show the voltage between each pair of terminals. The power supply may be controlled either at the supply line outlet or with a toggle switch. If a switch is desired, drill a 3/8" hole in one side of the chassis and connect the switch in the transformer side of the power line, as shown on the schematic diagram. Connect the line cord and plug to the transformer and the power supply is ready to operate.

SCHEMATIC DIAGRAM

CHASSIS LAYOUT

◆ 139. Drawing of half-wave selenium power supply.

◆ 140. A full-wave power supply using a power transformer and rectifier tube.

◆ 141. Wiring underneath the chassis of the power supply.

2. Full-Wave Rectifier.

Materials required:

1 Power transformer, 450 volts, CT, 50 MA, 5-6.3–volts (T)
1 Choke coil, 6-henry, 50 MA
1 Capacitor, electrolytic, dual 20 μf, 450 volts (C_1, C_2)
1 Capacitor, electrolytic, 4 μf, 450 volts (C_3)
2 Resistors, 20,000 ohms, 10-watt
1 Rectifier tube, 5U4
1 Tube socket
1 Toggle switch, single-pole
1 Rubber grommet, 3/8"
1 Rubber grommet, 1/2"
1 Piece masonite, 1/8" x 2" x 5"
5 Fahnestock clips
1 Line cord and plug cap
1 Piece sheet steel, 6" x 7", 20 gage

Lay out and drill the piece of sheet steel as shown on Drawing 142. Bend the ends along the broken lines to an angle of 90°. Mount the choke coil and the power transformer on the top of the chassis in the approximate positions shown on the drawing. Place the toggle switch in the 3/8" hole in the front end of the chassis. Make a ter-

minal strip with the piece of masonite and Fahnestock clips and secure it to the back end of the chassis. Secure the electrolytic capacitors and the two resistors underneath the chassis.

Wire the power supply as shown in the schematic diagram. The two resistors connected in series serve to keep the high voltage of the power supply at a constant value and to provide a means of getting an additional lower voltage. The voltage across the output of the power supply will be approximately 200 volts, and since the two resistors connected across the output have the same resistance, the voltage between the point where they are connected together and the negative terminal will be approximately 100 volts. Mark the terminals on the terminal strip so that the output voltages may be easily identified.

SCHEMATIC DIAGRAM

CHASSIS LAYOUT

◆ 142. **Drawing of full-wave power supply.**

REVIEW QUESTIONS

1. Why is direct current needed for radio receivers?

2. What kind of current is produced by a half-wave rectifier?

3. Explain the purpose of a filter.

4. What does the capacitor do in a filter system?

5. Why are electrolytic capacitors used in filter systems?

6. What are the elements found in a diode electron tube?

7. When a single diode is used, what is that kind of rectifier called?

8. Explain the advantages of a full-wave rectifier.

9. How many diodes are needed in a full-wave rectifier?

10. What is the purpose of a choke in a filter?

UNIT 30
TRANSMITTING RADIO WAVES

Radio Frequency Signals

We have studied the basic principles of receiving radio signals. Now we will learn about the transmitting of radio waves. A fundamental transmitter consists of a *radio frequency generator,* a *power supply* for the generator, and the *antenna.* As illustrated in Figure 143, the radio frequency generator is connected to the antenna which sends the signal out through space. A radio frequency generator is called an *oscillator.* Frequencies above 15,000 cycles per second (15 kilocycles) are called radio frequencies because they are useful in radio transmission.

Because of the very wide range of radio frequencies, they have been divided into different classifications as shown below.

◆ 143. A block diagram illustrating that the basic requirements for a transmitter are a power supply, radio frequency generator, and antenna.

FREQUENCY	CLASSIFICATION	ABBREV.
15 to 30 kc.	Very-low frequencies	v.l.f.
30 to 300 kc.	Low frequencies	l.f.
300 to 3000 kc.	Medium frequencies	m.f.
3 to 30 Mc.	High frequencies	h.f.
30 to 300 Mc.	Very-high freq.	v.h.f.
300 to 3000 Mc.	Ultra-high freq.	u.h.f.
3000 to 30,000 Mc.	Superhigh freq.	s.h.f.

Basically, all radio frequency signals are used to establish communications.

Different kinds of radio signals are used to carry the desired information. We have already learned about amplitude modulated signals and frequency modulated signals that are used to carry audio frequencies. Another method of sending information is through the use of the international Morse code. Here the signal is interrupted by a key so that the radio frequency waves are started and stopped at regular intervals, as shown in Figure 144. These signals are called *continuous wave telegraphy,* often abbreviated as *c.w.* Television and facsimile are two other kinds of signals used to send information.

DASH   DOT

◆ **144. A continuous radio frequency wave is interrupted to produce dots and dashes for International Morse code signals.**

Oscillation

One of the requirements of a transmitter is to generate a radio frequency wave with the use of an oscillator. A basic oscillator circuit includes an inductance L and a capacitance C connected as in Figure 145. If we charge the capacitance, it will start to discharge by having an electron flow through the coil, toward the positive plate of the capacitor, setting up a magnetic field about the coil. As the electron flow starts to die down the magnetic field about the coil collapses and this collapsing of the field induces a back electro-motive force into the coil. The back electromotive force, induced by the collapsing of the magnetic

◆ **145. In a parallel L-C circuit the charging and discharging of the capacitor produces a sine wave.**

field, recharges the capacitor. When the capacitor is recharged, it will have an opposite polarity. Energy is again stored in the capacitor and again the capacitor will discharge through the coil.

The back and forth flow of electrons produces an oscillation in the LC circuit. The frequency of oscillation is determined by the value of the capacitance and the inductance. We have already learned that the formula for this is:

$$F = \frac{1}{2\,\pi\,\sqrt{LC}}$$

These oscillations in the LC circuit would continue if it were not for the resistance that is in the circuit. Since every circuit has some resistance, the signal would soon die out; therefore, it is necessary to use some device to keep the circuit oscillating.

The Regenerative Oscillator

The regenerative circuit in Figure 146 uses an electron tube to produce a continuous wave oscillation. Energy

◆ **146. A basic regenerative oscillator circuit. The frequency of the circuit is determined by the value of L and C. This circuit is known as the Armstrong oscillator.**

from the tickler coil is fed back into the grid circuit, and oscillation takes place in the LC circuit. This LC circuit is called the *tank circuit*.

When the circuit is first turned on, the rush of plate current produces a magnetic field in the plate or tickler coil. This magnetic field induces a current into the grid coil. The feeding of energy from the plate back into the grid starts the circuit into oscillation. To get regeneration or oscillation, it is important that the output of the plate coil be correctly coupled to the grid coil. The feedback must be in step with the oscillations occurring in the grid circuit. If the circuit fails to oscillate, it may be necessary to reverse the connections to one of the coils.

The grid leak plays a very important part in the operation of the oscillator. It is used to obtain "self" grid bias for the electron tube and provides for efficient operation of the tube.

The Hartley Oscillator

There are many different types of electron tube oscillators. For the most part, the variations in circuits depends upon the method used for feedback. Figure 147 illustrates another type of oscillator called the *Hartley oscillator*. It differs from the plate coil regenerative oscillator in that only one coil is used. The single coil is tapped for the cathode connection. The oscillating frequency of the Hartley oscillator is determined by the value of L and C.

We must remember that the current flowing in the plate circuit is also flow-

◆ 147. The Hartley oscillator circuit. Feedback is obtained by coupling some of the plate energy back into the grid circuit by means of an inductance. The feedback circuit is shown in color. L_1 and C_1 make up the basic oscillator and L_2 is the portion of the coil which couples the plate feedback into the grid circuit. C_B is a blocking capacitor which keeps the B+ voltage from reaching the oscillator.

ing in the cathode circuit. Electrons leaving the plate must flow through the cathode coil to get back to the cathode. Thus, the section of the coil shown below the cathode tap in Figure 147 induces a current into the grid circuit and provides the necessary feedback.

The transistor can also be used as an oscillator. A Hartley transistor oscillator is illustrated in Figure 148. The LC circuit is the same as for the electron tube. Voltage from the collector circuit is developed across a portion of the coil, inducing a current of the proper phase into the base circuit, in order to maintain oscillation.

◆ 148. A transistorized Hartley oscillator.

◆ 149. A crystal is placed between two metal plates. The frequency depends on the thickness of the crystal. Thick crystals vibrate slowly, thin crystals vibrate rapidly.

◆ 150. A basic crystal oscillator circuit. Feedback is obtained through the inter-electrode capacitance of the tube.

The Crystal Oscillator

In the unit on *Producing Electricity* the piezoelectric effect of crystals was studied. We learned that if a voltage is applied across the opposite sides of a crystal, a vibration will be set up in the crystal. These vibrations become very strong when the frequency of the applied voltage is the same as the mechanical resonant frequency of the crystal. When properly connected with an electron tube or transistor these crystals can be used in oscillator circuits. They provide very excellent frequency stability, and, in circuits where just one frequency is needed, they are very desirable.

The method of cutting the quartz and the thickness of the material determines the frequency at which it will vibrate, and this is called its *fundamental frequency*. A quartz crystal may be about one half inch square, and several thousandths of an inch thick. It is placed between two metal plates in a crystal holder as in Figure 149. The plates called electrodes, just touch each side of the crystal so that it is free to vibrate. Each plate is connected to a terminal or prong of the holder, so that these two connections provide contact with the crystal.

A crystal oscillator circuit is shown in Figure 150. The crystal represents an LC circuit in the grid circuit. If the plate circuit composed of L_1 and C_1 is tuned to the same frequency as the crystal, energy from the plate is fed back to the grid through the capacitance in the tube elements. This is possible because there is a capacitive effect between the plate and grid that acts as a coupling capacitor from the plate to the grid circuit; this is called the inter-electrode tube capacitance. Because the energy from the plate is fed back into the grid at the same resonant frequency as the crystal, the crystal is set into vibration. The frequency of the oscillation is determined by the crystal. Because of the crystal, the oscillator has very good frequency stability.

Radio Frequency Amplifiers

Since oscillators usually do not provide a great deal of power output, they are coupled to radio frequency amplifiers. The amplifier is used to increase the power output of the signal so that it can be received at a much greater distance. Then the amplifier is connected to a transmitting antenna. If additional power is necessary, more

♦ 152. The capacitor, in capacitive coupling, provides a low impedance path for the radio frequency signal. It also keeps the DC voltage of the oscillator plate from being applied to the amplifier grid.

♦ 151. The top drawing illustrates inductive coupling using the plate tank coil of the oscillator as the primary of a radio frequency transformer and the grid coil of the amplifier as the secondary. The bottom drawing shows inductive coupling through the use of a link. Link coupling permits the oscillator and the amplifier to be located some distance apart.

than one amplifier stage may be used. The oscillator is coupled to the radio frequency amplifier either by inductive coupling (Figure 151) or capacitive coupling (Figure 152).

To obtain high efficiency from power amplifiers, operated at radio frequencies, it is desirable to use an amplifier called a *Class C* amplifier. Amplifiers are divided into classifications such as *Class A, Class B* and *Class C*. These classifications are made according to the operating conditions under which the tube works. In Class *A* amplifiers the grid bias is such that plate current flows at all times. Because of their excellent frequency response, Class *A* amplifiers are used in radio receivers and in high fidelity amplifiers. The Class *B* amplifier is biased so that very

little plate current flows when no signal is applied to the grid. A class *B* amplifier provides much greater power output than a Class *A* amplifier and they are used for the final power amplifier in many audio amplifier systems.

The efficiency of a Class *C* circuit may be as high as 80%. In a Class *C*

♦ 153. A block diagram of a transmitter using an oscillator and a radio frequency amplifier coupled to an antenna.

◆ 154. An oscillator and a Class C amplifier circuit using capacitive coupling. The grid and coupling circuits are shown in colored lines. Bias for the grid of the amplifier is supplied through an RF choke which also prevents the signal from the oscillator from flowing to ground. Milliammeters measure current flow and may be used for tuning the circuit.

operation, the plate current flows for less than one half of the radio frequency cycle. Since the plate is drawing current for only a portion of the time this increases the efficiency of the tube. Stated in another way, the plate consumes power for just a fraction of the time required for the entire cycle.

The Class C Grid Circuit

To see how a Class C amplifier functions we must first review the grid circuit. Grid bias is placed on the grid of the tube as illustrated in Figure 154. This bias is usually about twice cutoff. By this we mean that if a −20 volts of bias, on the grid, will stop the plate current from flowing for a particular tube we must use a −40 volts for Class C operation.

With no signal applied to the grid no current flows in the plate circuit. Now we must couple the oscillator to the grid of the amplifier so that a signal is applied to the grid. In this particular circuit capacitive coupling is used. The capacitor must have a low reactance to the frequency applied, and capacitors of about $100 \mu f$ are frequently used. The signal, called the drive, from the preceding amplifier or oscillator must be strong enough to overcome the negative bias of the tube and drive the grid positive.

A radio frequency choke is used to keep the radio frequency applied to the grid. This choke has a high impedance to the applied signal so that it will keep the signal from flowing toward the ground. A 2.5 millihenry choke is often used for this purpose.

When the grid becomes positive, electrons will flow from the cathode to

◆ 155. A graph showing the effect of the applied grid signal on the plate current of a Class C amplifier. The horizontal waveform on the left represents the signal on the grid. When this signal causes the grid to go positive as shown by the solid color portion of the signal then current flows as indicated by the plate current pulses in the drawing.

the grid and current will flow in the grid circuit. This grid current can be shown through the use of a milliammeter connected in the circuit. The graph of the current flow in a Class C amplifier is shown in Figure 155. At the bottom of the drawing we can see the effect of the input signal on the grid.

The Class C Plate Circuit

The plate circuit shown in Figure 154 consists of the inductance and capacitance, called the tank; the radio frequency choke; the by-pass capacitor; and the plate voltage. The tank circuit must tune to the resonant frequency of the applied signal. The radio frequency choke and by-pass capacitor are used to keep any radio frequency from flowing back to the power supply. The plate voltage is determined by the type of tube used. Some Class C amplifiers use up to 3,000 volts on the plate.

With the grid biased to twice cutoff, no current will flow in the plate circuit until a signal is applied to the grid. As a strong signal is applied to the grid, the grid voltage varies with the signal. This variation of grid voltage produces pulses of plate current as illustrated in the graph, Figure 155.

To reproduce the applied grid signal in the plate circuit, we must tune the tank to resonance. When this circuit is in resonance, the pulses of plate current flow through the coil and capacitor. The charging and discharging of the capacitor, through the inductance must be at the same rate as the pulses of plate current. Thus, the fly wheel effect of the tank circuit produces a continuous wave signal at the desired frequency.

It is extremely important to have the tank tuned to resonance to avoid burning up the electron tube. The milliammeter, shown in Figure 154, is used to indicate the current flow, and it also can be used to show when the circuit is tuned to resonance. The plate tank is a parallel resonant circuit and when tuned to resonance it presents a maximum impedance. At resonance the high impedance of the circuit results in a reduction of plate current. Thus, when tuning an amplifier to resonance we can watch the plate milliammeter and observe a drop in the plate current. Before resonance the plate current will be extremely high, but at resonance a very definite dip will show on the milliammeter.

Preventing Amplifier Self Oscillation

Power amplifiers are used to amplify the signal of the oscillator; therefore, it is not desirable that they generate their own signal. Because of the interelectrode capacitance in an electron tube, it is very easy for the energy from the plate to feedback into the grid. When this occurs the tube starts oscil-

lating and generates a new signal. To avoid self oscillation, it is necessary to neutralize the amplifier.

One method of neutralization is through the use of screen grid tubes. Tubes with a screen grid help eliminate feedback because the screen grid is placed between the grid and plate inside of the tube. The screen grid reduces the coupling between the plate and grid and thus tends to prevent self oscillation.

The Dipole Antenna

If a radio frequency amplifier is to send out a signal for communication purposes, we must connect the transmitter to an antenna. The antenna is a wire that takes the energy from the transmitter and radiates it into space in the form of electromagnetic waves. To operate efficiently, the antenna must be resonant with the signal from the transmitter.

A fundamental radio transmitting antenna is called a *half-wave dipole*. A dipole is a length of wire that is equal to one half the wave length of

◆ 156. One wavelength is the distance that the radiated energy will cover, travelling at the speed of light, during one cycle of the radiated energy.

the radio frequency signal. This wire acts like a resonant circuit. The wire includes inductance, capacitance, and resistance just like a regular tuned circuit. We can calculate the length of wire needed, providing we know the operating frequency.

The formula for determining one wavelength is:

$$\text{Wavelength in meters} = \frac{300}{\text{Freq. in Megacycles}}$$

$$A\ meter = 39.29\ inches$$

This formula is not quite accurate for an actual wire. These formulas apply to a wave traveling in space. Because of the resistance in a wire a practical half-wave antenna is actually about 5% shorter. Thus an average formula for a resonant length of wire would be:

$$\frac{1}{2}\text{ wavelength in feet} = \frac{468}{\text{Freq. in Mc.}}$$

We may calculate the length of a half-wave dipole to be used on a frequency of 7,000 kilocycles by using this formula. The 7,000 kilocycles is equal to 7 megacycles.

$$\frac{1}{2}\text{ wavelength in feet} = \frac{468}{7}$$

$$Length\ of\ half\ wave\ dipole = 66.85$$

Transmission Lines

To get the energy from the radio frequency amplifier to the antenna we

◆ 157. Transmission lines used to carry power to the antenna usually consist of a coaxial cable shown at top, or a twin lead line, shown at bottom of the photograph.

need to use a transmission line. A transmission line consists of two parallel lengths of wire that are spaced an equal distance apart from each other. These two wires have an impedance to current flow since they include capacitance, inductance and resistance. There are a number of different transmission lines available. One of the most common types is *coaxial cable*. Coaxial cable includes an inner conductor centered within an outer shield. A polyethylene insulator is used to insulate the inner conductor from the outer shield as illustrated in Figure 157. Another type of transmission line is the *twin* or *ribbon lead* also illustrated in Figure 157.

When an antenna is connected to a transmission line, it is important that all of the energy going from the output of the amplifier through the transmission line be transferred to the antenna.

◆ 158. Construction of a half-wave dipole fed with a 75 ohm twin-lead transmission line.

◆ 159. A coaxial cable transmission line inductively coupled to the output of the final amplifier.

◆ 160. The frequency multiplier stage of a transmitter. The plate circuit is tuned to twice the frequency of the grid, so that for each cycle on the grid, two are produced in the plate circuit.

A maximum transfer of energy occurs when the transmission line impedance equals the antenna impedance.

The half-wave dipole usually has the transmission line connected in the center. Figure 158. Such an antenna has an impedance of about 73 ohms. Therefore, to get a maximum transfer of energy from the transmission line to the half-wave dipole, the transmission line must also have an impedance of about 73 ohms. Both the coaxial cable and the twin lead may be obtained with 73 to 75 ohms impedance. The antenna impedance depends on the design of the antenna. Each type of antenna requires that the transmission line be made to match the impedance of the antenna.

The transmission line may be coupled to the output of the power amplifier using inductive coupling as shown in Figure 159.

Frequency Multipliers

Oscillators are far more stable at low frequencies than at high frequencies. Since transmitter stability is very essential the oscillator is often placed in operation at a lower frequency than the final amplifier. To increase the frequency of a signal it is possible to use

a frequency multiplier. The frequency multiplier stage operates on a harmonic of the lowest frequency called the fundamental frequency. The fundamental frequency is called the *first harmonic* and the second harmonic is twice the fundamental frequency. Thus, the third harmonic would be three times the fundamental frequency. If a fundamental oscillator frequency is 4 megacycles, the fourth harmonic would be 16 megacycles.

A frequency multiplier circuit is very similar to a regular Class *C* amplifier. In the regular amplifier the plate signal is tuned to the same frequency as the input or grid signal. The multiplier stage tunes the plate circuit to a harmonic or a multiple of the grid circuit signal. To double the frequency of a 4 megacycle oscillator, the output of the frequency multiplier stage must be tuned to 8 megacycles, Figure 160.

To act as a doubler, the plate circuit must be tuned to twice the input frequency. The multiplier is able to multiply the frequency because of the flywheel action of the tank circuit. A signal on the grid produces a pulse of plate current in the tank circuit. Since the tank circuit is tuned to twice the frequency of the input signal the circulating current in the tank will produce two complete cycles of current before the next pulse of plate current. These pulses of plate current keep the tank circuit oscillating. The action of a multiplier to triple or quadruple the frequency is the same.

It should be pointed out that each time the frequency is increased the efficiency of the output is decreased. Therefore when the harmonic frequency is several times that of the fundamental frequency it may be necessary to use several stages of amplification to make up for the loss in signal strength.

If the oscillator and the frequency multiplier do not provide enough driving power for the final amplifier, another stage of radio frequency amplification may be used. Such an amplifier is often called a *buffer*. A buffer may also be used between the oscillator and the final amplifier to prevent the

◆ 162. Placing the telegraph key in the cathode circuit permits the plate current to be turned on and off.

amplifier from changing the operating frequency of the oscillator.

Keying the Transmitter

If we wish to operate a transmitter using the international Morse code, we must have some method of stopping and starting the carrier. Code transmitters, called c.w. transmitters use a telegraphy key to turn the carrier off and on in the form of dots and dashes. There are a number of methods used to key a transmitter. One of the most popular methods uses a key to open and close the cathode circuit, Figure

◆ 161. Block diagram of an amplitude modulated transmitter.

◆ 163. Complete schematic for a 7 Mc. transmitter. The keying circuit is shown in color.

162. When the key is closed current flows in the tube. If the key is open, no current flows. In Figure 163, the cathodes are opened in both the oscillator and final amplifier stages.

Modulating the AM Transmitter

In an amplitude modulated signal, the audio signal is used to vary the amplitude of the carrier. When the audio signal or modulating voltage is "positive," the carrier amplitude is increased; when the modulating voltage is negative, the carrier amplitude is decreased. To modulate a carrier it is necessary to apply the audio wave to the carrier so that the amplitude is varied in accordance with the sound waves. This requires the use of a modulator. A modulator is an audio amplifier that is connected to the radio frequency amplifier so that the audio signal can be superimposed on the carrier signal.

A complete modulator system might be compared to a public address system that is used to amplify audio frequencies. First, we must have a microphone that is used to change the audio waves into a very weak pulsating current. The weak pulsating current produced by a microphone is connected to a speech amplifier to increase or amplify the audio signal. After the audio signal has been amplified by the speech amplifier, the signal is then applied to the modulator or output tube. In a public address system, the output of the amplifier is coupled to a loudspeaker; in a modulator the output is coupled to the RF amplifier.

◆ **164. Plate modulation of a Class C amplifier.**

Types of A.M. Modulators

There are a number of different methods used to apply the audio frequency signal to the radio frequency amplifier. One of the very popular methods is called plate modulation. In this system, two tubes are used in a circuit called a *push-pull class B amplifier,* Figure 164. The output of the modulator is coupled to the final radio frequency amplifier through the secondary of a modulation transformer. The audio signal from the modulator is induced into the secondary of the transformer and this voltage is applied to the plate voltage of the radio frequency amplifier. Thus, the audio signal adds or subtracts from the DC plate voltage. The principal disadvantage of plate modulation is that a considerable amount of audio power is necessary. Large audio amplifiers are very expensive to build.

◆ **165. Grid modulation of a Class C amplifier.**

◆ **166. Screen grid modulation of Class C amplifier.**

Another modulation system that requires less audio is called grid modulation. In grid modulation the audio signal is applied to the grid of the radio frequency amplifier as shown in Figure 165. A serious disadvantage of grid modulation is the reduction in carrier output.

Screen grid modulation is another method used to apply the audio signal to the radio frequency signal. Figure 166 illustrates how the audio is applied to the screen grid through the use of a transformer. The carrier output of screen grid modulation is only about one fourth to one third of that obtainable from the same radio frequency amplifier with plate modulation.

INTERESTING THINGS TO DO

Short Range Voice and Code Transmitter

Materials needed:

1 Variable capacitor, midget broadcast type, $400\mu\mu f$, C_3
1 Fixed capacitor, $0.05\mu f$, 450 volts, C_1
1 Trimmer capacitor, $100\mu\mu f$, C_2
1 R. F. choke coil, L_1 (see text)
1 Antenna coil, broadcast type, L_2 (see text)
1 Potentiometer, 250,000 ohms, R
1 Transistor, PNP, CK 722 or equivalent
1 Toggle switch, S. P. S. T.
1 Transistor battery, 9 volts
1 Base, sheet metal, $3\frac{1}{2}$" x $3\frac{1}{2}$"

This transmitter will permit you to send voice or code signals to your home radio receiver. Since its range is limited to about 50 feet there is little possibility that it will interfere with other radio receivers outside your home.

All of the parts are mounted on a metal base to reduce the effect of body

◆ **167. Form for winding choke coil, L₁.**

chased or made by winding 130 feet of No. 32 enameled wire on the form shown in Figure 167. Connect the parts as shown in the wiring diagram. If you wish to use a crystal microphone, connect a piece of wire across the key terminals and connect the microphone as shown by the dashed line. The length of the antenna, which is a piece of flexible wire, should not be longer than 10 feet.

capacity when you adjust the set. The coil, L_2, may be purchased or made by winding 160 turns of No. 32 enameled wire on a piece of wood dowel, $\frac{3}{4}'' \times 2\frac{1}{4}''$. The choke coil, L_1, has an inductance of 2.5 mh and may be purchased or made by winding 130 feet of No. 32 enameled wire on the form shown in Figure 167. Connect the parts as shown in the wiring diagram. If you wish to use a crystal microphone, connect a piece of wire across the key terminals and connect the microphone as shown by the dashed line. The length of the antenna, which is a piece of flexible wire, should not be longer than 10 feet.

When we studied radio transmitters we learned that a circuit must be in an oscillating condition before it can generate a radio frequency signal. In this circuit oscillation is maintained by feeding back energy from the collector to the emitter by means of capacitor C_1. To adjust the transmitter, place it close to a radio receiver that is tuned to a point on the dial where no station

◆ **168. The completed transmitter. The home-made choke coil is shown at the left of the tuning capacitor.**

can be heard, preferably in the 600 to 800 kc range. Adjust capacitor C_3 on your transmitter until a signal is heard on the radio receiver. Next, adjust capacitor, C_2, until oscillation occurs. This will be indicated by a high pitched squeal from the radio. If you retune the radio receiver carefully you will find a point on the tuning dial where the oscillation signal fades out and then builds up again as the tuning dial is turned. Retune either the radio receiver or transmitter to the "dead" spot and the transmitter is ready to operate. Final adjustments can be made with the transmitter located away from the radio receiver. The potentiometer serves as a volume control for the transmitted signal.

◆ **169. Short-range voice or code transmitter.**

REVIEW QUESTIONS

1. What is the purpose of a radio frequency signal?

2. What determines the frequency of a parallel *LC* circuit?

3. Explain the function of the tickler coil in a regenerative circuit.

4. In a Hartley oscillator, where does the feedback take place?

5. List the advantages of a crystal oscillator.

6. What determines the frequency of a crystal?

7. What is the function of the tank circuit in a Class *C* radio frequency amplifier?

8. Explain why it is not desirable for a radio frequency amplifier to pro-

duce self-oscillation.

9. Calculate the length of wire needed for a half wave dipole antenna which will operate efficiently on 3,000 kilocycles.

10. Why should the transmission line impedance match the antenna impedance?

11. Name two kinds of transmission lines.

12. What is the function of a frequency multiplier in a transmitter?

13. What is the purpose of a telegraphy key in a c.w. transmitter?

14. Name three methods of modulating a radio frequency amplifier in an AM transmitter.

UNIT 31
ELECTRONIC DEVELOPMENTS

The Television Camera Tube

Television has been one of the greatest inventions in the field of electronics. The ability to send pictures through the air waves and to make these pictures visible in a television receiver is a wonderful development.

A television station has two transmitters sending out high-frequency radio waves. See Diagram 171. One transmitter sends out the sound signals, and the other sends out picture signals. The picture signals are first picked up by a television camera. The camera uses a tube that is sensitive to light like the photoelectric cell. This tube changes light into a flow of electrons.

It is not possible to send a complete picture. It is necessary to break the picture up into a group of tiny parts of light. A beam of electrons called a *scanning beam* is made to move across the picture picking up the light received by the camera. The beam starts at the top of the picture and goes from one side to the other to the bottom of the picture.

This scanning beam sweeps across the picture and breaks it up into 525 lines. Each complete picture is made up of particles of light found in the 525 lines. It takes $\frac{1}{30}$ of a second for a picture to be completed; thus, 30 pictures are sent out every second. See Illustration 172.

The Television Transmitter

The electron flow from the camera is then made stronger by an amplifier called a *video amplifier*. These picture

Courtesy San Diego City Schools

◆ 170. A television camera being used in a station studio.

TRANSMITTING
ANTENNA
FOR
PICTURE SIGNAL

CAMERA

VIDEO
AMPLIFIER

PICTURE
TRANSMITTER

SCANNING
AND
SYNCHRONIZING
CIRCUITS

TRANSMITTING
ANTENNA
FOR
SOUND SIGNAL

MICROPHONE

AUDIO
AMPLIFIER

RADIO-FREQUENCY
TRANSMITTER
OF
SOUND SIGNAL

◆ 171. A block diagram of a television transmitting station. One transmitter sends out the picture signal and the other transmitter sends out the sound signal.

waves are combined with the high-frequency carrier of the transmitter. A transmitting antenna then sends these waves out into the air.

Television signals travel in a straight line like a beam of light. For this reason transmitting antennas are placed in as high a location as possible so that the signals can cover a fairly large area. See Illustration 175.

Frequency Modulation

In a standard broadcast station the sound waves and the carrier wave are

combined so that the carrier wave is increased and decreased in strength by the sound waves. This is called *amplitude modulation*. Television uses another method of combining the sound waves and the carrier wave called

START OF
FIRST
262 1/2 LINES

START OF
SECOND
262 1/2 LINES

◆ 172. A drawing of the scanning lines of a picture picked up by a television camera. Each picture takes $\frac{1}{30}$ of a second to complete and it is made up of 525 lines. Two sets of lines are used to make the 525 lines of the picture. The beam scans half of the lines (262½) as shown by the solid line. Then it starts back again between the first lines and scans the other 262½ lines as shown by the broken lines.

Courtesy Radio Corporation of America

◆ **173. This high-power television station has an ultra-high-frequency transmitter with a radiated power of one million watts.**

Courtesy Bell Systems

frequency modulation. In frequency modulation the sound waves vary the frequency of the carrier as shown in Illustration 176.

Frequency modulation is also used in ultra-high-frequency broadcast stations called *FM* stations. The main advantage of using frequency modulation is that noises made by such things as electrical circuits in the home, lightning, and automobile ignition are not

◆ **174. Radio relay stations and towers, spaced about 30 miles apart, provide a line-of-sight route over which telephone calls and television programs can be relayed great distances. The radio waves that do the work are of super-high frequencies and travel in fairly straight lines, like a beam of light.**

◆ 175. Television signals travel in a straight line like a beam of light, so antennas are made as high as possible.

heard in the receiver. Also, better sound quality is possible through the use of frequency modulation.

The Television Receiver

The television receiver has a tuner that is used to select the various stations. It tunes in both the sound signal and the picture signal. Since both the sound and the picture signals are on slightly different frequencies, they are separated in the receiver. The sound signal is amplified and is heard from the loudspeaker. The picture signal is amplified and is seen on the picture tube.

The Cathode-Ray Tube

The picture tube is called a *cathode-ray tube.* It is the face of the cathode-

ray tube that we see when we look at a television set. Inside the face of the tube there is a coating of a material that will glow when electrons strike it. The stronger the flow of electrons the more the tube will light up. This glow from the electrons hitting the face of the tube is what makes up the black and white of the picture.

The picture tube is adjusted so that the beam of electrons can keep in step

◆ 177. The video wave is picked up by your television receiver, and fed into a picture tube, or *kinescope.* There it varies the strength of a stream of electrons. As the electron stream plays across the fluorescent screen at the wide end of the tube, it paints the same picture seen by the camera.

◆ 176. In frequency modulation the carrier is varied in *frequency* by the sound waves, while the amplitude remains unchanged.

◆ 178. This simplified block diagram shows fundamental arrangement of a television receiver.

with the beam in the television camera. Special circuits, called synchronizing circuits, keep the beam of the television camera and the beam of the cathode-ray tube together. As in the camera, the cathode-ray tube beam must move across the face of the tube making 525 lines 30 times per second. This means that the electron beam is traveling 15,750 times per second across the face of the screen. As the beam moves across the screen, it paints the picture that the camera is picking up.

Color Television

A color television transmitter uses three camera tubes for the picture signal. Each camera picks up a different color from the scene being broadcast. One camera selects the red light from the scene, the second camera selects the green, and the third camera selects the blue light. These three color signals are all sent out by the transmitter. Combinations of these color signals are used for the brightness of the picture and also provide a black and white picture for black and white television receivers.

The tube in a color television receiver contains three electron guns which shoot the red, green and blue signals against the face of the tri-color picture tube. The inner face of the tube is coated with many thousands of dots of red, green, and blue phosphors which glow when the electron beam hits them. A screen that has the same number of openings as there are colored dots is located next to the phosphor face inside the picture tube. The holes in the screen are placed so that the beam of electrons sent out by the electron gun that makes up the red part of the picture can hit the red phosphor; the beam that makes up the green part of the picture can hit the green phosphor; and the electrons from the blue part of the picture can hit the blue phosphor. Since the color dots are so small and so close together, your eye brings them together into a true-to-life picture.

◆ 179. Airborne radar enables pilots to peer deep into thunderstorms, detecting areas where rough air may be encountered. Dotted lines on radar scope in cockpit show possible corridors pilot can follow for smooth flight through storm which appears solid to unaided eye.

Courtesy United Air Lines

Radar

Radar is an electronic development made during World War II that has been put to very valuable use during peacetime. In navigation, both at sea and in the air, radar plays a most important part.

You are familiar with an echo of your voice. The sound waves hit a cliff or building and bounce back. You heard your voice when you spoke, and you hear it again when it returns from the cliff or wall that it has hit. This is what happens in radar except that high-frequency radio waves are used instead of sound waves. The radar set sends out a radio wave that strikes an object and receives the same wave when it returns. The set then performs its most important duty by automatically showing the distance that the object is from the radar set. See Illustration 180.

For example, an airplane can determine its height above the ground through the use of radar. A transmitter is used to send out a radio wave. The signal is beamed toward the ground.

◆ 180. The face of a cathode-ray tube used on a radar screen. The two pips, on the screen, show the distance between the original transmitted signal and the echo signal after it bounced back to the receiver. By using the calibrated scale below the beam, it is possible to determine the distance that the object is away from the radar station.

After it strikes the ground it bounces back up to the airplane. The wave that bounces back is picked up by a radio receiver that is connected to a cathode-ray tube. The signal sent out by the transmitter shows on the screen of the tube by a little bump called a *pip*. The signal that bounced back from the ground also shows on the screen by a pip. It only takes a fraction of a second for these radio waves to go to the ground and bounce back. The time between pips can be calibrated in distance since the speed of radio waves is known to be 186,000 miles per second. By looking at the scale on the front of the tube, it is possible to measure the distance between pips to determine the distance of the airplane from the ground.

Radar is used in many ways. Ships at sea can get a picture of the shore line near them with radar. Other objects in the air or at sea can be located by radar. More and more the principle of

Courtesy Convair

◆ 181. Radio-controlled guided missiles shown aboard a Navy ship. The development of these devices depends upon electronics.

radar is being used for navigation purposes to make air and sea travel safe.

Radio-Controlled Rockets

Rockets and airplanes can be controlled through the use of radio waves. Rockets, or guided missiles, fired into the sky carry a radio receiver with them. The transmitter from the home station sends out radio signals that are picked up by the receiver in the rocket. All of the direction controls in the rocket are connected so that they can be moved by signals coming into the receiver. A radar station watches the rocket. It keeps the operators informed as to the speed and location of the missile. In this way the operators have complete control of the flight of the rocket.

High-altitude research rockets carry transmitters with them. These transmitters inform the ground stations as to how the rocket is performing. Information regarding air pressure, temperature, and other important facts is sent out by the rocket transmitter.

Satellites and Space Capsules

While rockets and missiles are valuable as a means of defense, their role in research has been replaced by the satellites and space capsules that are now being sent into space. These are capable of sustained orbits outside the earth's atmosphere and provide information on weather, solar radiation and valuable new data on communication.

In the construction of these satellites and man carrying capsules such as the *Mercury* in which Gordon Cooper made his historic flight, every component represents the latest advance in

Courtesy Bell Laboratories

◆ **182. Telstar with its launching shell removed. Part of the 3,600 solar cells which provide its operating power may be seen in the square frames around its outer surface. The spiral antenna for telemetry signals is located on top of the satellite. Two sets of microwave antennas for receiving and transmitting T.V. signals encircle the satellite at the center behind the small openings.**

electronics. As a satellite must be self sustaining in operation and provide the many forms of information necessary, it must be extremely compact and reliable. This is accomplished by "packaging" the electronic circuits in microminiature component blocks and using solar cells to provide for a portion of its operating power.

Many satellites have been put into orbit and have provided valuable information necessary for further exploration in space. The Van Allen radiation belt was discovered and plotted through the use of these space devices.

Telemetering

Preparation of man's first flight to the moon is marked by the accumulation of data which will report accurately some of the conditions he will encounter when he makes his initial attempt to reach that distant planet. Much of the desired data is being obtained from transmitters in satellites which respond to signals from ground transmitting stations. The signals from the satellites are in the form of pulses of such strength and duration that they can be interpreted in terms of the desired information. The science of transmitting and receiving measurements and other data from a distance is known as *telemetering*.

As many as one hundred fifteen forms of data are available from the various satellites, among which are density of radiation, effect of radiation on the solar cells, amount of sunlight hitting the satellite, voltages on many of the components, pressures within and outside the shell, and condition of the power plant.

Geiger Counters

One type of instrument used to locate radioactive materials is a *Geiger counter*. When the Geiger tube is brought near uranium ore or other radioactive items, it will make an indicating device operate. The indicator can be a clicking in the earphones, a flashing neon light, or a swinging meter needle.

The most important part of the counter is the small Geiger tube. This glass tube is filled with a gas and has two metal plates, called *electrodes*, inside of it. When radioactive materials are placed near the tube, rays from the material start a current flowing between the plates in the tube. An amplifier is then used to amplify the current flow. The stronger the radioactivity, the stronger the indication on the counter. Faster clicks are heard in the earphones, the neon flashers speed up, or the meter needle moves farther.

Geiger counters have many important uses. Prospectors use them to locate uranium ore deposits. In places where radioactive materials are being used, the Geiger counter can determine whether or not the people or their clothing have come in contact with these dangerous rays.

◆ 183. Using a Geiger counter to locate uranium-bearing ore. In the field these units are usually operated with small flashlight cells.

INTERESTING THINGS TO DO

◆ 184. The Neon Lamp Flasher

1. Neon Lamp Flasher.

Materials required:

1 Neon lamp, Type Ne-2
1 Fixed resistor, ½-watt (see text)
1 Fixed capacitor, 150 volts (see text)

Many pieces of industrial equipment use a timing circuit similar to the one shown in Diagram 185 to turn an electrical circuit on or off. With its use extremely accurate timing may be obtained whether the time intervals are a fraction of a second or many minutes apart. The timing is governed by the values of the resistor measured in ohms and capacitor measured in farads. If we multiply the value of the resistor by the capacitance of the capacitor in farads, the product will be the time interval in seconds at which the neon lamp will flash.

The flasher shown in Photograph 184 is arranged to flash at one second intervals by using a 1,000,000-ohm resistor and a 1 µf capacitor. The term *farad* represents such a large value that it is seldom used in electronic circuits, but since 1,000,000 microfarads equal one farad, we can see that one microfarad can be expressed as .000001 farad. If we wish to increase the timing interval we have only to increase the value of the resistor or the capacitor, so that when both are multiplied together, the product will be the desired timing in seconds.

The input terminals should be connected to a source of direct current, 90 to 135 volts. If it is desired only to observe the flashing rate, a piece of wire should be connected across the output terminals. If it is desired to control another circuit, connect a sensitive relay across the output terminals.

INPUT
90 TO 135 VOLTS
DIRECT CURRENT

CONNECT
TWO TERMINALS
TOGETHER

NEON FLASHER CIRCUIT

INPUT
90 TO 135 VOLTS

OUTPUT
CONNECT
SENSITIVE RELAY
HERE
(2,000 OHMS TO
5,000 OHMS RELAY)

NEON LAMP CONTROL CIRCUIT

◆ 185. Diagrams of the neon lamp flasher and control circuit.

◆ 186. Transistor code-practice oscillator.

◆ 187. Wiring diagram of the transistor code-practice oscillator.

2. Transistor Code Practice Oscillator.

Materials required:

1 Piece wood, $\frac{1}{2}$" x 3" x 3"
1 Transistor, G. E. 2N107 or Raytheon CK 722
2 Fixed capacitors, .01 μf (C_1, C_2)
1 Resistor, 47,000 ohms (R)
2 Pen light cells
4 Fahnestock clips

This transistor oscillator provides a very compact set with which you may learn the radiotelegraph code to qualify for an amateur radio license. Mount the parts in the approximate positions on the wood base as shown in Photograph 186. Wire the set according to Schematic Diagram 187. Two of the Fahnestock clips should be marked "key" and two should be marked "phones." If all of the connections have been made correctly, a high-pitched buzz should be heard in the phones when the key is pressed. For the best results the phones should have an impedance of 2,000 or more ohms. To reduce current drain from the pen light cells, the headphones should be disconnected from the oscillator when it is not in use.

REVIEW QUESTIONS

1. Why are two transmitters used in a television station?

2. How many complete pictures are sent out every second by a television station?

3. Each picture is divided into how many scanning lines?

4. Why is it necessary for a television antenna to be located as high as possible?

5. What is the picture tube in a television receiver called? Explain how it works.

6. Explain how a radar set tells the height that an airplane is from the ground.

7. How can radar be used to make airplane travel safer?

8. What is the advantage of having radio-controlled rockets?

9. For what is a Geiger counter used?

STANDARD SYMBOLS FOR ELECTRONICS

ANTENNA

PIEZOELECTRIC CRYSTAL

Single pole, single throw
SWITCH

GROUND

One Cell   More than one cell

BATTERY

CHASSIS

OR

FUSE

Incandescent–filament
LAMP

JACK   OR

BELL   BUZZER

MOTOR   GENERATOR

*Appropriate letter symbol may
be inserted to identify kind
of speaker

LOUDSPEAKER

Filament   Cathode or heater

Grid   Plate

VACUUM TUBE ELEMENTS

Fixed   Variable

CAPACITOR

*Letter inside circle
denotes type
METER

Fixed   Tapped

Adjustable   Variable

RESISTOR

Magnetic core   OR

Tapped

Adjustable   Variable

COIL

HEADPHONES

SELENIUM PHOTOCELL

E   C   E   C

B   B

P–N–P   N–P–N

TRANSISTOR

No connection   Connection

CROSSING OR JUNCTION OF
PATHS OR CONDUCTORS

PICKUP

RECTIFIER

Air Core   Magnetic core

TRANSFORMER

318

SOLDERING HINTS

In all electrical work, good soldering joints are essential. Solder is intended to provide a good electrical contact, to prevent corrosion at the joint, and to add strength to the joint or splice. Most electrical soldering is done with an electric soldering iron or a soldering gun.

Procedures for Soldering

1. Clean the Soldering Tip

When using an electric soldering iron, it is advisable to remove the copper tip from the iron before filing. File the tip as shown in Illustration 1 so that the four sides of the copper are smooth and come together to a point. The tip should be taken out of the iron at least once a week so that the corrosion can be removed from the copper. If the tip remains in the iron for long periods of time, it will corrode in the iron barrel. Should this occur, it is very difficult to ever remove the tip.

The soldering gun tip should be cleaned with steel wool or with sandpaper.

2. Tin the Tip

Heat the tip and then apply a thin coat of rosin core solder. Sometimes the solder will not stick even though the tip looks clean. When this occurs, rub the heated point with steel wool and again apply the rosin core solder. The tip should now be tinned and will have a shiny appearance. If excess solder remains on the tip, it can be removed by wiping the point with a rag.

3. Use Rosin Core Solder

Wire-shaped solder with a hollow core filled with rosin flux is recommended for all electrical connections. Acid core solder or paste fluxes are not desirable because they corrode connections.

4. All Parts to be Soldered Must be Clean

Solder will not stick to wire or terminals that have not been cleaned. Lugs, wires, and other parts to be soldered should be scraped with a knife until the metal appears bright. Thin wires covered with enamels can best be cleaned with sandpaper as shown in Illustration 2.

5. Make a Good Mechanical Connection

◆ 1. The copper soldering iron tip should be filed.

◆ 2. The insulation on small wires can be removed with sandpaper.

◆ 3. To conduct heat away from transistors the leads should be held with pliers when soldering.

◆ 4. The small tip of a soldering gun is preferred when soldering printed circuits.

Before soldering, the wires should first be wrapped around terminals or securely clamped. After the wire is tight and secure, the solder can be applied.

6. Heat the Connection

The hot iron tip should be held against the parts to be joined until they are heated. Enough heat should be applied so that the solder melts when it touches the wires being joined together. The solder will then flow freely over and through the joint.

7. Keep the Connection from Moving

While the joint is being soldered and while the solder is cooling, the connection should be held perfectly still. Movement of the connection will result in a cold solder joint that may have a high resistance.

8. Use the Proper Amount of Solder

Use only enough solder to do the job.

Excessive solder does not help the connection, and this extra solder may cause a short circuit. If excessive solder appears, re-heat the joint and remove the extra solder by wiping it with a rag.

9. Protect Certain Parts from Heat

Certain parts such as diodes and transistors can easily be damaged by excessive heat. To avoid ruining these parts when soldering, the leads should be gripped with pliers as shown in Illustration 3. The pliers will conduct the heat away from the part.

10. For Small Spaces Use a Small Tip

Crowded electronic circuits may have a number of components in a very small space. A large soldering tip can easily damage the parts or the other connections. In such instances, a small tip such as found on soldering guns should be used. See Figure 4.

SUPPLEMENTARY PROJECTS

The following four projects are included in the appendix for use by the instructor as deemed most profitable for his particular class.

MAKING A MAGNETIC FIELD PATTERN DEVELOPER

Materials needed:

1 Tin can (size of 3 lb. shortening can or a 2 lb. coffee can)
1 Lamp socket
6 ft Lamp cord
1 ft Wood dowel, ¼"
1 Wood base
2 Pieces wood for can support
2 Pieces wood for pattern platform
1 Piece heavy cardboard
1 Attachment plug
1 Rubber grommet, ⅜"

Make a platform approximately 3" high with two pieces of wood and a piece of heavy cardboard and secure it to the wood base. In securing the parts of the platform together and to the wood base, use glue instead of nails or screws. Mount the lamp socket on a wood block and drill a ¼" hole lengthwise through the center of the block for the wood dowel. Drill two ¼" holes through the sides of the can near the bottom, so that the piece of wood dowel can be inserted in the holes, and through the hole in the wood block which holds the lamp socket. Glue the piece of wood dowel to the wood block and secure the lamp socket to the bottom of the can.

Drill a ¼" hole in each of the can supports so that when the can is mounted and rotated the edge of the can will clear the top of the pattern platform by ¼". Drill a ⅜" hole in the bottom of the can near the lamp socket for the rubber grommet. Attach one end of the lamp cord to the lamp socket, extend the cord through the

◆ 1. Sprinkling steel wool on the wax paper held under the lamp of the magnetic field pattern developer.

grommet and attach a plug cap on the opposite end. Insert a lamp in the socket and the field pattern developer is ready to operate. The size of the lamp may vary from 75 to 150 watts, depending upon the type of wax paper used in making the patterns.

To make a permanent magnetic field pattern, place a magnet, either permanent or electromagnetic, under the platform and close to the cardboard top. Place a piece of waxed paper on top of the platform and sprinkle fine iron filings on the paper. Pieces of steel wool rubbed together will produce very satisfactory results. Tap the cardboard top of the platform gently un-

WOOD UPRIGHT
LAMP CORD
WOOD DOWEL
HEAVY CARDBOARD
WOOD BASE
FRONT VIEW

LAMP CORD
WOOD BLOCK
GROMMET
LAMP SOCKET
LAMP
CAN

SECTIONAL VIEW
OF CAN
TO SHOW LAMP
HOUSING

SPACE FOR MAGNET
WOOD SUPPORT
FOR
PATTERN
PLATFORM
3"
SIDE VIEW

◆ **2. Magnetic Field Pattern Developer**

til the desired pattern is formed, then swing the can with the lamp lighted over the pattern. Within one minute the heat from the lamp will cause the filings or pieces of steel wool to sink into the wax on the paper. When the heated lamp is removed a permanent pattern of the magnetic field will remain on the waxed paper.

◆ **3. The magnetic pattern is permanently impressed on the wax paper.**

PISTON TYPE MOTOR

Materials required:

2 Fiber washers, 1/8" thick, 1 1/8" diameter
1 Piece wood dowel, 3/8" x 2"
1 Piece soft steel, round, 1/4" diameter, 2 1/4" long
1 Piece steel, round, 1/8" diameter, 3 1/4" long
1 Piece sheet brass, 1/16" thick, 1/4" x 1 1/2"
2 Pieces sheet steel, 18 gage, 1 1/2" x 2 1/2"
1 Piece brass rod, round, 1/2" diameter, 3/16" long
1 Piece spring brass, 26 gage, 3/16" x 2 3/4"
1 Piece wood, 3/4" x 1 1/2" x 2"
1 Piece wood, 1/2" x 4" x 6"
2 Terminal screws
100 ft Magnet wire, No. 22, enam.
1 Flywheel (see text)

◆ 4. Piston Type Motor

This type motor has an action somewhat like a steam engine in that the power is supplied to the flywheel by a piston moving back and forth. Make a coil form by drilling a 17/64" hole through the piece of wood dowel and place a fiber washer at each end of the dowel. Drill two small holes in one washer for the coil leads and wind eight layers of No. 22 magnet wire on the form. Shape one end of the wood block to match the curve of the coil and glue the coil to the block. Secure the coil mount to the wood base with screws or glue in the approximate position shown in the assembly view. Shape and drill the piece of sheet brass to serve as the connecting rod.

File away one end of the piston rod so that the end of the connecting rod will fit against it and drill and tap the end of the rod as shown on the drawing for the piston. Secure the connecting rod to the piston with a 6-32 machine screw. Tighten the screw so that the connecting rod can move freely, then solder the end of the machine screw to the piston. The flywheel may be turned from wood with a piece of pipe serving as a rim to give it weight, or it may be made by casting plaster of Paris in a jar lid, as was done with the motor shown in the photograph. Bend the piece of steel rod as shown in the drawing to serve as the crankshaft. Drill, shape, and bend the two pieces of sheet steel for the bearing stands, as shown in the drawing.

Assemble the crankshaft, flywheel, and bearing stands by first placing a 6-32 machine screw nut that has been drilled out to 1/8" over the straight end of the shaft. Next place a bearing stand on the shaft, then the flywheel, and finally, the other bearing stand and another drilled out machine screw nut. Place the whole assembly on the wood base and insert the end of the crankshaft through the hole in the connecting rod. Line up all of the parts so

ASSEMBLY VIEW

COIL MOUNT

COIL FORM

PISTON

CONTACT CAM

BEARING STAND

BRUSH

CRANK

CONNECTING ROD

◆ 5. Piston Type Motor

that the moving parts work freely, then secure the bearing stands to the base with wood screws. Secure the flywheel to the shaft so that it will be centered between the bearings. Solder the machine screw nuts to the shaft to keep the flywheel centered.

Shape the piece of round brass rod to provide a cam approximately 160 degrees wide as shown in the drawing and place it on the end of the shaft. Drill and shape the piece of spring brass to serve as the brush, as shown in the drawing, and secure it to the wood base so that its end will rest against the contact cam. Adjust the cam so that it makes contact with the brush slightly after the piston begins its backward stroke and breaks contact with the brush just before the piston begins its forward stroke. In some instances the edges of the cam may need further dressing with a file to provide maximum operating results. Solder the cam to the shaft when it has been adjusted to the correct position. Wire the motor as shown in the assembly view and the motor will be ready to run. Direct current from 3 to 8 volts will operate the motor satisfactorily.

RADIO AND TELEVISION TUBE FILAMENT TESTER

Materials required:

1 Piece sheet steel, 20 gage, 5½" x 6"
1 Resistor, 100,000 ohms
1 Neon lamp, NE-51
2 Octal sockets
2 Miniature sockets, 7 pin
1 Miniature socket, 9 pin
1 Rubber grommet, ¼"
1 Rubber grommet, ⅜"
6 ft Lamp cord
1 Attachment plug

One of the frequent causes of a radio or television receiver failing to operate is the burning out of one or more tube filaments. With this filament tester you can locate such tubes quickly and accurately. Tube manufacturers use different combinations as filament terminals for octal sockets and seven pin miniature sockets. Thus, two sockets of each type are provided to handle all present-day filament terminal arrangements. Since nine pin miniature tubes have only one filament terminal arrangement at present, only one such type tube socket is required.

Lay out, shape, and drill the piece

♦ 6. Diagram of Radio and Television Tube Filament Tester

of sheet steel as shown in the drawing. Bend the sides and ends of the chassis along the dotted lines and solder the corners together. Attach the tube sockets to the chassis in the holes provided. Secure a rubber grommet in the hole in the top of the chassis and press the neon lamp into the grommet with the terminals inside the chassis. Wire the tester according to the schematic diagram and attach the line cord after passing it through a rubber grommet in the end of the chassis. When testing either an octal base or a seven pin miniature tube, first place the tube in the socket on the left side, then in the socket on the right side. If the neon lamp lights in either case, the tube

◆ 7. **Radio and Television Tube Filament Tester**

filament is good. If the neon lamp fails to light, the filament is defective. To test a nine pin miniature tube, place it in the socket and observe the neon lamp as directed above.

TRANSISTOR AMPLIFIER

Materials required:

  1 Piece wood, $\frac{1}{2}''$ x 3″ x 3″
  1 Transistor, Raytheon CK 722
  1 Fixed capacitor, electrolytic, 10 μf, 25 volts
  1 Resistor (see text) R_1
  1 Resistor, 220,000 ohms, R_2
  2 Penlight cells
  4 Fahnestock clips

This transistor amplifier will provide more volume for either the crystal diode receiver or the transistor receiver which are described elsewhere in this book. Mount the parts in the approximate position on the wood base as shown in Photograph 8. Wire the set according to Diagram 9. Two of the Fahnestock clips should be marked *input* and two should be marked *output*. For best results the value of resistor R_1 should be about 470 ohms when the amplifier is used with the transistor receiver and about 47,000

◆ 8. **Transistor Amplifier**

◆ 9. **Wiring Diagram of Transistor Amplifier**

ohms when it is used with the crystal diode receiver. To reduce current drain from the pen light cells, the head-phones or speaker should be disconnected from the output side of the amplifier when it is not in use.

HIGH GAIN DETECTAPHONE AMPLIFIER

Materials needed:

1 Transistor input transformer, T_1
1 Transistor driver transformer, T_2
2 Resistors, 470,000 ohms, R_1, R_4
1 Resistor, 100 ohms, R_4
1 Potentiometer, 10,000 ohms, R_3
2 Capacitors, electrolytic, 10 μfd, 6 volts, C_1, C_2
1 Capacitor, electrolytic, 50 μfd, 6 volts, C_4
1 Capacitor, ceramic disc, 0.01 μfd, 150 volts, C_3
2 Transistors, PNP, CK 722, TR_1, TR_2
1 Transistor battery, 9 volts
1 Switch, S. P. S. T.
1 Microphone jack
2 Phone tip jacks
1 Plastic case with cover, 1" x 3" x 4½"
2 Terminal strips, 4 lug

This high gain amplifier is small enough to be carried in a shirt pocket, yet sensitive enough to pick up conversation within a house 50 to 70 feet from its source. If a sensitive microphone is attached to it and held against a wall, sounds occurring in a room beyond may be readily understood. If the microphone is suspended in front of a bowl or reflector, its range can be extended to several hundred feet.

Obtain a plastic case first, then cut a piece of insulating material such as bakelite or plastic, $\frac{1}{16}$" thick, for mounting the parts. Arrange each component so that the leads will be as short as possible. Connect a transistor to three of the lugs on each terminal strip and use the extra lugs for securing other parts. Secure the microphone jack and potentiometer to one end of

◆ 10. The detectaphone parts may be assembled into a compact unit that may be attached to a belt or slipped into a pocket.

the plastic case and the phone tip jacks to the opposite end. Although the potentiometer and switch are listed as separate items, they may be obtained in one unit. The high gain of this circuit is due to the fact that transformer coupling is used. While resistance-capacity coupling would provide better quality of sound, its gain would be far less than that obtained with transform-

◆ 11. Schematic diagram of high gain detectaphone amplifier.

◆ 12. If a microphone is mounted on an adjustable rod in the center of a reflector, the detectaphone will amplify sounds such as bird calls from a distance of several hundred yards.

ers. Their audible range is more than sufficient to give excellent reproduction of all the voice frequencies, which fulfills the purpose of the amplifier. When transformer coupled amplifiers are used there is a tendency for them to break into a low frequency oscillation when the components are placed close together. This effect is called "motor boating" and it may be identified by sharp clicks in the headphones which occur two or three times a second. To eliminate that possible effect a capacitor, C_4, is connected across the battery as shown in the diagram.

Connect the parts as shown in Figure 11, taking particular care to wire the capacitors so the polarities will be as shown in the diagram. When all wiring is complete, plug a crystal or dynamic microphone in the microphone jack and a pair of sensitive headphones in the pin jacks. Turn on the battery switch, adjust the volume with the potentiometer, and the amplifier is ready to operate.

INDEX

A

Alkaline manganese cell 42, 43
Alternating current
    effective value of 76, 77
    frequencies 53
    generators 53-55, 58, 128-130
    motors 187-191
    R.M.S. value of 77
    transformers 138
    voltmeter 76, 77
    wave form 55
Alternators 202, 203
American wire gage 98
Ammeters 81-86
    construction of 83
    current ranges 84
    experimental 86
    shunts 84
Ammonium chloride, in electrolyte 40
Ampere, defined 81
Amplifiers
    audio 253-266
    buffer 301
    class A 295
    class B 295
    class C 295-298
    electron tube 253-256
    high-fidelity 258-264
    light 11
    radio 253-266
    radio frequency 264, 265, 294-298
    resistance coupled 253-256
    transistor 273-275
Amplitude modulation 220, 221, 303, 304
Antennas
    receiving 219-221
    transmitting 298-300
Armature 53-58, 186-188
Armored cable 161
Atom
    structure of 37-39
    nucleus 38, 39
Audio amplifiers 253-266
Audio frequencies 212, 220, 221
Audio transformers 257
Automation 6, 12
Automobile
    batteries 44-47, 198
    circuit breakers 208
    fuses 208
    generators 57, 58, 200, 201
    ignition system 203, 207
Autotransformer 144, 145

B

Baffles, speaker 263
Ballast, fluorescent lamp 174-176
Bar magnets 25, 51, 52
Base, transistor 270-272
Batteries 44-46
    parallel connection 115, 116
    series connection 114, 115
    storage 44, 45, 49, 198
Binaural reproduction 263, 264
Blueprints, electrical 166
Branch circuits 151
Breaker points, in automobile 204-206
Broadcasting, TV 307-309
Brushes, motor 54-56
Buffer amplifiers 301
Bulbs, automobile headlights 207
Bypass capacitor 256

C

Cable
    armored (AC) 161
    nonmetallic sheathed 161
Calrod heating elements 177-179
Camera, television 307-311
Capacitance
    formulas 228, 229
    in parallel 228
    in series 228
    unit of 226
Capacitive reactance 230
Capacitors
    color codes 228
    construction of 225, 226
    dielectric in 225, 226
    electrolytic 227
    in filter circuits 283, 284
    grid 245, 246
    mica 227, 228
    rotor plates 223, 224
    stator plates 223, 224
    types of 227
    variable 223, 224
    working voltage 227
Carrier wave 220, 221
Cartridge fuses 151, 152
Cathode in electron tube 241
Cathode-ray tube 310-313
Cells
    alkaline manganese 42, 43
    chemical action in 40, 41
    dry 41, 42

330